Violence, Monkeys and Man

By the same authors

HUMAN BEHAVIOUR

Violence, Monkeys and Man

Claire Russell and
W. M. S. Russell

Macmillan
London · Melbourne · Toronto
1968

© Claire Russell and W. M. S. Russell 1968

Published by

MACMILLAN AND CO LTD
Little Essex Street London W C 2
and also at Bombay Calcutta and Madras
Macmillan South Africa (Publishers) Pty Ltd Johannesburg
The Macmillan Company of Australia Pty Ltd Melbourne
The Macmillan Company of Canada Ltd Toronto

Printed in Great Britain by
RICHARD CLAY (THE CHAUCER PRESS) LTD
Bungay, Suffolk

Contents

Contents

Illustrations

Authors' Note on Appendices, Notes and Bibliography

THE Appendices of this book are written in the same style as the text. They are not technical elaborations; they are more like additional chapters. They contain important matter omitted from the text in order to avoid breaking the thread of the main arguments.

The Notes and Bibliography require some explanation. In a book on a compact subject, some discussion of the sources for its study occupies a proper place. In a book on so vast a field as ours, source references are bound to be selective, and special discussion of sources would appear arbitrary, except where they form an integral part of our story (as in the case of field studies of monkey societies, briefly surveyed in Chapter Two). Moreover, we have frequently interwoven material from several sources in one paragraph, and an apparatus of footnotes on factual sources would have swamped the book, and sometimes left only a trickle of actual text at the top of each page.

Some means had to be provided, however, to give readers access to the sources of our facts, some of which may be unfamiliar or even startling. We have separated this apparatus from the rest of the book, so that the text itself (including the Appendices) can be read as an uncluttered narrative. Anyone wishing to find the source of a particular fact, or group of facts, can turn to the Notes (pp. 301–312) and look up the references given under the appropriate page of the text. Under each page, facts or groups of facts are there specified as brief headings. In brackets after each such heading, the reader can find numbers, which will lead to the appropriate source or sources in the numbered list that makes up the Bibliography (pp. 313–331). It should be possible to get from fact to source in less than a minute. Finally, the Bibliography itself is divided into numerous categories, and each source is followed by references to the

*

pages of text where it has been used. Tracing in the other direction, therefore, the Bibliography can be used as a general subject index.

Acknowledgements

WE should like to thank Professor S. L. Andreski, Miss Maureen Canning, Mr Arthur Cook, Mrs Violet Frieslich, Dr Caroline Loizos and Dr Piet Sevenster for information used in this book. We had the great benefit of consulting unpublished material by Dr M. R. A. Chance, Dr Hans Kummer and Dr Vernon Reynolds, to whom we are most grateful. Dr Reynolds kindly permitted us to draw largely on his thesis for the University of London on the rhesus monkeys at Whipsnade, the subject of a forthcoming book by him. However, we alone are responsible for any errors there may be in the present book.

To Michael Chance

To Michael Chase

Violence, Monkeys and Man

Deathdance

Violence, Monkeys and
Man

The music I hear in my head,
And that's driving me nearly mad,
Goes furioso, staccato,
Lento, obligato —
Furiously staggered into a rage,
Slow obligations building a cage —
Those little grey cells create with a will
Grey little hells with rhythms to kill.

In those grey little hells in my brain,
Fiddling devils drive me insane;
For they idly decide
Life to deride,
And with lack of true feeling
And true feelings reeling,
Since their play's left to chance,
To play the 'Totentanz' dance.

If trapped grey little cells
In grey social hells
Reflect lack of true feeling
And true feeling's reeling,
Will the 'Totentanz' dance
Be played by pure chance?

Introduction

THIS is a book about violence in higher mammals (chiefly monkeys) and man. The whole argument of the book can be reduced to two essential points. First, we have tried to show that violence is not the result of an innate propensity to aggression irrespective of conditions, but a response to stress in societies. Second, we suggest that violence is part of a complex of responses evolved to achieve drastic reduction of a population that is in danger of outgrowing its resources. We have sought evidence, bearing on these two ideas, from societies of monkeys and other mammals, from human tribal societies, from the history of human civilisations and from the age we live in.

The subject of the book is so large that it may be useful to define our main term in advance. Animals inflict injury or death upon each other in three situations. A predatory animal will naturally attack its prey. A prey animal, in defence of itself or its young, may attack a predator. Finally, an animal may attack another (of the same or a related species) which exploits the same natural resources of food, shelter or the like. It is this third kind of attack that we commonly call 'aggression', and we have used the words 'aggression' and 'violence' throughout the book in this restricted but not unusual sense. (The grounds for this restriction are discussed in Appendix One.) We are concerned, therefore, essentially with social aggression and social violence.

On the other hand, in discussing human violence, we have used the term in its widest sense within this restriction. Some scientists regard violent crime and organised war as separate problems. On the contrary, we consider that they are closely related. This follows from our two main points; but we also present a great deal of special evidence in favour of this relationship (notably in Chapter Three). From the outset of the book, there-fore, we discuss social violence in general, bracketing together violent crime, civil disturbance and war.

In covering our very wide field, we have used evidence from the work of a variety of specialists, and we should like, in this introduction, to address a few comments to two kinds of specia-list in particular, zoologists and historians. We have not tried to present a comprehensive account of social aggression or popu-lation control in animals. Apart from monkeys, and the impor-tant special case of rats (Appendix Four), few mammalian species are discussed, fewer birds and only one fish. There are many interesting behaviour patterns and mechanisms for regu-lating populations which we could have digressed upon, but we chose to restrict ourselves to cases with a close bearing on our main themes. Copious examples are to be found in books such as those of Konrad Lorenz, Niko Tinbergen and V. C. Wynne-Edwards, listed in the Bibliography, and we felt no need to duplicate their work. Zoologists will therefore, we hope, excuse us if we have omitted their favourite species or problem. Natur-ally, however, we have tried to ensure that any generalisations about mammals, or animals in general, are valid.

Some zoologists may feel concern about our use of words like 'establishment' and 'electorate' in discussing monkey societies. They are rightly anxious not to ascribe specifically human properties to these simple and inarticulate communities. We have, however, always *described* the behaviour we have labelled in this way. There seems little fear that anyone will be misled into supposing that monkey establishments draw up written marriage settlements or operate corporations with overlapping directorates. Our object has been to draw attention, in a com-parative way, to the simpler automatic patterns of behaviour which often underlie human complexities, and which are seen in uncluttered form in monkey bands (in the case of establish-ments, the fundamental principles of alliances). Social scientists, familiar with the more automatic aspects of human social be-haviour, are more ready to accept this comparative language. In a recent broadcast, one of us discussed monkey societies, using nearly all the terms of this kind we have used in this book, with an anthropologist, a sociologist and a social psychologist; they saw nothing to object to in the implied analogies, and developed them further with human examples.

As with terms, so with analogies. When we compare Henry VIII of England with a monkey at Whipsnade (in Chapter Three), we are not forgetting that the Tudor king was a literate, highly educated and gifted human being, who wrote lyrics and music and probably designed buildings and ships and certainly understood a great deal about parliaments. We are only observing that he (like many less gifted people) was subject in his personal relationships to certain automatic patterns, so simple that we can see them at work among the Whipsnade monkeys.

Our historical material itself is of two kinds. In the first four chapters, and in some of the appendices, we have had to select a few cases for relatively detailed study, out of a vast possible field of choice. We have picked cases which we felt were richly illustrative without being unrepresentative. In the last two chapters we have covered great sweeps of history, with generalisations of the broadest kind. In both cases, we were conscious of omitting, again and again, the rich complexities that enter into any historical event. In discussing the population crises of Europe, for instance, except for the case of Elizabethan England (Appendix Five), we have scarcely mentioned the many special local factors that cushioned, sharpened, advanced or retarded the impact of each crisis in different regions (for instance, the Dutch overseas empire, or the vicissitudes of medieval German advance into eastern Europe). We hope to make up for this, to some extent, in a later book. In this one, here again, we have concentrated on presenting a bold outline.

One specific historical topic deserves special mention. It is sometimes supposed that there was no essential difference between the Nazi régime (discussed in Appendix Four) and other tyrannical police-states of the nineteenth and twentieth centuries. We consider, on the contrary, that the Nazi régime was profoundly unlike other tyrannies, and that it is dangerously confusing to lump it with the rest. The peculiar nature of this system is discussed in detail in Appendix Four. For the present, it may suffice to point out that the Nazi outburst produced violence on a literally unique scale. It is difficult to be cool about massacres; but, as a matter of simple arithmetic, the Nazis directly murdered more than twice as many people (chiefly Jews and Slavs) as any other régime in history. More fundamental, they started the Second World War, in a much more real and meaningful sense than (say) the German Imperial Government started the First World War; and the Second World War was the most lethal in history, killing an estimated total of fifty million people by violence. We have, therefore, devoted special attention to this remarkable and terrible outbreak, as a phenomenon of a particularly dangerous kind.

The larger human societies are incomparably more complex than those of monkeys, and violence in man is no doubt a correspondingly more complex problem. Some of these specifically human complexities (for instance, price revolutions) we have considered in Chapters Five and Six; many others, of course, we have not considered at all. But we do not wish to qualify our theory out of existence. If it is true, there is no doubt that the effective regulation of human populations by voluntary birth-control would be by far the most important first step towards eliminating human violence.

One/Violence, Man and Monkeys

1

MORE than a thousand years ago, the poets of the T'ang Dynasty of China were much concerned with the senseless cruelty of war. 'Three hundred and sixty thousand men,' wrote Li Po, 'dragged from their homes, weep as they bid their families farewell. Since it is the order of the prince, they must obey, but who is to cultivate the fields?' And in another poem of the same age his friend Tu Fu tells of a frightened old man jumping a wall to escape the recruiting officer; his elderly wife, the only other fit person left in the family, offers herself as a camp-follower in his place. 'The night was dead, the sound of talking ceased. I seemed to hear sobbing and lamentations.'

For thousands of years, poets and peasants have looked on at the spectacle of human violence, and in every age a few people have tried to come to grips with the problem. But, quite suddenly, in the sixties of the present century, this problem of human violence has begun to excite more serious and widespread attention than ever before. Symposia are held, conferences are summoned, books are written, research projects are financed on an increasing scale. There are at least four reasons for this.

To begin with, we are living in an unusually violent age. On average, every hour of the year 1964 saw two or three people wounded in Britain and one person murdered in the United States. Every such crime of private violence causes suffering to some, but public violence in the modern world can reach a far more menacing scale. Since the Second World War almost every country on earth has been the scene of civil disturbances, ranging from brief riots with few casualties to the conflict in the Congo, which has already caused hundreds of thousands of deaths and is classified as a war. Some of these local conflicts appear only sporadically in our newspapers, like the Kurd revolt in Iraq, which is said to have produced some 200,000 refugees, the civil war in Indonesia which (including executions) may have killed more than 300,000 people, and the fighting in southern Sudan, which is reported to have reduced the local population by about one million. Between 1945 and 1964 thirty conflicts were sufficiently international to be called wars; the most murderous were the mutual massacres of Indians and Pakistanis and the Korean conflict, which brought a death-roll of millions. Since then, an organised war has been fought between India and Pakistan, and the war in Vietnam has become steadily more ferocious; by February 1966 the Americans were bombing there at two and a half times the rate used in Korea.

Since man first lived in cities and wrote history, there have always been wars. Between A.D. 1500 and 1900, for instance, 250 major wars were fought by European powers, each involving more than 50,000 troops; they included thirteen general wars, involving nearly all the great powers at once. Many past wars have given rise to large-scale atrocities. In 260 B.C. King Chao Hsiang of the state of Ch'in in China cut off the heads of more than 400,000 men who had surrendered on a promise of quarter. Similar procedures by Mongol armies, assisted by famine and disease, reduced the population of China by about forty millions in the course of the thirteenth century A.D. But death-rates by violence in the twentieth century are without precedent. It is probable that, during the winter of 1941–2 alone, the German army deliberately starved or froze to death something like two million Russian prisoners of war.

These monstrous death-rates result in part from the fact that modern populations are so large: there are now more people to kill. Everything in our populous age is on the grand scale, even death. But even proportionately, in numbers of troops (and especially civilians) killed per million of population, ours is one of the more violent centuries in history, much more so, for instance, than the preceding one. In 1933 Pitirim Sorokin worked out an index of violence which took account of differences in total population. By that year (in which Hitler rose to power) the twentieth century was *already*, on Sorokin's reckoning, more than twenty-five times as violent as the nineteenth. As the present century continues, wars are becoming more and more bloody, brutal and destructive. By human violence alone (not counting deaths from disease), the First World War killed about ten million people, the Second World War killed about fifty millions; and the Korean war, though localised to one country, killed more than nine millions. In the First World War civilians made up only 5 per cent of the dead, in the Second World War between 50 and 75 per cent (estimates vary), in the Korean war, 84 per cent. In Vietnam the percentage may turn out to be even higher. Thus, to an increasing extent, war is affecting the whole life of the peoples exposed to it. To produce this record of mounting savagery, nuclear conflict was not required. The two atom bombs dropped on Japan were insignificant weapons by the standards of the sixties; the conventional bombing of Hamburg in July 1943 (Operation Gomorrah) killed about as many people as the atom bomb dropped on Hiroshima.*

The violence of our age is one reason for the present concern with the problem; a second is the lurking presence of nuclear weapons. By November 1965 the load of the combined rocket forces of the United States and the Soviet Union was equivalent to nearly two tons of high explosive for every person on earth. The earlier wars of the century already caused drastic interruptions of technical and social progress. Graphs show that the progress of industrialisation in Russia (compared, for instance, with that of the United States) was grievously set back by the civil war (with foreign intervention) that followed the revolution of 1917. The Second World War inflicted a similar set-back on the world consumption of agricultural chemicals, a very general indicator of technical advance. Both these set-backs were,

* Comparisons of violence in different centuries, by Sorokin and others, have been collated by Quincy Wright in *A Study of War* (2nd ed., 1965). They are discussed further in our Chapter Five, pp. 170 ff. The absolute war casualty estimates are taken from Wright's massive book and from another well-documented work, T. Stonier's *Nuclear Disaster* (see Notes, pp. 301 ff., and Bibliography, pp. 313 ff., where these and all other authorities used are specified). Popular accounts often tend to underestimate the casualties in recent wars.

however, transient, and were followed by recovery. Wars have always left legacies of trouble; in 1965 there were still 200,000 foreign refugees left in West Germany, including a second generation. But the effects of nuclear war would be very much more devastating.

It is true that war has led even in the past to destruction on a massive scale, irreversible for centuries. The most spectacular example is supplied by the history of a vast belt of land, which extends from Morocco to Turkestan and includes the Near and Middle East. Throughout this region, rainfall is irregular and drought a constant menace; but, by the control of rivers and streams, irrigated crops could once be grown on an ample scale. It was within this region that civilisation began; by the second millennium B.C., cities had reached populations of several hundred thousands, and they continued to be greater than any European cities built before the sixteenth century A.D., except those (like ancient Rome) which imported their food from North Africa and the Near East. Places like Tunisia, Israel, Jordan and Syria were among the granaries of the world. High civilisation prevailed over large parts of the belt at times when Europe was barbarous and illiterate. Yet, by the twentieth century A.D., the whole belt lay in ruins. In the days of the Caliph Harun al Rashid (eighth–ninth centuries A.D.), Iraq had a population of over thirty millions, densely settled over the land. A cock that crowed in Mosul, they said, could be heard (by rousing a chain of other cocks to crow) in Basra, 700 miles away. Baghdad alone housed two million people. By the twentieth century, the population of all Iraq had shrunk to less than five millions. In Afghanistan, once the seat of great empires (like the Ghaznavids in the eleventh century A.D.), less than 3 per cent of the land was under crops in 1964. Remains of great Roman cities dot the deserts of Tunisia. Near Qal'at Sim'an in Syria, the ruins of forty-two ancient towns may be compared with the fourteen hamlets still occupied: the desert around is littered with ruined oil and wine presses. By the early twentieth century A.D. nothing but wilderness covered the area where, early in the second millennium B.C., 'Lot lifted up his eyes, and beheld all the plain of

Jordan, that it was well watered everywhere, even as the garden of the Lord.' Today every country in the whole belt (except subsidised Israel and the smaller oil-rich Arab states) is a 'developing' country — that is, a poor one, with a low average income, relatively little industrial development, low rates of literacy and all the other marks of national poverty.

Many factors combined to bring about this great reversal of fortune, the largest-scale tragedy in the history of man. The climate made the region vulnerable. On the river Euphrates, the only method of irrigation possible without modern technology had the effect of making the surface soil gradually more salty and sterile. High taxation helped to ruin agriculture; the European crusaders, who built their castles in the Levant, were welcomed by their subjects because they took *only half* the peasants' produce in taxes. But there is no doubt that the main cause of the tragedy was human violence, in the form of wars between the agricultural civilisations and, above all, between them and the nomadic shepherds on the fringes of the surrounding deserts. The high taxes were themselves partly due to this. A general sequence of events can be followed all over the belt. Destructive wars and invasions led to the neglect and collapse of irrigation works, and in these times of anarchy the shepherds swarmed over the land, cutting down trees and overgrazing the vegetation. For lack of protective plant cover, large areas dried up, and others were devastated by soil erosion. Meanwhile, in many places, neglected irrigation canals turned to stagnant marshes, ideal breeding-grounds for malarial mosquitoes. Malaria incapacitates those whom it does not kill; it demoralised the farmers and prevented reconstruction. And now the efforts of a century at least, with all the resources of modern technology, will be needed to restore this vast region to anything like its former prosperity.

All this was the consequence of human violence. But it took thousands of years, with two outstanding catastrophes in succession (the Arab conquest of the seventh century and the Mongol invasion of the thirteenth century A.D.), and this in a region liable to terrible drought. Thermonuclear warfare would operate on a different time-scale: it could ruin a society in months, even in a temperate climate.

The consequences of a thermonuclear attack would be manifold, and their combined effects are difficult to predict. It is calculated that one large bomb, exploded in Manhattan, New York, would probably kill at least seven million people directly, chiefly by fire; London would fare even worse. This, of course, would only be the beginning. The loss of other cities, let alone the capital, could knock out a nation's economy; the American machine-tool industry, for instance, (vital for all other industries) is concentrated in half a dozen cities other than New York. The disruption of transport, the strain on all services and the loss of skilled manpower would start a vicious spiral. (In milder form, such disruptive effects could result from large-scale evacuations or retreats into shelters, even without a bomb dropped.) Most menacing of all is the threat to public health, precariously maintained in the modern world by a network of services, already under strain from population growth. In the First World War epidemics killed three times as many people as direct violence. In the Second World War only one-sixth of the deaths were from disease, owing to improved control of public health. No such immunity could be expected in a thermonuclear war, which would create conditions ideal in every way for the outbreak of large-scale epidemics. In 1962 two famous exercises were held in Europe to simulate the effects of a thermonuclear attack; the hospital services were shown to break down immediately.

Bombs bursting on or near the ground throw quantities of dust into the atmosphere and cause a fall-out of radioactive material over wide areas. The effects of this are themselves manifold and often bizarre. Observations have been made on Rongelap Atoll in the Marshall Islands, accidentally exposed to fall-out from the test explosion on Bikini in March 1954. They show that insects are much less vulnerable to radioactive fall-out than either the plants they attack or the birds and mammals that normally prey on them. Extensive fall-out could thus bring about explosions of insect populations, which might destroy large areas of vegetation and create the conditions for wide-spread soil erosion. The quantity of dust particles in the atmosphere after the bomb explosions could even affect the world climate. The eruption of Mount Tomboro, on Soembawa Island in Indonesia, in April 1815 made the following year famous, on the other side of the world, as 'eighteen hundred and freeze-to-death', or 'the year without a summer'. It has been calculated that the great wheatlands of Canada could be rendered too cold to grow wheat for several years, by the explosion of a few hundred bombs *somewhere else*.

These effects (all acting and interacting together) are only a few of the known hazards of thermonuclear conflict, not to speak of the ultimate weapons of biological warfare, the deliberate spread of diseases of man, livestock and, above all, crops. The menace of all these weapons is a second reason for the present concern with the problem of violence. A third reason arises not from possible risks but from a more immediate threat: the mounting cost of what is nowadays called 'defence'. British military expenditure doubled in the course of the 1950s. World expenditure on war preparations in 1962 has been estimated as about £43,000 million; by January 1966, a defence budget of nearly half this sum was being presented in one country (the United States) alone. The cost of the Vietnam war at that date was officially stated as more than £10 million a day; by April 1966, according to Sir Robert Thompson, leader of the British Advisory Mission to Vietnam, it was already costing appreciably more still. It is not only the bigger and more publicised wars that drain money; in 1965, armed intervention in the Yemen was costing the United Arab Republic (Egypt) £357,000 a day.

Much of the expenditure on defence is literally thrown away, in consequence of the pace of modern weapon technology. The arms race has given rise to two new principles of military economics. The first (established in the United States by a detailed investigation of seventeen projects) is that any weapons project eventually costs, if all goes according to plan, between twice and seven times the original estimate. The second principle has been summed up in the epigram 'if you can use it, it's obsolete'. In 1963, in response to a request made in the House of Commons, the British Minister of Aviation published a list of thirty major projects cancelled before going into service since 1951, at a total cost (on the Ministry's estimate) of £239,465,000.

The amount budgeted in the United States in January 1966, to pay for one year of the war in Vietnam, would have covered two-thirds of the total budget proposed in the Third Five-Year Plan (1961–6) for developing the vast society of India, where (famines apart) some 150 million people were already reckoned to be grossly undernourished in 1961. But military expenditure is not only a tragic waste from the world viewpoint, it is a serious menace to the developed nations themselves. In the American budget just mentioned, the expansion of the government's campaign against poverty at home was severely slowed down to pay for the Vietnam war; and the United States is not, of course, the only developed nation where war expenses are paid out of the people's welfare. But this is not all. War expenditure, even without the fabulous expenses of modern technology, has actually bankrupted nations in the past, such as France in the eighteenth century (generally losing the wars) and Spain in the sixteenth (generally 'winning' them). The cost of defence must have helped to rock the pound sterling in the 1960s; it may now begin to dislodge the dollar. On 27 January 1966 President Johnson warned Congress that the cost of the Vietnam war was liable, unless special measures were taken, to lead to rising prices in the United States.*

Human violence, in short, has never been more prevalent, dangerous or costly than it is today. It has also never been more constantly before people's eyes, and this is the fourth and perhaps the chief reason why the problem is arousing more interest

* The war costs continued to mount and, sure enough, the prices rose. Between January and August 1966 the increase in the cost of living in the U.S.A. was nearly three times the average increase between 1958 and 1964. This was reported soon after our paragraph was written.

than ever before. In the past, despite all the fighting that was taking place, it was possible for many individuals at favoured times and places to live out their lives without coming into contact with the more extreme forms of violence. Even during a major war, those not in the firing-line could be remarkably unconcerned. We possess the journal, written by a certain Joseph Farington, of a sightseeing tour of the north of Britain in the summer of 1801. Mr Farington's party visited Nuneham Courtenay, Blenheim Palace, Dovedale, Mr Arkwright's Manufactories at Cromford (at the spearhead of the Industrial Revolution), Harewood House, Edinburgh (where they met Boswell's daughter and heard about the fashionable portrait-painter Raeburn) and Perthshire. The journal is full of detail; it tells us that Arkwright's child-labourers earned up to 3s 6d a week at the age of ten, that a fire in an Edinburgh hotel room cost 9d a day, that the Duke of Devonshire's horse Childers had broken a record at Newmarket. The tourists reached Perth, according to the journal, at an inconvenient time, when all the inns were crowded with locals attending the annual balls. News of peace with France reached Perth when Farington's party was staying there, but the journal does not mention this; nor does it anywhere make any reference to the increasingly serious war which Britain had been fighting with her neighbours across the Channel for the past eight years.

Modern transport and communications, making the world one, have changed all this. Newspapers with high circulation, radio, the cinema, and above all television bring violent events daily before our eyes from the ends of the earth. Today those without first-hand experience do not have to read history books to learn what human violence can do to individual people. They have only to watch the films on television of the men, women and children of such stricken lands as Vietnam. The sufferings that lie behind statistics of crime, riot and war are presented to us in their most vivid and personal terms. No wonder then that man is at last preparing in earnest to tackle, and it may be to solve, the age-old problem of human violence.

2

Any approach to the problem of violence must depend on the view taken of the nature, causes and origin of human aggression. For thousands of years there have been essentially two schools of thought about human aggression and its expression in violent crime, riot and war. In various guises this fundamental difference has recurred again and again, cutting across many other divisions (for instance, in religious beliefs); exponents of both views can be found in widely different civilisations.

Some people have said that aggression is human nature, and in some form or other will always be with us. Aggressiveness is 'a fundamental property of human beings, which is very difficult to suppress by any environmental influences'. It is 'an innate disposition in man'. 'The idea that we can get rid of aggression seems ... to be nonsense.' Violence will out; it is a natural means of self-assertion. It is a thing we have to live with, for which we must find outlets. It is idle to remove frustrations and stresses and improve the lot of mankind. People are so inherently murderous, however well they are treated, that they will always have to be sternly controlled by punishment or the threat of it, or deluded into expressing aggression in relatively harmless ways. They may even have to be allowed what are nowadays called limited wars, like the war in Vietnam. Since all alike are naturally aggressive, people differ only in their readiness to face the fact; and those who are most aware of their aggressiveness are best qualified to keep the rest in order. Conflict between human groups is inevitable, and the relations between nations are simply a struggle for absolute dominance status, in which one side must always win, and one side must always 'back down' and lose; in the conduct of these relations, the only way to limit violence is by gradations of threat designed to terrify the opponent into submission. Not all believers in inherent aggressiveness have pushed the argument to these lengths; many have been humane and thoughtful people. Nevertheless, this line of thought, with all its ramifications, is based on the notion of an inherent urge to aggressive behaviour *irrespective of conditions*; we may call it the *unconditional** view of human aggression.

Other people have taken a *conditional** view: that human aggression is a response to intolerable frustrations, and that violence is a *symptom* of stresses in human societies, and in their relations with their natural surroundings: for instance, the stress of shortage of food. Treating symptoms is never a complete solution in medicine or elsewhere. However, we can use this symptom to diagnose social disease. On this view, violence is no more inevitable than famine or pestilence. It is a problem we can hope to solve, just as we have solved to some extent the problem of epidemic disease. It is not an easy problem, but we can at least set about finding the social stresses, and how to relieve them. Some people, who have suffered unusual stresses in their upbringing, are likely to be very much more aggressive than others. These people are suffering from a real sickness, and should not be permitted to exert wide influence on their societies. On the contrary, the ideal leaders are those best able to satisfy their own and other people's needs with the least aggression; and such leaders can do much to reduce violence. In world affairs the problem is to determine the real needs and fears of different peoples, and how to meet them in a realistic way to the benefit of all.

This age-long debate between unconditional and conditional views of aggression is by no means a cloudy argument. The balance between the two views affects the handling of a wide variety of important practical issues. Ultimately it must help to determine how much mankind spends on 'defence', and how much on research and action to improve the conditions of human life. To decide between these two views of aggression, on the

---

* The words 'unconditional' and 'conditional' are used here in their ordinary English sense (with no reference to the technical terminology of 'conditioning' or 'conditional reflexes'). All we mean is that one school of thought postulates an unconditional urge to aggressive behaviour, while the other suggests that this urge arises only in some conditions, and not in others.

basis of objective evidence, is therefore a question of considerable importance for the future of mankind.

The evidence of past history (and even prehistory), right up
to the middle of the twentieth century A.D., appears to favour
the conditional view. It provides abundant indications that violence is a reaction to stress, and that human aggression becomes
serious only when things are getting tough. In the twelfth century A.D. the Chinese author Hung Mai examined the evidence
from Chinese history on the incidence of civil violence. 'Since
the days of antiquity,' he concluded, 'the appearance and cessa-
tion of brigandage has been dependent on famines brought
about by floods and droughts. Driven by cold or hunger, men
gather together with loud cries intent on pillage.' The rule has
continued to operate since he stated it. The Boxer Rising of
1900, for instance, in which many people were massacred, began after two ruinous harvests, a plague of locusts and a particularly disastrous flood of the Yellow River; it started, like
many earlier risings, in the Province of Shantung (at the mouth
of the river), which is especially subject to floods. A few examples
from other parts of the world will suffice at this point to provide
material for conclusions like that of Hung Mai.

In the course of the fifth and fourth millennia B.C., pioneers
from the Mediterranean brought the practice of agriculture to
northern Europe. The earliest of these pioneers entered the
region from the Balkans by the valley of the Danube, and have
therefore been called the Danubians; they eventually spread
right across Europe as far as Belgium. They kept strictly to a
particular kind of soil called loess, which forms a corridor
across the Continent. This soil was naturally well drained, easy
to till with their simple stone-bladed hoes, and occupied by a
woodland less dense than the forest which then covered the rest
of Europe. The Danubians, who had few livestock animals,
would clear a piece of ground, grow wheat and barley till the
soil of the plot was exhausted (in about ten to twenty-five years)
and move on, to return later when the soil there had recovered.
This method of 'shifting cultivation' was developed in the
tropics, for various reasons, into an elaborate farming system;

in A.D. 1957, it was estimated that 200 million people were still using it there. In Europe it was eventually completely replaced (except in parts of Finland) by systems of settled farming, in which the same land can be used year after year.

Shifting cultivation, especially in the primitive form used by the Danubians, requires a large amount of land and a low density of population. As their numbers rose, the surplus Danubian population pressed ever farther west into the forest; by about 4220 B.C., they had reached Magdeburg. But eventually the supply of loess land, the only kind they could tackle with their simple equipment, began to run short.

Now the earlier villages of the Danubians were unfortified, and their graves then contained only tools for farming and hunting. Evidently, when there was still plenty of land, they lived at peace with one another. Their later villages, built when land was running short and the pressure of population began to be felt, had business-like fortifications, and their graves contained weapons of war. From the nature of shifting cultivation, the same places were often occupied more than once, with long intervals between; so the evidence of earlier peace and later war can be found at the same sites. At Köln-Lindenthal, near Cologne, the earlier Danubian village of twenty-seven households was merely fenced against wild beasts; the later village of thirty-five households was protected by a defensive ditch and rampart, which must have taken nearly 3000 man-days of labour to make. Evidently war among the Danubians was a direct consequence of land shortage for a rising population. These people began to fight only when hunger stared them in the face.

In more recent periods, with a money economy and elaborate relations between distant regions, matters become more complicated; but the same fundamental connection between stress and violence can still be traced. In the Southern States of America, the terrible practice of lynching Negroes was already well established by 1880, after the successive stresses of the pioneering epoch, the slave economy, the Civil War, and the dreadful period of 'Reconstruction', in which Northern politicians inflicted ruin and disruption on the South. (Why violence took this particular form, we shall consider later, pp. 107 ff.) By the same date the region's economy had become dangerously specialised for cotton production. Between 1880 and 1940 the economic condition of the South was closely geared to the price of cotton on the world market, and a falling price meant disaster, one way or another, for the whole region.

The overproduction of Southern cotton led to a glut on the world market, which caused the price to start falling in the 1880s. In the last decade of the nineteenth century, the price of cotton plunged to its lowest level in history. In that same decade 1111 Negroes were lynched (about one-third of the total of 3397 lynchings in the fifty-six years between 1882 and 1939). In the first decade of the twentieth century, because cotton production had drastically fallen in the general ruin, the world price began to recover; at the same time, the establishment of mills for processing the cotton in the South offered new forms of employment and brought some measure of improvement in the economy. In that decade the number of lynchings dropped to 791. From 1910 to 1929 the price of cotton rose, the Southern economy improved, and the number of lynchings steadily declined: only seven occurred in 1929 itself. But by this time cotton was again being overproduced in the South, other parts of the world had begun to produce it in competition, and the world demand began to be affected by the beginning of the Great Depression. The price of cotton fell again in 1929–30, and completely collapsed in 1931. At the same time the depression itself hit the South. Lynching showed an immediate resurgence; from 7 in 1929 the number rose to 20 in 1930, and in the following 5 years there were 75 lynchings. The situation was gradually improved by drastically reduced cotton production, a renewed rise in the world cotton price after 1933, Roosevelt's New Deal and the beginnings of a new boom in the later thirties; in 1936, only 8 Negroes were lynched; in 1937, 8; in 1938, 6; in 1939, only 3. Thus, over the whole sixty-year period, lynching increased when the price of cotton fell, and declined when it rose. Clearly here too violence was related to stress.

Often in the past particular incidents of rioting have been ascribed to mere wanton aggressiveness, without real cause for discontent. This has been the theme of many 'easy speeches, that comfort cruel men', and many self-deceptions practised by well-meaning but frightened and confused members of oppressive upper classes. When such incidents are placed under the microscope of history, a different picture generally emerges. A case in point was the rioting by farm-labourers, in the early summer of 1816, in various parts of East Anglia (the English counties of Norfolk, Suffolk, Essex, Cambridgeshire and Huntingdonshire). The most serious of the riots occurred at Bury St Edmunds, Brandon, Norwich, Downham Market, and especially Littleport and Ely. The episode (one of many disturbances in England that year) appears minute on the scale of world history, but, like all such episodes, it caused grave distress to a number of people. The violence was mainly on the side of those who suppressed the riots. The rioters beat up several people, and seriously wounded one soldier in a pitched battle; the authorities shot one rioter while he was trying to escape, hanged seven and punished a number of others by transportation to Australia (sometimes a death-sentence for as many as two-thirds of a ship-load of convicts at that time, owing to the terrible conditions on board).

One of the three judges who tried the rioters in the Special Assizes of 1816 was Edward Christian, who held the odd post of Chief Justice of the Isle of Ely; it is said to have carried a salary of £1500 a year. His career had been, in a way, not uneventful. In 1792 he had campaigned for an enactment which forbade magistrates to issue vagrant passes* until the bearer had either been whipped or imprisoned for at least a week. In 1805 he took part in a disputed election for another legal post, in the course of which he barricaded himself for two days in the office where the records were kept, was ejected, returned and finally got his

---

* Unemployed labourers, genuinely looking for work outside their own parishes, were usually regarded as 'vagrants', up to no good; they were sent home with a pass to be shown to constables on the way.

B

head stuck in the door until he gave in and 'begged permission to withdraw it'. At Cambridge, where he was Professor of the Laws of England, he was connected with a movement to promote a savings bank, which is said to have 'involved many persons in a heavy loss'. He was also once approached by the authorities of St John's College, some of whose trees had been uprooted by persons unknown. They asked him to draw up a handbill to induce the culprits to own up; his solution was to threaten the offenders with capital punishment. Captain William Bligh was ill advised to ask for this man's younger brother, Fletcher, as mate of the *Bounty* in 1787; after what he must have gone through at home, it is no wonder Fletcher Christian led the most famous mutiny in history.

Because of Edward Christian's special post at Ely, where the chief riot had occurred and the assizes were held, it proved impossible to rid his fellow-judges of this embarrassing colleague. At the end of the trial he gave an address on the subject of the riots. He announced that the rioting labourers had not been suffering any distress; they were 'robust men, in full health, strength and vigour . . . who were receiving great wages', and they had rioted for rioting's sake (expressing, evidently, their innate aggressiveness). The magistrates of the Isle of Ely asked for the speech to be printed and posted up throughout the countryside. This view of the rioters, which was shared by Christian's respectable colleague Charles Abbott (later Chief Justice of England), gained currency in contemporary books about the riots. On these books, inaccurate in several respects, all later accounts of the episode were based, up to as recently as 1954.

In 1965 the historian A. J. Peacock published the results of his new discoveries about the East Anglian riots of 1816. He began by finding a new set of documents about the Littleport and Ely riots that had only just been deposited in the Cambridgeshire Record Office, and proceeded to explore the Treasury Solicitor's Papers at the Public Record Office. Among many other new facts, these documents gave the actual wages being earned by the individual rioters (when employed at all). He built up a general picture of the condition these people were in at the time; parts of it were common to most of England, parts applied specially to the riot areas in East Anglia.

Throughout the wars with France (1793–1815) what is called the 'enclosure' movement went on steadily and rapidly. That is, well-to-do landowners obtained Acts of Parliament entitling them to fence off and appropriate areas which had formerly been common pasture and woodland for all local farmers. Having monopolised the commons, they used them for growing wheat and other cereal crops. They had every incentive to do so, because during the wars, with no foreign competition, the price of home-grown wheat rose like a rocket. The poorer peasants, losing their free pasture, had to get rid of their farm animals, and also had to buy fuel (the price of this was rising too). Many of them had to give up their farms and became landless labourers on the estates of the better-off farmers. As the contemporary reformer Arthur Young put it, 'the poor in these parishes may say: "Parliament may be tender of property; all I know is I had a cow, and an Act of Parliament has taken it from me."'

At the end of the wars, in 1814–15, foreign competition came back and lowered the price of wheat. Many farmers cut down production and laid off their labourers, and a serious unemployment problem arose. In East Anglia other employment was not available, because the only local industry (textiles) had collapsed. The problem was aggravated because new farm machinery, introduced during the wars, made a good deal of farm labour redundant anyway. Public assistance was grossly inadequate, and the workhouses were overcrowded death-traps, where epidemics abounded, and where the inmates often had to wear badges of their pauper status (in one place in Norfolk the badge bore the words 'Infamous Liar'). If the unemployed labourers went poaching to feed their children, they were liable to end up on a prison treadmill, taking 48–50 steps a minute for ten hours a day.

While many labourers were laid off, the others had their wages sharply cut down, and might in any case only be employed for part of the year. The 'great wages' of the eighty

rioting labourers tried at the Special Assizes have been cata-
logued by Peacock. They varied from 4s to £1 per week, but
most of them were getting between 6s and 15s, 'some were unemployed; many were obviously underemployed'. One of them,
for instance, had five children, earned 15s a week, and received
2s a week of public assistance; another, with four children,
earned 8s and got assistance at 1s 3d a week. Beef, veal or lamb
at this time cost about 8d a pound. Coal cost 40s a chaldron;
1816, as we have seen (p. 13), was 'the year without a summer'.

In 1815 the wealthy farmers had succeeded in getting an Act
to prohibit the entry of cheap foreign wheat. In April and May
1816 the price of bread rose steeply; by May a loaf of 4 lb. 5½ oz.
cost 11¾d (evidently a day's wages for some of the rioters). The
riots occurred in these two months, and the first ones broke out
as soon as the price increase began. 'Driven by cold or hunger,
men gathered together with loud cries intent on pillage.' The
rioters, though confused and disorganised, were explicit enough
about their problems. At Brandon, for instance, they told a
magistrate they wanted 'cheap bread, a cheap loaf and pro-
visions cheaper', and a young woman rioter (described as 'very
good looking') produced a piece of paper, on which a literate
labourer had written: 'Bread or blood in Brandon this day.' In
the riot at Littleport and Ely the crowd demanded cheaper
flour. At the village of Upwell a rioter summed up all their feelings. 'Here I am,' he said, 'between Earth and Sky — so help
me God. I would sooner loose my life than go home as I am.
Bread I want and Bread I will have.' Such were the rioters of
East Anglia in 1816, believed for nearly 150 years to be well-
paid people expressing their inherent aggressiveness in violence.

The Ely judges were simply unaware of the connection between violence and the stress of food shortage. Not all authorities have been so blind, as we can see from an incident in the
history of show-business. In the year 1594, when the London
theatre boom was well under way, somebody in the biggest
management group came up with the bright idea of a play
about Sir Thomas More, the Lord Chancellor of England beheaded by King Henry VIII in 1535 for refusing to accept the

authority of Crown and Parliament over the Church. In the reign of Henry's daughter Elizabeth I, this was political dynamite; nevertheless, Philip Henslowe (the tycoon who controlled the group) decided to risk the investment. A treatment and a skeleton script were commissioned from Anthony Munday, a writer on the pay-roll with a reputation for being 'the best for plots'. A script conference probably followed, at 'the tavern in Fish Street', and the usual gang of script-writers (Chettle, Dekker, possibly Heywood and Kyd) was called in to provide additional scenes and dialogue.

The treatment called for one scene (based on historical fact) in which a crowd of Londoners, excited by a rise in the price of bread, is mobbing some foreigners whom they illogically blame for their troubles; Sir Thomas More makes a speech and stops the riot. Nobody wanted to touch this scene, so it was offered to an expert from another management. Maybe he was interested, maybe he wanted to help out his fellow-writers (he was that kind of man), or maybe the money was right. Anyway, the expert took on the hot scene and wrote a fine speech for the hero, in which he warns the crowd that violence is catching, and that if this sort of thing got out of hand, 'men like ravenous fishes would feed on one another'.

The whole product (in six handwritings) was eventually sent to Edmund Tilney, Master of the Revels, the official stage censor. Sure enough, he took one look at the crowd scene, and wrote firmly in the margin: 'Suppress the riot and the causes thereof, at your risk and peril.' The cut did not help Henslowe's investment, because on second thoughts Tilney decided to ban the whole show, which was never printed or staged. (The script stayed in Tilney's files, and was only discovered by a scholar in 1844.) The author of the riot scene (the best thing in the show) had his consolations for the disappointment; he even managed to use some ideas from it in later works. Unlike most writers, he got into management (a group of actor-managers); this gave him considerable control over his own scripts, most of which he wrote without co-authors. He never made much as a writer, but his position in management gave him a cut from all these properties. He died a wealthy man, in a fine new house in his hometown of Stratford on Avon.

The censor's reaction to William Shakespeare's riot scene was never exactly surprising (it certainly cannot have surprised the script-writers). But this official sensitivity about bread riots is even more understandable in the light of a study published in 1964 by the economic historian W. G. Hoskins. He compiled lists and graphs of the changing price of bread in England from 1480 to 1619. He found that, in the early Tudor period, the price showed wild fluctuations. He ascribes this to very low margins of food and money, so that a poor harvest, caused by bad weather, produced a serious immediate shortage of bread, which drastically raised the price for that year.

Hoskins also found that, during this part of the period, high bread prices tended to occur in *runs* of several years in succession. He suggests that, after a bad harvest, part of next year's seed had to be used for food; hence next year there was less grain to sow, and things got worse and worse until the next year of exceptionally good weather. This terrible dilemma of eating next year's seed is not a thing of the remote past only; it was experienced in parts of China during the 1950s, for lack of food or money reserves after decades of invasion and civil war. And English farming methods in Tudor times were very much less productive than those of modern (or even ancient) China. At Heighton St Clair in Sussex, according to the historian J. Cornwall (writing in 1954), the bad harvest of 1562 gave only three times as much grain (of wheat, barley and oats) as the amount that had been sown.*

In early Tudor England both the bad years and the bad runs meant really desperate shortage of food; as Hoskins writes, 'death [from starvation] must have been as common a sight as on a battle-field'. He observed that the bad years and

* In Elizabethan England the ratio of wheat yield to seed sown could be as high as 8 : 1 in a good year in a productive district. This is still low by more recent standards. The *average* ratio for all the years from 1895 to 1914 over the whole of England was 11·4 : 1. Already by that time, the ratio of yield to seed had ceased to be a critical problem. Modern ratios may be over 20 : 1.

the bad runs corresponded in time to outbursts of violence: political crises, rioting and executions. There was, for instance, a very bad year in 1549, bad enough to keep prices high for the next two years. The year 1549 saw Ket's Rising, one of the most serious revolts of the century. Violence in Tudor England was thus an outcome of the same kind of stresses as those present in East Anglia a couple of centuries later. Here, too, on a much larger scale, it was a case of 'bread or blood'.

In 1558–93, during more than three-quarters of the reign of Elizabeth I, the price fluctuations were much smaller, and there were noticeably fewer bad years and especially bad runs. Over the same period, relatively speaking, England enjoyed an unprecedented relief from public violence. The reign is of extraordinary interest from this point of view, and we have devoted our fifth appendix to it; a crucial factor was the outstandingly good leadership provided by the queen. A marginal reserve of food and money was created, which made the country proof against the occasional bad harvest; there was generally enough to eat and enough seed for next year. Permanent grain stores had already been set up (since 1556) in many towns, such as Norwich and Great Yarmouth. An Act passed in 1563 restrained the tendency to take land out of food production (for producing wool, then extremely profitable). The export of wheat was prohibited. Above all, largely through Elizabeth's own efforts, the finances of the country were restored and maintained (see Appendix Five), so that money was available for importing cheap foreign grain in years of bad harvest at home.

Unfortunately, in the 1590s the weather did its worst. In 1593, after three excellent harvests, the laws promoting food production and prohibiting wheat export were relaxed. There followed four appalling years (1594–7), when rain fell solidly over Europe from Ireland to Silesia, producing a *natural* run of bad harvests at home and abroad. Even Elizabeth could not cope with this. The price of bread rocketed, the population had risen since early Tudor times, and the violence that now broke out was on a larger scale than ever. In 1597–8, the agricultural measures were re-enacted, together with the first important

welfare legislation in modern Europe. But the catastrophe had
been great, and the reign of Elizabeth ended with several years
of violent unrest. This final outbreak is the measure of her earlier
achievement in reducing violence.

It is no wonder the government censor in 1594 wanted no
public performance of scenes about bread riots, no wonder he
wrote: 'Suppress the riot and the causes thereof.' At this stage,
there was not much the government could do to relieve the situation (unlike the government of 1816, which could have brought
in cheap food from abroad). Elizabeth may have been alone (as
we shall see) in grasping the importance of stringent economy
on the part of the government. But the connection between food
shortage and violence was familiar to everyone in that government, from the queen to the censor. The experience of these
practical and unsentimental people was admirably summed up
by one of the ablest among them, Francis Bacon, in his essay
Of Seditions and Troubles. 'The Rebellions of the Belly,' he wrote,
'are the worst.' He made no mention of inherent aggressiveness. Indeed, he well expressed the conditional view of human
aggression and violence: 'The first Remedy or prevention is to
remove by all means possible that materiall Cause of Sedition
...; which is Want and Poverty in the Estate.'

3

In 1932 the 528 members of the American Psychological Association were sent the question: 'Do you as a psychologist hold
that there are present in human nature ineradicable, instinctive* factors that make war between nations inevitable?' 346
replied 'No'; 10 replied 'Yes'; 22 replied ambiguously; and
150 (as usually happens on such occasions) did not reply at all.
These psychologists may be taken as representative of civilised

---

* At that time, the word 'instinctive' was used by many scientists
to mean 'innate', and not simply 'automatic' or 'impulsive' (as in
the sentence 'I instinctively switched on the radio'). The Latin word
'instinctus' simply means 'impulse'.

opinion at the time. Evidently there was an overwhelming majority for the conditional view. Enough evidence had accumulated to make Bacon's approach to violence and its causes more generally acceptable than ever before.

A quarter of a century later, civilised opinion became less unanimous. Voices began to be heard in favour of 'inherent aggressiveness'. The quotations on p. 16, used to illustrate the unconditional view, are taken from publications of the 1960s. Clearly there has been a resurgence of the unconditional notion that violent aggression is human nature. This is not a meaningless swing of the pendulum. It is the result of recent social changes without precedent in human history, which appeared to offer a kind of test case for the conditional approach to the problem.

By the 1950s the world was divided into highly industrialised ('developed') nations and those in early stages (some in very early stages) of industrialisation (the 'developing' nations). The developed nations (especially those of western Europe and North America) had very much higher national incomes than the others, and in 1958 they were labelled, by the American economist J. K. Galbraith, the 'affluent societies'. The people of these nations, it was said, had 'never had it so good'. The teenagers appeared to have more and better food and more money than their parents or grandparents had dreamed of enjoying.

It is true that these teenagers did not always count their blessings, and this led to considerable complaint from older people, some of them (who had really had it much worse) honestly and understandably bewildered, others more or less envious and bitchy meanagers. Great social changes always bring about misunderstanding between the generations. There is nothing new about complaints of teenage restlessness and ingratitude. The first people in history to become appreciably more affluent were the literate office-workers of ancient Iraq. A collection of clay tablets from the eighteenth century B.C. (translated by the American scholar S. N. Kramer) records the moans of a father in this class to his teenage son. He complains of loafing ('don't stand about in the public square'), insubordination ('be humble

*

and show fear before your monitor'), noisy arguments ('because of your clamourings I was angry with you'), ingratitude
('I never sent you to work to dig up my field'), and lack of enthusiasm for office work ('it is in accordance with ... fate ...
that a son follows the work of his father'). He declares that his
heart is sated with weariness of his son, who has become so 'fat,
big, powerful and puffed', and he ominously remarks that the
rest of the family 'waits expectantly for your misfortune'. And
yet this man is not ignoble, not just a meanager or a heavy father.
In the midst of the tirade he is moved to a passionate defence
of the uses of literacy, for which his son shows so little respect:
written words, he says, bring counsel down the ages, as the
canals bring water from distant places. And after he has got his
complaints off his chest, he ends with a prayer to the gods for his
son's safety, welfare and success. In short he is a well-meaning,
mixed-up adult, like many of us 3700 years later, incapable of
listening to the teenager side of the story — 'I kept away from
you, and heeded not your fears and grumblings, no, I heeded
not your fears and grumblings.'

But whatever the 'fears and grumblings' of the teenagers in
the modern affluent societies, they did appear to be better fed
and clad than their parents had been. For the first time in history, the changes were affecting masses of people, not just a
small élite as in ancient Iraq; and the changes were continuing.
Surely, it was argued, if the conditional view was the right one,
violence should now be on the decrease in the affluent societies;
for were not the old stresses being removed?

On the contrary, there was every evidence from these societies that violent crime was on the increase. The period 1950–60
in England and Wales has been carefully studied from this point
of view by F. H. McClintock and others of the Cambridge Institute of Criminology. Between 1938 and 1950, the annual
number of indictable offences of violence against the person
rose from 2721 to 6249, an increase of 130 per cent. Between
1950 and 1960 the number rose from 6249 to 15,759, an increase
of 152 per cent. This rise is not simply due to population growth
(more people to be violent). In 1950, there were 14·3 such

crimes per hundred thousand of the population; by 1960, the corresponding figure had more than doubled, to 34·4. All kinds of crime have been rapidly increasing, but the proportion of violent crimes has also risen; they made up 1 per cent of all crimes in 1938, 1·4 per cent in 1950 and 2 per cent in 1960. From time to time in the sixties, improved police communications have brought about local improvements (as in Manchester, Birmingham and, by the use of hidden television cameras, in Soho in 1965). But the main trend goes inexorably on. In 1964, the crime total in England and Wales was greater than at any time since records began to be kept; for the first time, there were more than 2000 cases of felonious wounding (there had been less than 200 in 1935). In 1965 crime and violent crime showed further large increases; in London, combined cases of wounding and assaults were 7·5 per cent more numerous than in 1964.

In the United States developments have been similar, except that the problem is on a worse scale. It has been called a 'crime explosion'. Between 1958 and 1962, according to an F.B.I. report, crime increased four times faster than population. In 1965 the increase in major crimes of violence in New York was 13·8 per cent. It was against this background of increasing violence that serious rioting occurred in several American cities in the summer of 1966.

In England and Wales the rate of actual murder has risen far more slowly than that of other violent crimes. (This slow, steady increase has been quite unaffected by changes in the law concerning the death penalty.) In the mid-thirties the average rate was 3·2 murders per million people per year; if we include all killings then classified as murder (some of these have been treated as manslaughter since the Homicide Act of 1957), the corresponding figure for 1964 is 4·0 per million. At a conference in July 1965 Francis Camps, the Home Office pathologist, suggested that some overworked hospital pathologists, when carrying out post-morten examinations, may be missing cases of murder; so the murder rate may not be quite so stable as it looks. Even so, the rise is unlikely to be explosive. In the United States, murder is more prevalent — in 1963 there were 549 murders in New York, compared with 26 in London — and the American murder rate is certainly rising steeply. By 1965, the F.B.I. was reporting one murder every hour, and President Johnson set up a commission for an urgent investigation of the causes of crime in the United States.

Another sign that things are getting worse is the tendency towards violence among the young. The Cambridge criminologists examined the percentage increases from 1950 to 1960 in the numbers of people of different ages convicted of crimes of violence in England and Wales. The increases are as follows: age over 30, *47* per cent; age 25–30, *106* per cent; age 21–5, *130* per cent; age 17–21, *150* per cent; age under 17, *229* per cent. In the United States in 1964, 37 per cent of the serious crimes solved by the police were committed by teenagers under 18 years old; in some places, as many as 79 per cent of arrests for serious crimes were of people under 25. Even in the United States, teenage violent criminals are, of course, a small minority of the nation's teenage population; but it is the trend which is so disturbing. Teenage unrest and violence by some teenagers are not confined to countries of one politicial complexion. Wage increases (e.g. in 1964) and gradual increases in production of consumer goods and retail trade (e.g. the figures for 1961–3) show that the Soviet Union is gradually beginning to move towards Western-style affluence, and is certainly far ahead of most developing countries. In January 1966 teenage violence in Moscow was so acute that the government imposed a temporary street curfew on teenagers. The immediate occasion for this measure was a fight with *finkas* (flick-knives) in Red Square (very like the battles between British 'mods' and 'rockers' a few years earlier) between two gangs who had met to celebrate, with guitars and dancing, their graduation from high school.

To the new exponents of the unconditional view, all this appears proof positive that man is inherently aggressive, and actually needs objects for this causeless aggression. Better his conditions, they say, give him more money, and he becomes more violent than ever, a 'rebel without a cause'. Relief from economic pressures is simply taking the lid off human violence. Relaxation of rigid customs only leaves an exaggerated concern with 'material' things. (This particular argument is probably played down in the Soviet Union, where a form of 'materialism' is the ideology of the State; there the emphasis is on giving the teenagers more hard work.) One British psychiatrist has even suggested (in 1963) that modern teenagers are *not frustrated enough* by their parents; they can no longer find excuses for venting their innate aggressiveness at home. 'The notable increase in juvenile crime in the last twenty years', he writes, 'may actually be connected with the lessening of external frustration. If parents cannot be treated as scapegoats, aggression finds other objects to attack.'

This line of argument, so much at variance with mankind's whole experience before the 1950s, demands careful scrutiny. The affluent societies are certainly hotbeds of crime. One obvious first question is: how affluent are the people of the affluent societies? The affluence of a country is measured in one of two ways: either by totalling the national income, or by counting the total amount of money in circulation. Both measures can be adjusted to take account of different costs of living, and they are divided by the country's population, to get the *average* income or expenditure per head. The two measures give somewhat different results; in 1966 France is lower than the United States by the first measure, and higher by the second. But on either count, the nations of western Europe and North America are enormously richer than the developing nations, and may justly be called affluent societies.

But a high *average* income and a large amount of circulating money do not necessarily mean that everybody is well off. They could mean that a very few people are fabulously wealthy, while the overwhelming majority are extremely poor; this situation has actually occurred for a time in oil-owning Arab states. Average wealth is only half the story; we need to know how the wealth is *distributed*. If many people are poor, then there is obviously plenty of stress to stimulate violence. This was fully appreciated by Francis Bacon, when he wrote the essay we quoted earlier. 'Above all things,' he insisted, dealing with the remedies for violence, 'good Policie is to be used, that the Treasure and Moneyes in a State be not gathered into few Hands. For otherwise, a State may have a great Stock and yet starve. And Money is like Muck, not good except it be spread.'

In 1962 careful studies of the distribution of national wealth were published by R. M. Titmuss for Britain and by G. Kolko for the United States. Kolko showed that inequality in the United States was so extreme as to make the 'affluent society' almost a myth. The motor-car, for instance, is often taken as the symbol of affluence for the masses (though in countries like the United States it is often a necessity for getting to work). In 1956 the richer 50 per cent of the American people bought 88 per cent of the nation's cars. In Britain, Titmuss concluded that 'there is more than a hint from a number of studies that income inequality has been increasing since 1949, while the ownership of wealth . . . has probably become still more unequal, and, in terms of family ownership, possibly strikingly more unequal, in recent years'. Present-day increase in inequality, like teenage crime, is not restricted to countries of similar political institutions. According to the British economist Margaret Miller, in the early days of the Revolution the highest-paid Russians received only twice as much as the lowest-paid ones; by about 1930, the ratio was 8 : 1; by the fifties it was up to 15 : 1.

Inequality will be an important theme of our book, but at this point we need only consider how much 'Want and Poverty' it means. Any study of present-day poverty in the 'affluent societies' (especially the United States) at once removes much of the force of the unconditional argument about violent crime. In the United States, the Works Progress Administration before the Second World War, and the Bureau of Labour Statistics after it, worked out levels of family income called 'maintenance' and 'emergency' budgets. A maintenance budget will maintain 'a level of adequate living', but *not* 'an abundant life'; in such a family, for instance, the wife can only buy a new skirt once in five years, but there are cheap cuts of meat on the table several days a week. An emergency budget is defined as 70 per cent of the maintenance one; those forced to live at this rate 'for an extended period may be subjected to serious health hazards'. On Kolko's careful reckoning, in 1957 *at least 44 per cent* of American families had incomes below the maintenance level, and at least 27·5 per cent were below the emergency level. The corresponding figures for 1935–6 were 49 per cent and 28 per cent. Kolko concludes that the poverty in the United States is as serious as ever, and growing: 'the predominantly prosperous middle-class society is only an image in the minds of isolated academicians'. Between 1953 and 1964, the number of recipients of public assistance rose by about 40 per cent. Teenagers have special problems of their own; between 1953 and 1962 the percentage of young people (under 24) unemployed more than doubled, to 11 per cent. 'I'll tell you, man,' said one seventeen-year-old, quoted in 1964 by the American journalist Edgar May, 'I go to Catholic Charities, to the Youth Center, down by the employment people — a couple of weeks ago I tried to buy a job. . . . You go from place to place, you know, and you get tired. . . . Guys say no work, no nothin', no work. . . .'

Elderly people do not, of course, make much direct contribution to violent crime; but their living conditions are some indication of what many people can look forward to in the 'affluent society'. At the time of his death in 1963, the late Senator Estes Kefauver was performing his last act of public service, as chairman of the Senate Subcommittee on Anti-trust and Monopoly. In his book on the subject, written just before he died, he tells how certain big American drug houses were arranging among themselves to keep the prices of essential drugs as high as possible, while spending large sums on competitive advertising (not always accurate). The Subcommittee hearings had already resulted in the passage of the Kefauver–Harris legislation in October 1962, which put a check on these practices. They had been remarkably profitable. In 1929, a druggist in Atlantic City paid less than $1000 for some shares in one of the big drug corporations. The stock was still in his safe when his widow died in 1958: the lucky heirs discovered that by that time it was worth $477,000. The case of a drug marketed by another firm casts light on the position of many older people in the United States. A number of letters came in to the Subcommittee from elderly people suffering from arthritis. Because of the artificially high price of the drug prescribed to relieve their pain, it cost them exactly half their social security payments. Their budget simply could not cover both food and drugs; regularly, towards the end of every month, they had to choose between the alternative pains of hunger and arthritis.

The British National Health Service is, as we shall see, under strain from population growth. As long as it lasts, however, old people in Britain will be free from such cruel dilemmas. In general, poverty in Britain (like violence) is on a less frightening scale than in the United States. Nevertheless, British affluence is distinctly patchy, as is particularly obvious in places like Glasgow and Belfast. In 1964 a physician working in a London clinic described the 'fairly typical budget' of an unmarried coloured mother. She earned £7 17s a week as a cleaner, paid £3 10s in rent and £1 10s to a baby-minder, leaving £2 17s per week to feed and clothe herself and the child. 'How she manages on this money I have no idea', writes the doctor. 'Hers is by no means the worst case of poverty I have come across.' He contrasts this budget with the Ministry of Labour statement that in 1962–3 the *average* British family spent £18 7s 4d per week. In 1962, British economists D. Cole and J. E. G. Utting published the results of a survey of the living conditions of elderly people in several places in England and Scotland. They made a tentative estimate that in 1959–60 nearly two and a half million old people were living 'very near to the poverty line as determined by National Assistance standards'. 'If my shoes have to go to be repaired', one seventy-year-old widow told them, 'then I have to rely on selling something from the garden to make it up, otherwise I couldn't manage.' A doctor in the county of Somerset has calculated that a hard winter will kill anything from 20,000 to 100,000 old people from diseases associated with 'hypothermia' (Greek for 'underheating'), because they cannot afford adequate fuel. In the freezing winter of 1963, one eighty-three-year-old in Worcestershire was found dead in front of his cold fire-grate; he had gradually bricked it up to take smaller (cheaper) fires, till it measured 2½ inches across and 4 inches deep. Old people and unmarried coloured mothers are not, of course, the only British sufferers from poverty; in 1961, 20 per cent of households in the United Kingdom had incomes of less than £10 a week. In 1965, the British sociologists Brian Abel-Smith and Peter Townsend made a serious effort to measure the extent of poverty in Britain. They concluded that in 1960 about 14 per cent of the British people (more than seven million) were living below 'a defined national assistance level of living' which 'reflects what is the official government view of the minimum standard which is tolerable'.

In a left-handed way, business institutions in the 'affluent societies' have shown a definite recognition that many incomes are too low. Business needs a market for consumer goods, and if not enough people can afford to pay for them, credit has to be supplied in the form of hire-purchase arrangements. In the United States, for instance, between 1947 and 1957 this kind of credit rose from 3·5 per cent to 9·9 per cent of the total amount people were earning. The amount of debt, relative to annual income, is naturally heaviest among the poor; this is a reflection, as Kolko has observed, of their need 'to exploit credit in order to keep body and soul together'. Hire-purchase debts naturally give rise to what is sometimes called 'an excessive concern with material things' — in plain English, more or less desperate worries about money.

In Victorian England Benjamin Disraeli observed that the rich and the poor were virtually two nations. Today it is as if each of the 'affluent' developed countries has a developing (poor) nation at home, which is apt to be forgotten in discussions of the plight of developing nations abroad. It is true that, in the scale of human misery, even the slum-dweller of Chicago is probably less wretched than those who sleep in the streets of Bombay; at least he is more unlikely to starve to death.

This reference to the underfed and often literally starving millions of India may serve to remind us that the name of affluent societies, without inverted commas, is justified by a real

difference in certain respects from the developing countries of
today and the developed countries as they were in the past. Real
wages (the amount of goods wages will actually buy) are much
higher for even the poor in Britain and the United States than
they are for the poor in most developing countries; for the
majority of people in the United States, and the great majority
in Britain, they have certainly risen. By 1947 the real wage per
hour of the average American industrial worker was at least
four times as high as it was a century earlier. If social progress
since the thirties has been patchy in Britain and small in the
United States, technical progress has been spectacular in ways
which greatly change the conditions of daily life. On 15 May
1940 the first nylons were on sale in the United States. The
coming of cheap synthetics and plastics has changed human life
in the affluent societies out of all recognition. All except the very
poor are better clad than they were thirty years ago, and in
Britain, at least, habitually barefoot children have become a
rarity. Technical advance has brought other changes without
precedent in history: by 1962 three out of every four British
households had vacuum-cleaners (even if they had not finished
paying for them). Above all, in the affluent societies, people are
better and more regularly fed. There is never the slightest need
to eat next year's seed. Death from starvation is no longer, as it
was in Tudor England and is in modern India, a real and ever-
present threat; malnutrition is no longer (as probably in fourteenth-century Europe and certainly in modern India) the fate of
a third or more of the population. This improvement in nutrition, as well as improved control of infectious disease, is reflected
in length of life. In Tudor England (1550), the average individual at birth could expect to live eight and a half years; today
he or she can expect very nearly the Biblical three-score years
and ten. Average life expectancies in the affluent societies are
the longest in the world. Unlike average incomes, average ages
really do tell us something about a people as a whole. Since
there is still an upper limit, a high average age cannot be the
result of a few centuries-old Methuselahs and a majority who
die young. In fact we can still legitimately use the term 'affluent

societies' (and shall so use it in the rest of this book), if by affluence we mean that there is *no serious shortage of food.*

Despite all the evidence of poverty in these societies, therefore,
they do raise a real problem about violence. In most of the
examples we gave from past history, violence was a result of
failure to get enough to eat; people were driven to it by hunger.
Clearly this is no longer, in these societies, an important driving
force. All the people are better fed, all but the poor are wealth-
ier, even the poor are not getting *less* money or food than before, and very few are actually starving. The removal of desperate hunger might reasonably be expected to reduce violence.
Yet, as we have seen, rates of violent crime have been rising
steeply in the affluent societies since the fifties, and about this
there is no ambiguity or doubt. Does this mean that the unconditional view is right after all, that man is inherently aggressive,
that violence will out, even that people are not being frustrated
enough?

It is at this point, when the human story has become confused
and seemingly ambiguous, that we need another perspective;
we need to look at a simpler situation which will help us to return to the human problem from a new angle. We can find this
new angle in recent evidence, some of it very recent, about violence in societies of higher social animals, especially monkeys
and apes.* The comparison is not as far-fetched as appears at
first sight. The gap between any individual human being (ancient Iraqui, modern Londoner, or Australian aborigine) and
any individual monkey is vast: the human (whatever his or her
racial origin) can learn to talk, read, and gain access to all that
human civilisation has to offer. But the other gap, between a
simple food-gathering human *society* of African bushmen or
Australian aborigines and a food-gathering *society* of monkeys, is
far narrower; in many respects the two are closely comparable.

* Chimpanzees, gorillas, orang-utans and gibbons are called by
scientists 'apes'; they are alike, and different from monkeys proper,
in certain aspects of bodily structure. However, in this book, we shall
be discussing many things common to monkeys and apes, and for
convenience we shall refer to them all as monkeys.

Anthropologists, studying small societies of tribal peoples who use no writing, have enabled us to read between the lines much that goes on in large literate civilisations. The study of monkey societies without even spoken language can help us, in analogous ways, to understand much that goes on without words in human social behaviour. These monkey societies are probably not much unlike those small, chiefly food-gathering bands from which the human genus arose, by the latest count, well over a million years ago.

In 1932, while the American psychologists were declaring their scepticism about man's inherent aggressiveness, a remarkable book was published in London, called *The Social Life of Monkeys and Apes*. It was the work of a young South African anatomist, Solly Zuckerman (now Sir Solly, with a long record of work as both scientist and scientific adviser to British Governments, particularly on defence matters). In 1929–30, Zuckerman had made a detailed study of a large colony of hamadryas baboons at the London Zoo in Regent's Park. The colony had been set up in 1925 by liberating about one hundred baboons on Monkey Hill, 'a large oval rock-work enclosure one hundred feet long and sixty feet wide'. Two more baboons were added somewhat later, and thirty-five more in 1927.

Zuckerman's account of this baboon colony was a pioneering contribution to the study of monkey societies. His observations have been abundantly confirmed by later observers of zoo colonies; his descriptions were clear, objective and precise. Many features of monkey social behaviour in the zoo, studied in detail by later workers, were first recorded and correctly described in Zuckerman's book, which had a deservedly wide influence.

The colony of baboons on Monkey Hill was, of course, an affluent society, supplied by the keepers with a regular abundance of food for all. The behaviour of the colony showed that an affluent society, monkey no less than human, can be anything but peaceful. The monkeys were arranged in a rank order of dominance status, in which high rank was secured by brute strength expressed in aggression, often quite unprovoked. Might was right, and brutal inequality prevailed between those of high and low rank. If a number of bananas was thrown to a group of adults and young, the most dominant animal 'crammed his cheek pouches full of fruit, keeping at his feet what he failed to push into his mouth', while his subordinates made no attempt to get any. When a small baboon was eating, it would 'stop and drop the food from its mouth in evident terror' on the approach of a more dominant individual. At every level of this society, the weaker went to the wall; monkey mothers would snatch food out of the hands of their own babies.

An atmosphere of tension pervaded the colony. Each monkey seemed 'to live in potential fear lest another animal stronger than itself will inhibit its activities'. Quarrelling was so frequent and widespread that the rule of the bigger bosses seemed to be a necessity, if only as a system of brutal repression; and indeed highly dominant monkeys would interfere (often indiscriminately) in the quarrels of their juniors. But in the hierarchy of rank, 'a state of balance is only temporary, and at any moment may be disturbed to a greater or lesser extent'. Violence was therefore a constantly recurring event, and any major disturbance of the equilibrium (such as the death from disease of a high-ranking boss) caused the society to collapse into an anarchic mob, capable of orgies of wholesale carnage. Just as there were no restraints on domination, so in the fighting no holds were barred. Females and young were the principal victims, being the weakest. Sometimes they were injured or killed accidentally in the course of battles raging around them; but Zuckerman saw one male bully twice deliberately attack a baby monkey, which 'was found dead that evening'. The autopsies at Regent's Park are a catalogue of slaughter; they read like a despatch from a war front. Disease, especially in winter, was a serious cause of death; but 8 out of 61 males died by violence, and many others had severe wounds which may have contributed to their deaths. The weaker suffered worse. Of 33 female deaths, 30 were the result of fights: 15 of these died in just over one month of particularly savage conflict. Autopsies were performed on 5 young monkeys born in the colony; all 5 had died of wounds. Such was the nature of life and death in an affluent society of monkeys.

It was a natural conclusion that violence is monkey nature, that monkeys, however well off, are inherently domineering and aggressive. It was a wonder their societies survived at all. As we shall see, Zuckerman himself was too imaginative to suppose that the last word had been written about monkey societies. But, as often happens, the cautions scattered through his book seem to have gone unheeded, to judge from the writings of students of monkey behaviour for a long time afterwards. The notion of violent aggressiveness as an inherent quality of monkeys (or at least of baboons) was impressed upon a whole generation of scientists. By the fifties, when the crime returns from the affluent societies began to hit the headlines, the apparent results of Zuckerman's work may well have influenced a wider public, and helped to bring about the resurgence of the unconditional view of aggression. Alike in monkeys and man, it seemed, the improvement of living conditions is no guarantee against violence; aggressiveness is human nature, monkey nature, a fact of nature in the most fundamental sense. It was against this gloomy setting that news began to filter through from the plains and forests where monkeys live in the wild, news of discoveries that cast a much-needed light on the nature of aggression and the causes of violence in monkeys and man.

Two/The Wild Ones

1

TWENTY years were to pass after the publication of Zucker-man's book, before the British zoologist Michael Chance started (also at Regent's Park) a new wave of research on monkey societies in the zoo. The new observations fully confirmed the original impression of affluent captive monkeys as tense, domineering and aggressive — whether they are hamadryas baboons, cynocephalus baboons, rhesus monkeys, patas monkeys, night monkeys, gibbons or chimpanzees. Meanwhile, however, work was beginning on the more complicated problem of studying monkeys under more natural conditions.

One approach was to install a group of monkeys in a larger, opener and more natural environment than a zoo enclosure. In September 1938 the American scientist C. R. Carpenter trapped over 500 rhesus monkeys in twelve districts near Lucknow, transported them to Calcutta, and shipped them on a 14,000-mile voyage to Cayo Santiago, a warm, damp, well-wooded islet of forty acres off Puerto Rico. Here, in December, he released the 409 survivors. On this island Eden, the monkeys were allowed to roam free, but they were offered pelleted food at five stations, where they came regularly and could be relatively easily observed. The colony is still there; it has been studied in turn by Carpenter himself (1939–40), Stuart A. Altmann (1956–8) and Carl B. Koford (1958 onwards). The monkeys on Cayo Santiago are obviously living in much more natural surroundings than Zuckerman's baboons. But the islet is of limited size. Moreover, the original colony was formed abruptly from monkeys hitherto strangers to each other; and, as we shall see, the stresses of their capture and transportation left enduring marks on the societies they developed. This colony is a kind of half-way stage between the zoo and the wild.

Another kind of opportunity was provided by the extraordinarily stubborn religious taboo against harming the monkeys of India. The monkeys take full advantage of their immunity; according to an estimate made in 1950, the annual bill for damage by monkeys amounts to about £6 million. The scene reported in the *Hindustani Times* in 1960 must surely be unique in the annals of military security. A band of monkeys entered the offices of the Ministry of Defence in New Delhi, seized official documents from the files, tore some of them up and held others to ransom in exchange for sweets or pieces of fruit. Public opinion may be tolerant everywhere about military expenditure on obsolete projects, but it was adamant in India on the subject of injuring monkeys; and there was absolutely nothing the unhappy Ministry staff could do about the invasion.

The taboo applies mainly to langur monkeys, but other species enjoy a kind of reflected glory and privilege. One result is that large numbers of rhesus monkeys live around Indian villages, towns and temple precincts, where they are relatively easy to watch and study. In 1959–60, Charles H. Southwick, Mirza Azhar Beg and M. Rafiq Siddiqi took advantage of this to make detailed observations on the rhesus monkeys of a temple area in Aligarh, in the state of Uttar Pradesh. Here, one might think, if anywhere, monkeys are free for the pursuit of monkey happiness. Yet these urban monkeys are very different from those in the surrounding forests. Even if they or their ancestors have chosen it, their urban environment, crowded with human beings and their buildings, does result in 'certain behavioural distortions', as we shall see. According to their investigators, 'they are essentially living in an unconfined zoo'. Phyllis Jay, who worked in India in 1958–60 on common langur monkeys, found a similar difference between urban and forest communities.

The monkey colony on Cayo Santiago had been through the stresses of abrupt uprooting, transportation and coming to terms with strangers; the monkeys of Aligarh were under the stress of an urban environment. None of these stresses arise in the monkey societies that are being studied in Japan. That country is exceedingly hilly; on more than 60 per cent of its land area slopes are steeper than fifteen degrees. In such terrain, there is danger of flooding and soil erosion unless a good cover of forest is present. The Japanese were among the first peoples to practise forest conservation, and Japan is still rich in woodlands. On the other hand, cultivation is pushed as far as it can be with safety, and in the last century urban development has been spectacular; so the farms, roads and buildings of man spread everywhere in the valleys, splitting the original forest cover into isolated pockets of wooded hillside. Nowhere are human habitation and wild nature so closely intermingled; as a European friend of ours put it, after a recent visit, Japan is like one big park. Throughout Japan (except the northernmost island, Hokkaido), the separate pockets of forest (and small islets off the coasts) are occupied by isolated colonies of the Japanese monkey, a species related to and rather like the rhesus.

Soon after the end of the Second World War, enterprising Japanese scientists (notably the Primate Research Group of Kyoto University) began to study their monkey neighbours. The woods are still dense enough to make observation difficult; but in the summer of 1952 scientists working on the islet of Kōshima found that the local monkey community would take food from them. The monkeys remained free, but they regularly turned up, and stayed for hours, at the place where food was provided; here they could be observed much more closely than before. By the end of the year, the method was being used to study another monkey community (on Mount Takasaki). Later, more than a dozen monkey bands in different places were put under this kind of observation, and in 1956 the Japan Monkey Centre was set up at Inuyama, near Nagoya, to supervise the whole project. The public was generally admitted for a fee to visit these 'open zoos' (which helped to finance the research). The behaviour of the monkeys was somewhat modified (as also on Cayo Santiago) by the provision of food at one restricted spot, instead of scattered through the woods. In the long run, as we shall see, this had dramatic effects. But, at least to begin with, the monkeys were living under much more natural conditions than any we have mentioned yet; at the same time, the observations are as detailed as those made in zoos. The same individual monkeys crop up year after year in successive Japanese publications, till we begin to know them as living personalities; and the Japanese method has provided some of the greatest insights (and surprises) in the study of monkey societies.

But the final comparison, and much additional information, could only be obtained by field workers ready to spend long periods in the plains, hills and forests where monkey societies live wholly in the wild. A few such trips were made in the thirties. Some of the earliest were promoted by Robert and Ada Yerkes, who had been studying the behaviour of individual monkeys for many years in America. Under their auspices, C. R. Carpenter (later the founder of the Cayo Santiago colony) went to the island of Barro Colorado in Central America. This island was formed in 1914 when surrounding areas were flooded as part of the Panama Canal project. Here, in 1931–3, Carpenter studied the societies of howler monkeys, which had lived here continuously, being cut off when the waters rose. The howlers in this natural enclosure, which has been described as a scientist's paradise, have been studied repeatedly, like the Cayo Santiago rhesus colony; further observations were made in 1935, 1951, 1955, 1959 and 1962. Carpenter also made field studies of red spider monkeys in the Coto Region on the borders of Panama and Costa Rica; and in 1937 he was watching gibbons on the hillsides of Thailand. He may fairly be called the pioneer of scientific field research on monkey societies.

But the great expansion of monkey field studies began in the 1950s, that period so critical in every way for the story of violence, monkeys and man. While Michael Chance in England was reviving interest in zoo studies, while the Japanese were setting up their open zoos, and while the crime returns were startling the affluent societies of man, a new tide of field exploration began to set in; by the sixties, it was a flood. In Japan itself, in India, in Central America, and above all in Africa, scientists were setting about the study of more and more monkey societies in wholly natural surroundings. The field workers often displayed all the courage and resource of the great Victorian explorers, together with infinite patience. In 1962, for instance, Vernon and Frances Reynolds and their African friend and guide Manueri were roaming the Budongo Forest of Uganda, on the track of the highly mobile parties of chimpanzees that live there. From their scientific publications, we learn how much they were able to discover. From Vernon Reynolds's charming book *Budongo*, we learn what they did to make the discoveries, and what life can be like in the field (and, surprisingly, how much they enjoyed a good deal of it). Every day they spent most of the daylight hours trudging through the rain forest, guided from time to time by the calls of the chimps; whole days, once whole weeks, passed like this without a sight of the animals. Once they were lost for hours in a jungle swamp, where they waded through mud infested with worms which enter and blister the skin, while they dodged trees armed with spikes as long as daggers, and from time to time had to shake off showers of biting ants that fell into their hair.

Meanwhile, in the more open woodland of the Gombe Stream Reserve in Tanzania, in 1961–3, Jane Goodall was becoming almost a member of another chimpanzee society. In the end, she writes, 'I was greeted almost as another chimpanzee', she knew individual chimps, three mature males would take food from her hand, and one would even let her groom his coat. How she achieved this is told in half a paragraph in one of her scientific papers. At first she was not allowed within 500 yards. After eight months, she could approach within fifty yards 'provided they were in thick cover and up a tree'. After ten months, she could go 'within 100 feet of most individuals', and after fourteen months, within fifty feet. The final stage of acceptance, which she reached after eighteen months, was not without its hazards; chimpanzees are powerful animals. 'On one occasion', she reports in another article, 'I was actually hit by a chimpanzee in the wild, but this was prompted by curiosity rather than aggression.'

The results of field studies are sometimes, inevitably, limited in detail. But they give much information we could not obtain otherwise, and they provide a check on the studies intermediate between the zoo and the wild. Sometimes they enable us to compare wild societies in rather different environments; chimpanzees, for instance, have been studied not only in Uganda and Tanzania by the British scientists just mentioned, but also, earlier, in the Congo by the Dutch zoologist Adriaan Kortlandt (in 1960). In 1960–1, the Swiss scientist Hans Kummer, assisted by F. Kurt, studied hamadryas baboons on the rocky plateaux of Ethiopia, between Addis Ababa and Diredawa. In this relatively open terrain, Kummer managed to get almost as much detailed information as can be obtained in a zoo; his reports are of special interest, since this is the species studied in the zoo by Zuckerman (and later, in 1955–8, by Kummer himself at Zürich).

In the spring of 1964, the Institute of Contemporary Art in London held a series of lectures on different aspects of violence, with art exhibitions on the same theme. It was a typical expression of the increasing public interest in the subject. We were asked to talk about violence in animals, and we felt the time was ripe for a survey of all the new information from the field.* Monkeys in the zoo, however well-fed, are violently aggressive. Is it, then, simply the nature of monkeys to behave like this? Are they just as violent under ideal natural conditions? Do the members of a wild monkey band fight fiercely and frequently among themselves? Do separate bands make war upon each other? As we shall see, conditions and conduct differ even in the wild, and the intermediate studies give intermediate results. Nevertheless, by 1964, we were in a position to answer the questions for about a dozen monkey species. Although we already had an inkling what to expect, we ourselves were surprised by the decisiveness of the answer. The reports of the field observers were virtually unanimous; and every new report since 1964 has told the same story.

In Carpenter's field study of wild *gibbons* in Thailand, al-

* The result of this survey was broadcast on the BBC Third Programme later that year, and published in the *Listener* (see Notes).

though he was 'much interested in pugnacious activities' and constantly on the watch for them during three months of daily observation, he saw 'no actual fights', either within or between bands. During a total of more than eighteen months of observation of the *howlers* on Barro Colorado, studying behaviour within and between bands, Carpenter only once saw a clash which appeared to result in wounds; Southwick, who studied the same howlers during two seasons eight years apart, writes: 'I have never seen a direct fight between two howling monkeys.' Among wild *red spider monkeys*, Carpenter observed 'few instances of fighting', always of 'short duration'.

A. J. Haddow made observations on thirty-nine bands of wild *African redtail monkeys* in Uganda; neither he nor two other observers of redtails 'have ever witnessed fighting', during 'many years of field experience'. In redtail individuals collected in the wild, scars were rare and, if present, indicated only slight injury. Rarity of signs of injury is itself a useful guide. *Rhesus monkeys* have not yet been studied closely in such undisturbed environments as the forests of India; but Southwick and his colleagues reported that 'wounded individuals were rarer' in forest areas than in urban surroundings (where they were mainly wounded in battles between bands). Since even among the Thailand gibbons one or two scarred individuals were collected, rarity of wounds clearly means great rarity of fighting.

Except under special stresses we shall describe later, serious fighting is rarely reported among *Japanese monkeys*, even in the open zoos. In the wild, more than one band is sometimes found in one of the isolated pockets of forest. S. Kawamura and K. Tokuda studied an area near Tokyo where several bands were present, and saw no fighting between them. Paul E. Simonds made 'intensive observations' for six months on two bands of *bonnet macaque monkeys* (related to rhesus and Japanese monkeys), occupying neighbouring rows of banyan trees in a farm area in southern Mysore State, India. No fighting occurred between the bands. Serious fighting did occur frequently within the band he was mainly studying; but these monkeys (like the urban rhesus monkeys) were found to be more crowded than the bands in a forest near by. Only a brief observation was made on one of these fully wild bands; it appeared to be much more peaceful.

In Madhya Pradesh and Uttar Pradesh States, India, Phyllis Jay carried out more than 850 hours of close observation of *common langurs*. She reports that 'fighting is very seldom observed' between males, and that wounds are rare. In females, fighting was not only rare but apparently never serious: 'no adult female was visibly wounded in such fighting'. In six months' study of *colobus monkeys* (related to langurs) in Tanzania, W. Ullrich saw no fighting between bands, and very little sign of aggression within bands.

In terms of social organisation, baboons are of two main kinds: The hamadryas group includes two well-studied species (hamadryas and gelada), the cynocephalus group three others (olive, yellow and chacma baboons). Wild *cynocephalus baboons* in Kenya and southern Africa have been the object of 2000 hours of observation by K. R. L. Hall and Irven DeVore. According to Hall, fighting within bands is 'extremely rare' (in southern Africa, he saw only one fight between adult males in a whole season of observation); and fighting between bands has never been recorded. Kummer's very detailed account of wild *hamadryas baboons* is specially telling, for he observed the very species studied by Zuckerman at Regent's Park. Kummer reports that even mild quarrels take up *less than 1 per cent* of the time wild hamadryas baboons spend in social behaviour. He tells us in a letter that, though fights did occur in the wild, they 'never resulted in serious wounds', in marked contrast to fights among captive hamadryas studied by Zuckerman and by Kummer himself.

Besides its howlers, Barro Colorado Island contains many bands of the little *night monkey*. Martin Moynihan found that any kind of overt fighting between these wild monkeys was 'rare', although they would fight fiercely when put together in cages. K. R. L. Hall made a similar comparison between captive *patas monkeys* under various kinds of stress, and wild ones in Uganda. In the captives under stress, aggression was common and serious fighting occurred. In 627 hours of observation, the wild monkeys had only 49 brief quarrels, and not a single actual fight.

On the borders of the Congo, George Schaller succeeded in making 466 hours of observation of the shy *mountain gorillas*; after endless patience on his part, they were even prepared to join him on the branch of a tree where he sat. His conclusion is simple and comprehensive: 'I have not witnessed serious aggressive contacts between gorillas'. During 300 hours of observation of *chimpanzees* (no mean feat in the rain forest of Budongo) the Reynoldses saw ' 17 quarrels involving actual fighting or displays of threat or anger, and none of these lasted more than a few seconds'. The field record is probably held by Jane Goodall, who clocked up over 3000 hours of observation on her chimpanzees at close quarters. She saw seventy-three brief episodes of tension, and one fight: 'no signs of injury were visible after the encounter'.

These unanimous reports from the field observers are even more impressive than they first appear, for many of the observers were expecting just the reverse. After Zuckerman's book (1932), the idea that monkeys are naturally violent was very firmly established; old travellers' tales had often suggested the contrary, but these were dismissed as old travellers' tales. Carpenter saw 'no actual fights' in three months' observation of gibbons; in the same paragraph of his paper (1940), he complains that he 'did not see an adequate sampling of' aggressive behaviour. After describing the fierce (often lethal) fights observed in captive gibbons, he writes: 'admittedly most of the above description of gibbon fighting is influenced by experience with captive animals'. It is clear that he was surprised and puzzled by the rarity of fighting in the wild (evidenced only by observation of four injuries in thirty collected individuals), though he is too good a scientist to ignore his own observations, and he proceeded to consider reasons for the difference between wild and captive gibbons. Moynihan still shows this feeling of astonishment, in his recent paper on night monkeys (1964). He describes the fierce fighting among them when they are caged, and continues: 'it is perhaps surprising, therefore, that overt fights between pairs and family groups of night monkeys seem to be relatively rare in the wild, at least on Barro Colorado Island'.

Often an observer, reporting the peaceful behaviour of a species in the wild, supposed that it must be in some way exceptional. Southwick, for instance (writing in 1963), describes the peacefulness of wild howlers as 'unusual', and contrasts them with rhesus monkeys in Aligarh (under the stresses of an urban environment). It now appears that the fifteen or so species of monkeys observed in the wild provide a veritable catalogue of peaceful 'exceptions'.

Emphasis, however, is still often laid on alleged differences in inherent aggressiveness between different species. In an issue published on 17 May 1965, *Life* magazine provided a useful and beautifully illustrated popular survey of monkey societies, in which rhesus monkeys and their relatives are described as 'the most aggressive of all monkeys'. We have seen that neither rhesus monkeys nor the related bonnet macaques have yet been closely studied at large in the forests, where, however, they are known to be more peaceful than anywhere else. Phyllis Jay appears to make a telling point when she observes that rhesus monkeys are more aggressive than langurs *in the same places* (near Indian villages). But even in the same place, one species may be under more stress than the other, for instance from human interference. Langurs are more sacred than rhesus, and anyway much better able to escape from the less devout villagers by taking refuge in the trees, where, as Jay herself writes, they take 'long graceful jumps with apparent ease', whereas 'the stocky, short, muscular rhesus', more at home on the ground, 'moves slowly and cautiously in trees'. The species usually described as most aggressive are baboons and rhesus, those best known in zoo surroundings. They also live in unusually large bands, often containing over a hundred individuals, where mild tensions must be difficult to avoid altogether even under mild stress. It is conceivable that, *under an equal amount of stress*, some species (such as chimpanzees) may be inherently more peaceful than others (such as baboons), as individuals; but this is obviously very difficult to prove, and remains an open question. Within species, indeed within particular bands, some individuals are certainly more aggressive than others; but as we shall see, there is already evidence that this may be due to differences in upbringing.

What is quite certain is that any such inherent differences, if they exist, are completely outweighed by the difference between *any* monkey species in the wild and *any other* monkey species in the zoo (or in conditions approaching those of the zoo). Chimpanzees in the wild generally impress people as the most peaceful species imaginable, and our catalogue might seem to bear this out. But chimpanzees in the zoo can be much more aggressive than baboons in the wild. Caroline Loizos, who, together with Gilbert Manley, has recently been observing chimpanzees at Regent's Park, tells us she has seen a whole group cowering in corners under the tyranny of a brutally domineering male, who was not above deliberately attacking mothers with infants; threats and disputes were frequent, and a fight occurred in which one female viciously wounded another before anyone could intervene.*

For all practical purposes, therefore, intense aggressiveness is not an innate feature of individuals, appearing in some monkey species and not in others.† On the contrary, *all monkeys are peaceful in some conditions, and violently aggressive in others. Violence is a property of mammalian societies exposed to stress.*

In the history of science, few results have been as decisive as this one, largely obtained in the last ten years. It would be hard

* After this chapter was written, T. E. Rowell reported on some unusual bands of cynocephalus (olive) baboons in Uganda which, unlike most baboons, spent 60 per cent of their time in forested country. Fighting and even threat were 'extremely rare – in contrast to a caged group of the same species'.

† Some people have suggested that man is inherently and unconditionally more aggressive than monkeys. This idea is based on a number of misconceptions, which are discussed in Appendix One. Zuckerman's observations, and many others, show that monkeys and human beings can be equally aggressive when their societies are under stress.

to imagine a more striking vindication of the conditional view
of aggression and violence. The reports from the plains and
forests bring a message of hope for mankind. The violence of
zoo monkeys is not a product of inherent aggressiveness; monkey societies in ideal conditions live in peace and harmony.
Violence is not some ultimate and irreducible feature of the
universe; it is simply a problem to be solved, and mankind has
solved many problems.

In approaching this problem, we now have an important
clue. It is not shortage of food that causes violence to rage in the
affluent monkey colonies of the zoo. There must be important
stresses other than food shortage, and these, we may expect, are
afflicting the well-fed, affluent societies of man, provoking the
rising rates of violent crime, which appeared so mysterious at
first sight. What are these other stresses, and how in detail does
stress of any kind act to produce violence? These are the questions we shall try to answer, or at least begin to answer, in the
remaining chapters of this book. The study of monkey societies
has much to teach us about these questions. But before we begin
to examine the stresses and their action, we must see how these
societies work in ideal or near-ideal conditions, and enter the
strange but strangely familiar world of monkey politics.

2

Monkeys are mammals (animals, usually furry, that provide
milk for their young). The higher mammals, especially monkeys
themselves, represent the culmination of an evolutionary trend
towards progressively lower fertility, with increasingly elaborate
parental care of individual young animals. (There have been
similar but less far-reaching trends in some groups of birds and
fishes.) It is on this foundation that higher mammalian societies
have arisen. They are fundamentally individualistic, the outcome of a high evolutionary valuation on the life and social contribution of each carefully reared individual in the society. In
this they differ fundamentally from the hills and hives of the

vastly fertile social insects, which are populous assemblies of automata, in which all but one or two individuals are replaceable and expendable. Despite appearances in some human societies, there is every reason to believe that human social behaviour follows the mammalian pattern, of which indeed it is the supreme expression.*

The maintenance of peace in a society of mammals depends on the contentment and freedom from frustration of the individuals who compose it. The society's resources have to be shared out in some orderly but not grossly inequitable way. In any situation where a dispute might arise, one animal must take priority over another, without a quarrel or at worst after a mild threat. Various social systems have been evolved to take care of all this. They have been listed recently (1965) by the German zoologist Paul Leyhausen, using observations by himself and by Rosemarie Wolff on what we are pleased to call 'domestic' cats.

Cats accept from their human friends a marginal reserve against food shortage. But cats cannot live by cat's-meat alone. They still like to go out foraging and exploring. Each cat has a *territory*, consisting of a small home area for sleeping or resting and a network of foraging routes. Within the home area, the owner is fearless, while the neighbours are timid and uncertain, because they find it unfamiliar (or, as the Scots say, uncanny). Hence in this area the owner's priorities are undisputed: home matches are always won. Female cats are particularly attached to their territories, especially when they have kittens, for it is in these safe and private surroundings that kittens are reared. In urban England, where more cats are kept than anywhere in the world, cats often get exceptional tolerance, attention and support from the human beings in whose houses or flats they set up their homes. Here, it seems to us, toms are almost as territorially minded as females. In France, Germany and rural Wales they are apparently less so, though even there, in the last resort, every tom's home is his castle.

Toms, however, do tend to wander far afield, especially when rutting. Thus, over a large area containing many cat territories,

* Violence among social insects is discussed in Appendix Two.

a number of toms are liable to encounter each other. Priorities
are allotted by an *absolute hierarchy* of rank. That is, the individual toms are arranged in a rank order, and a top cat takes precedence over a junior cat *whenever and wherever they meet*. Over a
wide area, a hierarchy of toms, all of whom are known to each
other, form a definite establishment. When a young tom grows
up, or a stranger moves in, the local establishment gather
around his home and invite him to come outside. After a series
of scraps, he and they know exactly who can lick him and
whom he can lick, and so where he is to fit in the rank order; he
then obtains membership in the establishment. Thereafter there
is no fighting at all. Females are not fought over, but choose
their own mates. Traffic problems on narrow pathways are
settled simply by the rank of the parties concerned, without any
fuss. The hierarchy is absolute only on common ground; toms
of the lowest rank are still masters of their own homes.

Territory and absolute hierarchy have been known about for
some time. But Leyhausen shows that there is a third, rather
subtle system, which he calls *relative hierarchy*. It is especially
clear in the relations between female cat neighbours. While
home areas are separate, foraging and exploring routes overlap,
so traffic problems are always liable to arise on narrow paths or
at crossways. After at most one serious fight, one neighbour becomes superior to the other. Thereafter, she normally takes precedence on common routes, and she may even occasionally be
allowed to visit her inferior's home. But, in return, the inferior
cat can use the senior one's hunting routes, provided she respects her precedence. And there are occasions when priority in
time grants precedence over rank. Cats are, to some extent,
creatures of routine, and the inferior cat will adjust her time-
table of hunting trips to keep out of her superior's way. If, after
this, the superior arrives at her favourite look-out post at an unusual time, and finds it occupied by her inferior, she will withdraw in a civilised manner and wait till it is free. Relative hierarchy is thus influenced by time and place; it involves a kind of
highway code.

Mammal societies vary in the balance between territory,

relative and absolute hierarchy. Leyhausen sees in this the evolutionary basis for various balances in human societies between individual freedom and privacy, social give-and-take, and public efficiency and order. Provided the balance works well, there is little tension and the members of the society are good friends. Cat neighbours greet each other when they meet, and often go hunting together. In the evenings the establishment and their girl friends gather at the local 'club', somewhere outside their homes. In a little square on the outskirts of Paris, Leyhausen watched the local cat club meeting night after night. The members were not meeting to mate (this was outside the mating season), but simply to sit around, side by side, sometimes licking and grooming each other in a relaxed way. Now and again, a tom could be seen 'parading a little just for fun'. After a few hours, the party broke up and everybody went home.

The members of a band of wild monkeys live close together all the time, moving around a much larger shared group territory, with feeding-grounds, day-resting-grounds, sleeping-grounds and travelling-routes between them, which they all hold in common. Sleeping-grounds are places (trees or cliff ledges) as safe as possible from predators. There may be more than one in the band territory; patas monkeys, for instance, never sleep in the same area two nights running. At the sleeping-grounds an inclination for individual territory-ownership can still be seen. Patas monkeys, for instance, spread out widely at night, each individual picking a tree some distance from his neighbour. Hamadryas baboons regularly sleep on the same ledges; each baboon has his own sleeping-place on a given ledge, and returns at night to within a radius of three metres of the spot where he last slept. The earliest human food-gathering bands no doubt had similar vestiges of the individual (or family) territorial system. Hence, when man developed settled agriculture and settled down in fixed homes, individual (or family) territory gradually appeared. In due course, human farmers and townsfolk became suitable companions for cats.

For the most part, however, the territory of the wild monkey band is common property. Just as between individual cats, the

monkey territory system serves to avert conflicts, this time between whole bands, each of which is familiar with one territory
and therefore fearless and dominant over other bands which
enter it. Within the band, an individual has rights of access to
the resources of the common territory, and rights of privacy
represented by the distance between himself and other monkeys.
Much the most prominent feature of monkey behaviour in the
wild is the extent to which they keep out of each other's way,
except when they make contact by mutual consent for grooming,
mating or huddling in cold weather. This elbow-room is a kind
of mobile territory around the individual's body; Michael
Chance has called it *social space*. Just as a mother cat brings up
her kittens within her territory, so a monkey mother keeps her
infants* near her own body. In fact, in the hamadryas baboons,
she keeps them within three metres, exactly the radius of their
sleeping-territories when they grow up. Social space, and the
conditions under which it is shared, are extremely important
aspects of monkey life. The British sociologist Stanislav Andreski
has told us of his observations at the end of the Second World
War, in transit stations for released prisoners of war (from ordinary camps, where privacy was irksomely restricted, not from
concentration camps, where behaviour could be seriously crip-
pled). When they sat down to a meal in the canteen, some of
these men would draw chalk lines round their bodies to show the
elbow-room they wanted, a perfect visualisation of social space.

Within the wild monkey band, priorities are generally allotted by a hierarchy of rank or status; it can often be literally
measured in social space, as the amount of room each monkey
is given by others making way for him. Hierarchical relations
tend to be absolute, but where there are plenty of food resources,
widely dispersed over the ground, and plenty of room to keep
out of a superior's way, no serious tension need arise. There is

---

* 'Infans' is Latin for 'unspeaking', and the term 'infant' applies
strictly only to human babies before they can talk. For lack of another
word, however, it is now generally used for very young monkeys.
Similarly, it is sometimes hard to avoid words like 'child' in writing
of monkey societies.

often a good deal of relative hierarchy in the form of privileges in special conditions. Nursing mothers, for instance, are treated with special tolerance, irrespective of their normal rank as individuals. There is often a class system, much more complicated than the simple tom-cat rank order of individuals, and this may work in favour of physically weaker monkeys. Unlike the cat hierarchy, which involves fighting with each change of membership, the monkey rank system is formed and adjusted with a minimum of friction. Finally, the top monkeys unquestionably earn their privileges by doing responsible jobs for the benefit of the whole band, so much so that (as we shall see) a potential top monkey may actually prefer to contract out of the job.

Monkey bands vary widely in numbers, from 2 to 6 (gibbons) to several hundreds (hamadryas baboons and Japanese monkeys). The larger bands are in the same size range as the simpler human societies, such as tribes of Australian aborigines or African bushmen, which gather their food (80 per cent vegetarian) in much the same way. There may or may not be a division of labour between the sexes; when it exists, the females are mainly concerned with bringing up the young, the males with finding feeding-grounds, organising travel and dealing with dangers from predatory animals; males then have higher status, as a necessary basis for their work as leaders. Division of labour is never absolute, and males generally pay considerable attention to the young, who are the main focus of interest holding the whole band together. Among monkeys well adapted to life in the trees of dense forests, where they can easily give predators the slip, there may be no rigid division of labour and no difference in status between the sexes: this is the situation in gibbons, for instance. At the other extreme, among monkeys living on the ground in open country, notably baboons, the need for big and powerful males to tackle predators has led to marked division of labour and difference in status. Among hamadryas baboons, where the distinction is most extreme, it has led to marked differences in body form between the sexes, the males being much bigger and equipped with imposing manes. Intermediate conditions of life partly in the trees and partly on the ground have given rise to a great variety of more complicated social orders.

The gibbons of Thailand lead a simple family life. They appear to be monogamous till death does them part, though this has certainly not been proved. The family band consists only of father, mother and 1–4 children. Father and mother act as leaders, their status being perfectly equal. Father helps to groom and play with the children, and may even carry them around; mother takes her full part in guarding the family territory against other families. Gibbon 'teenagers', male or female, leave home, either through restlessness or because they are made to feel they have overstayed their welcome (or both: the causes are uncertain). After a time of solitary life in the forest, boy gibbon meets girl gibbon and a new family sets up territory.

Very different are the large bands of cynocephalus baboons in Africa, ranging from 8 to 185 monkeys per band, usually more than 20. Each band is ruled by the adult males, under a president supported by an establishment, or central committee. In one well-studied band, for instance, there were six adult males, three of whom formed an establishment under the president. The females are markedly inferior, and have no very definite rank order; they tend to form shifting alliances. As in many but not all mammals, female monkeys tend to have sexual cycles (analogous to the human menstrual cycle) during the breeding season. Generally the skin of their genital regions changes its appearance at the peak of the cycle, becoming more attractive in monkey eyes, though hardly in ours (zoo visitors often tell the keepers some of their monkeys have skin diseases). The perquisites of the baboon president include the right to mate with fully adult females when they are at their most alluring; at other (also fertile) stages of the cycle, they are available for his colleagues of the establishment, while younger females are left to subordinate or young males. The females tend to quarrel (mildly) over status among themselves when one of them is attracting the attentions of the president. On the march to the feeding-grounds, the establishment and their temporary consorts form the centre of the band, together with mothers and infants; other adults and juveniles travel on the flanks and at front and rear. The male establishment is largely responsible for leadership, route-finding and defence against predators.

The hamadryas baboons, on the other hand, have developed an extreme democracy, unique among monkeys. As in many human extreme democracies (ancient Athens, medieval Florence, the Swiss cantons), the status of females is extremely low, and, as we have seen, the sexes look more unlike than in any other monkey species. Hans Kummer has made a detailed comparison of the cynocephalus and hamadryas societies. The bands are about the same size in the two kinds of baboon, but the hamadryas society shows two additional groupings. On the Ethiopian plateaux, cliff ledges for sleeping-grounds (safe from predators) are rare (6 per 450 hamadryas individuals, compared with 6 per 26 cynocephalus baboons in southern Africa). A number of hamadryas bands may therefore have to share the same ledges, and for this purpose they combine into very large troops, of as many as 750 members. In the day-time, the separate bands of the troop go their several ways, and they do not always all sleep on the same ledge. Nevertheless, the troop is a definite tribe or nation: bands from other troops are not welcome. Kummer once captured a male with his two wives and an infant and released the family in the middle of a strange troop. The females and infant were appropriated by troop members, after which 350 males stood round the foreign male in a circle, keeping their distance, sitting down and getting up and moving whenever he did. The foreigner soon decided to leave.

The band itself is quite unlike the compact, oligarchically ruled cynocephalus band. It is composed of a number of polygamous families, each consisting of an adult male with from one to nine females and their infants, and sometimes a nearly adult male hanger-on. Each adult male is absolute master of his own family, with a sexual monopoly of his females. The females themselves correspond to the lower classes of other monkey societies, and normally have no political influence at all. The females of a given family have very little to do socially with the other families in the band or troop. The adult males, on the other hand, frequently greet each other and co-operate in leading

*

their families about and defending them against foreigners. They are absolute equals among themselves, with no trace of a status hierarchy. Each male goes through a definite career. He begins to learn his job as apprentice hanger-on in a family. Then he acquires one or two females, and joins a two-family team. The junior partner in such a team often leads the way on the march, but the senior partner decides the route, by following or refusing to follow if he disagrees. For some time, the male concentrates on acquiring a large harem of females and breeding with them. Then he gradually loses interest in his family, and may allow them to drift away to younger males. By this time he is an experienced leader, involved and influential in public life. Older, experienced males of this kind become the acknowledged leaders of the whole band of families whenever it moves around together, deferred to with respect when they indicate or veto a particular route. No questions of status or rank are involved, and there is never any dispute over matters of practical leadership. The successive stages of their careers accustom the males to trust each other's judgement in proportion to experience.

Hamadryas 'teenagers' live dispersed among the whole band, just like cynocephalus ones. But, as Kummer has shown, slight divergences in the pattern of their social behaviour gradually bring about the complete change in social life. The resulting patriarchal democracy is strikingly like that of certain human societies, such as the ancient Hebrews, with their polygamous families moving about independently, their two-family teams (Abraham and Lot) and their combination of equal status (for the patriarchs) and respect for experience. Kummer observed that food was relatively scarce in Ethiopia, and the baboons had to scatter widely in the day-time to get enough to eat. Dispersal into small family units is evidently necessary in these conditions, and each patriarch has to develop the independence and initiative shown in cynocephalus baboons by the few males of the establishment. Leadership is thus spread among all the males.*

* In 1964–5 the British zoologist John Crook made a careful study of societies of wild gelada baboons, also in Ethiopia. He found their social organisation, in general outline, very similar to that of

The Hebrew patriarchs, travelling far and wide to find grass and water for their flocks, were in a rather similar position. In both cases the status of the female appears extremely low.

The hamadryas baboon females do not, of course, suffer from any innate incompetence for leadership; their place in society is, as we shall see, a product of upbringing. The only thing they lack innately is the imposing mane of the male. This became clear in Kummer's zoo colony at Zürich, where one adult male was an inert and ineffectual leader, as a result of some disturbance of his behaviour in captivity. One of his wives took over all his functions of keeping the family together and regulating quarrels, and was treated as a leader by his other females. To achieve this, she had to keep returning to the neighbourhood of the male, and, as Kummer has put it, to use his mane as a backdrop. Imperial or royal seals and signatures have been used in much the same way by human leaders (male or female) disqualified by sex or birth from wearing the crown themselves.

In the tree-loving langur monkeys, the males act as leaders in foraging, but are not allowed near the nursery. On six occasions, Phyllis Jay saw 'an offending male, who may have inadvertently frightened an infant'; he was at once beset by an indignant club of formidable females, and did not stop to argue the point. One male 'walked under a mango tree in which a small infant was playing. The mother was sitting under the tree and as the male approached she reached up to grasp the infant, who became alarmed and jumped up to the next branch just out of her reach. The female jumped up and chased the male 150 feet while the infant raced around squealing in the tree.'

the hamadryas species. But in some places the one-male family units rarely foraged on their own, and were difficult to pick out from the band, which moved as a whole. Studying the variations, Crook found that sparse food supplies did indeed go with independent activity by family units, while the band tended to move as a whole when food was more abundant. He points out that the gelada is not closely related to other baboons, and that hamadryas and gelada almost certainly evolved their social patterns independently, as a response to the same kind of surroundings and resources.

Macaque monkeys (rhesus, bonnet and Japanese) spend much time on the ground, but can climb trees. The males are somewhat bigger but otherwise not strikingly different from the females. Rhesus monkeys and bonnet monkeys have never been studied in completely wild conditions, but we can form some impression of their societies. Although the status of females is much higher (so that a female can hold second rank in a whole band), these macaques seem to have a male establishment very like that of the cynocephalus baboons. But the most elaborate societies of all, so far as our present knowledge goes, are those of the Japanese monkeys, studied thoroughly in the open zoos and to some extent in the wild forest.

The underlying constitution of these societies is a subtle one, reminiscent of the later Roman Republic, where only men could hold office, but women ran political parties and helped to decide *which* men could hold office. The typical Japanese monkey society has the usual male establishment, but ultimate control often rests with an unofficial female electorate. The complex social structure is reflected in a complex geometry of social space, in the form, literally, of social circles. At the feeding-ground, the inner social circle, or court, contains the babies (of either sex) and *all* the females, who enjoy throughout life the special privileges of this court circle: first access to the feeding-ground, and a safe central position on the march. Upper-class females occupy a central position at court; lower-class ones are disposed round the edge. The males are divided into three classes. The rank and file occupy an outer or peripheral ring. The leaders occupy a central position at court. On the fringe of the court circle are an intermediate class, the sub-leaders. At about the age of two, males are relegated to the peripheral ring as cadets. Their subsequent promotion to sub-leaders and then to leaders (who finally return to the centre) is partly a matter of age seniority, but mainly a matter of personal qualities. Their capacity to establish status and form alliances in the male hierarchy is only one factor. The females allow leaders and (in the leaders' absence) sub-leaders to herd them to and from the feeding-ground, and otherwise to take executive command. But they often reserve the absolute right to choose among male candidates for leadership. In a band at Takahashi, for instance, the male who ranks highest in status among his fellow-males is never allowed to lead; the females always drive him from court. The cadets, whatever their individual rank, become subordinate even to young females when they approach the inner circle. In these societies, individual rank order gives place to class distinction.

The choice by the females is practical, and based essentially on merit. They like a firm and efficient leader, but will not tolerate an aggressive one. Unlike langur females, they approve of an interest in infants. When females with young are having their next babies, middle-rank leaders and middle-rank sub-leaders may take charge of the one-year-olds. Baby-sitting is a means of ingratiating themselves with the females (and a natural test for competent and unaggressive leadership); baby-sitters tend to be rewarded by promotion. This particular means of social climbing is found normally in three of the bands studied, rarely in seven, and not at all in eight. This is typical of the wide differences between Japanese monkey societies, where the extent of female influence varies appreciably.

Among themselves, females are less concerned with merit than with family background. In the rank hierarchy within each class of males, each individual has his place mainly on the basis of his own personality. The females, however, are divided into family cliques, and the status of a female (and her likelihood of being a top leader's consort) depends on the status of her *mother*. At first the young daughter of a matriarch has a high 'dependent' status (as the Japanese scientist Masao Kawai has called it). She ranks high when she is near her mother, a formidable figure in the background. Later others have learned to know and respect her, and she acquires a high 'basic' status, even when her mother is not around, as a member of an upper-class family. Within each clique, the *youngest* daughter is favoured in each generation, because she has most recently been an infant, regularly in the company of her mother (this shows conclusively that high status is transmitted by direct family influence, and not by

the genetic inheritance of particular qualities of behaviour).
Hence a female rank order will run: top matriarch, younger
daughter with her children (youngest first), elder daughter
with her children, second matriarch and her family, and so on.
An upper-class mother is at first an advantage to a son, too, but
when he joins the outer (all-male) circle he has less and less to
do with her, and must make his own way. However, upper-class
females live in the centre of the court, and their infant sons
attract the personal interest of top male leaders (who also live
there) when they act as baby-sitters. In this way, upper-class
sons get to know 'the right people', and it is thought this may
smooth their path to the top (and hence back to court) during
their subsequent public career among the males. In two bands,
very powerful females have kept their sons at court beyond the
normal time (in one case for five years) instead of sending them
to the outer cadet circle, so we may be witnessing the birth of a
matrilineal nobility. In their opportunities for social advancement, all male Japanese monkeys may be equal, but some monkeys are decidedly more equal than others.

In the course of the revolutions which tore apart the Roman
Republic, males of both parties were the object of merciless
pillage in turn. In 43 B.C. the gangster general M. Antonius
(Shakespeare's Mark Antony) proposed to pay his troops by
taxing the property of women. He very soon had to think again.
A number of tough Roman matrons appeared in the Forum,
and placed their spokeswoman Hortensia on the platform. This
lady was the daughter of the famous orator Q. Hortensius, and
a chip off the old block: she made a resounding speech on the
theme of 'No taxation without representation'. The new tax
proposal was dropped at once.

In one Japanese monkey band at Minoo, the females came
into the open in a still more decisive way. Becoming dissatisfied
with their male leader Ata, they chased him out and installed
the top female, Zuku, as Madam President. Two adult males
were still tolerated in the band, but both ranked openly below
Zuku and one of them below all the upper-class females. A
clique society resulted. The grandsons of the second and third

matriarchs were relegated to the outer circle as usual; so it is possible the females may gradually begin to experiment again with male leadership.

Even bloodless *coups d'état* like the expulsion of Ata are rarities in the life of a wild monkey society. There is normally so little friction that it has generally taken field observers hundreds of hours to work out these status arrangements and political constitutions. Often they have only been able to do so by deliberate interference. Kummer and Kurt threw food on to a sleeping-ledge of hamadryas baboons; in the course of approaching the food, a number of families entered each other's social space, and fights broke out, which showed the division of the troop into bands. The Japanese scientists, in a similar way, throw pieces of food between two individuals, causing them to trespass on each other's social space, in order to see who outranks whom. Normally, the occasional episodes of pulling rank take up a minute fraction of the time wild monkeys spend in social behaviour, even at assembly points like the sleeping-ledge; on the march, they seem to be totally absent. Whenever observers have actually totted up the time spent in various social activities, they have always found by far the greater part of the time to be spent in the peaceful and sociable activity of grooming one another's fur.

In Japanese monkeys, Yoshio Furuya has found two kinds of grooming activity. The first kind we might call personal service; a monkey of lower rank grooms his superior, who does not return the compliment; however, in return, he allows the subordinate within his social space. The second kind is a matter of pure friendship between approximate equals, who usually groom each other in turn. It is practised between males or between females of equal class and near-equal rank, and also between males and their female consorts. In wild monkeys this kind of grooming is very relaxed, and seems to be enjoyed by both parties. Grooming partnerships, between couples of the same or opposite sex who regularly groom each other, reflect the presence of many personal friendships (not connected with mating), which help to weld the society together. Japanese monkeys spend literally hours in grooming parties, in which couples sit about companionably in the sunshine, dozing or grooming, without the slightest sign of tension; similar accounts have been given for other species. Grooming is not the only expression of friendship or courtesy. A hamadryas patriarch, for instance, when he intends to leave the sleeping-ledge with his family in the morning in search of food, will come and 'notify' his neighbour patriarch, by politely showing his coloured rump, which signifies: 'I'm off now, are you coming?'

All these societies are compact and 'closed', like nations. Each band (or hamadryas troop) has its own territory, and foreigners are regarded as such. Individuals generally can, indeed, migrate from one band and join another, just as individuals can leave a human nation and obtain citizenship in another. A certain number of Japanese male monkeys, including even leaders, leave their bands and live a solitary life in the forest. Hiroki Mizuhara has studied this in detail in a band at Mount Takasaki. The solitaries are not, in the first instance, driven out, and it is often uncertain why they leave. At Mount Takasaki, the fifth-rank leader, Bacchus, took this kind of vacation for eighty days, and on his return resumed his old class at once and his old rank a few months later. On the other hand, the fourth-rank leader, Monk, and the fourth-rank sub-leader, Uzen, who took similar vacations, were made so unwelcome on their return that they became permanent solitaries; but by that time, as we shall see, the band was under a certain stress. Lone monkeys like this often hang around the outskirts of their own original band or another one. They may have grooming and even mating relations with females who stray from the centre. They sometimes acquire membership in bands other than the one that reared them, and in one instance several solitaries actually became leaders of a new band which was in process of splitting off from the very large one at Mount Takasaki. According to Mizuhara, lone monkeys generally fall into two categories: idlers, too inactive to keep up with the others, or adventurous, active monkeys who tire of the routine movements of their band. No doubt it is the adventurers who seek and make their fortunes in other bands. Migration between bands is not confined to Japanese monkeys. Among the cynocephalus baboons studied in Kenya, a male called Lone was subordinate and somewhat persecuted in his original band; he left, joined another band, and eventually rose to be a member of its establishment. Among the rhesus monkeys on Cayo Santiago, whose societies are still rather unstable, individual monkeys (male or female) change bands at the rate of one migrant a month.

At any given time, however, each of these monkey bands has a definite membership, and defends its territory against other bands. Yet, as our catalogue showed (pp. 48 ff.), serious fighting between bands is virtually unknown in the wild. When two bands meet, numbers usually decide the issue without violence, the smaller band giving way. Thus large bands have large territories, which is a fair way of dividing the assets of the whole species. The only problem is to make it clear which band is the larger. In dense forest, where visibility is poor, gibbons and howlers have solved this problem by the simple method of setting up a howl: the louder band is recognised as the winner, and the less noisy band more or less gracefully withdraws.

There is another kind of monkey society which does not involve closed bands at all, the curious 'open' society of the chimpanzees. Both Jane Goodall and the Reynoldses often saw parties of chimps moving about together — all-male, all-adult, mothers and young, or all sexes and ages together. But these parties were *temporary* assemblages, and any given individual in a party might be in a different party, or travelling alone, the next time he or she was observed. 'The only group', writes Jane Goodall, 'that is stable over a period of months is a mother with her infant and older offspring.' Vernon Reynolds had the impression that one loose band, constantly forming and reforming into different parties, may generally occupy a given forest area of six to eight square miles. Mothers with their infants generally stayed near the middle of this area, but males, not so encumbered, were free to roam as far as they liked into the range of another loose band: 'there were no boundaries at all where small bands of chimpanzees did not cross over, meet and mingle'. Reynolds points out that the chimps' food is sometimes widely dispersed, and sometimes concentrated at isolated clumps of special fruit-trees, ripening at a particular time. The loose organisation is ideally suited for feeding in such surroundings. When food is scarce and scattered, chimps wander far, alone or in small, shifting parties. When a given clump of fruit-trees is in season, the first chimps to find it set up a great hooting which brings their friends from all around. Though the society is so loose, it is complex and has many of the familiar features — status differences, grooming friendships, and so on. It is just extremely flexible. Even when chimps from different ranges meet at a feeding-spot, there is no conflict. But everybody is then a little nervous, and the tensions are expressed in a tremendously noisy party — the chimpanzee 'carnival'. They swing about the trees, run along branches, jump to the ground and back up the trees, come up to each other and part again, stamp and beat the branches, while some of them drum with their hands on the buttress-roots of ironwood trees: the sound is that of a big bass drum, and carries for up to two miles. The first of these beat sessions watched by the Reynoldses lasted for fifty-five minutes: 'all we could do was stand in awe and say unscientific things like "Good heavens, look at that one!"' The chimpanzee carnivals were first described (with the picturesque but probably mythical addition of drum-sticks) by a missionary called Thomas Savage in 1844; nobody believed him until the modern field workers reported their findings about 120 years later.

To this day, human food-gathering tribes like the African Bushmen scatter singly or in small parties to find food in difficult seasons — and hold carnival-like festivities when many can gather together in times of plenty. On a variety of evidence, the Reynoldses have suggested that the ancestors of man lived in an open, flexible, highly individualistic society of the chimpanzee kind, and that closed bands are quite a late development in the evolution of human societies. Certainly chimpanzees, as individuals, are the most man-like of monkeys; and with their

strange and exuberant society we can fittingly conclude this
survey of the varieties of monkey political experience.

3

Monkey societies have turned out to be remarkably varied, but
their uniform peacefulness in the wild is connected with certain
principles common to most or all of them. Most of them have a
more or less absolute status hierarchy, and we might expect,
judging from the cats, that this would require at least one serious fight between each monkey and each of his colleagues to
settle their relative ranks. The scarcity of serious fights in the
wild shows that this is not so, and they must have other arrangements.

One critical factor seems to be the fact that monkey individuals are brought up in the society (and not, as kittens are, in
separate territories). At first, the very young monkey is indeed
kept always close to mother (just as is the very young human).
But, gradually, the mother permits the infant to spend more and
more time playing with other young monkeys, and receiving the
friendly, playful and educative attentions of adolescents or
adults, including the leaders. An interesting laboratory experiment has been made by the American psychologists Harry and
Margaret Harlow. They observed baby rhesus monkeys playing
together for twenty minutes a day in a large and commodious
play-room. At first the young monkeys explored and handled
everything in the room, living or inanimate. Then they began
to romp and wrestle with each other. Next they played games of
chasing each other, and finally they evolved elaborate games
including both wrestling and chasing. All this was entirely in
fun.

By the time they had reached this stage of elaborate play, the
young monkeys had developed friendly relations and special
friendships. Without any real aggression, they had formed some
idea of their relative strength, agility and resource, and so they
had the basis of rank hierarchy. Finally, they had become adept

at dodging and evasion. It was only after all this that fighting tendencies appeared, and so the monkeys at once formed a hierarchy to control it, without any serious injuries in the process. 'The monkeys had gained skills of evasion . . . during the more relaxed and carefree stages of infant–infant affection.' Although a rank hierarchy was now firmly established, 'firm affectional bonds, formed earlier, remained'. On the other hand, rhesus monkeys, reared for some time in total isolation from each other and their mothers, and then put together, fought long and fiercely; but the fighting never resulted in a stable hierarchy. Violence is neither necessary nor sufficient even for forming the monkey hierarchy itself.

From studies of a number of species, we know that the tendency to fight (in response to frustration or stress, and especially to unwanted contact) appears rather late in the natural undistorted development of a young mammal. Monkey societies have evidently become so impressively complex and smoothly organised by exploiting this fact: by the time they become capable of quarrelling, the young have been assimilated into society. Playgroups for the young, generally under the supervision of adults or adolescents, are a feature of all large monkey bands in the wild. To prove this rule of monkey education, an exception is provided by the hamadryas females. In wild cynocephalus baboons, young females belong to the play-groups for three years, by which time they are integrated into the society, at a somewhat lower status than the males. In wild hamadryas baboons, Kummer saw only six females in the play-groups, compared with forty-nine males. Long before they are three (sometimes before they are one year old), most females are kidnapped by young adult males setting up their future harems. Most of the females in each harem are therefore quite unequipped for public life and social relations (though, as we have seen, not innately so). They do not become a source of violence in the wild, because their lord and master prevents them from fighting each other and from having any contact with other families.

Stuart Altmann, studying rhesus monkeys on Cayo Santiago, showed how the male and female young in normal play-groups learn tolerance and restraint in potential quarrel situations. If a given monkey always won the games, nobody would play with him; so the older or stronger monkeys accepted 'handicaps': 'they played no more roughly than the younger monkeys would tolerate within the context of play'. It is also, no doubt, in the play-groups that monkeys learn when and how to use expressions of threat and bluff, like the fencing passes of hamadryas males, who, in their occasional arguments, snap their teeth without touching their opponents. Hence (in the wild) when adults do pull rank, they do so at most by chasing an inferior, and usually only by such hints as an upright swagger in their gait, keeping their tails up, or an old-fashioned look with raised eyebrows. In adult wild monkeys, high status is normally apparent to a human observer only by two indications, both originally demonstrated by Michael Chance in the zoo. The first is social space; a high-ranking monkey can occupy certain positions at the feeding- or resting-grounds, and is given a wide berth as he moves around. The second is the fact that subordinate monkeys tend to watch for and pay attention to the movements of a high-ranking monkey. This comes in useful in focusing public attention on those who become the leaders of society.

The complexity of monkey societies depends on another important principle, which is also developed in the play-groups. The rank of an individual tom-cat is determined entirely by his own unaided behaviour (unless his human friends interfere), and the relative ranks of any two toms are decided at the first encounter between them. The result is a simple rank order of individuals, exactly like those observed in birds and even fishes; what is new in mammals (such as cats), and rare or rudimentary in birds, is the presence of positive friendly relations, essentially an outgrowth of the long and affectionate relationship between mammalian parents and young. Monkeys, however, have developed a more sophisticated system, based on the tendency of one monkey to respond to a quarrel between two others by joining in on one side. This, too, develops from parental behaviour, for we have seen how in Japanese monkeys (brought up, like all monkeys, in the society) the support of a powerful mother confers a high 'dependent', and later a high 'basic', rank on her offspring (p. 65). In the play-groups, monkeys learn the art of gaining allies and enlisting public support. Hence status in a monkey society depends not merely on a monkey's fighting qualities, but on his personal relations with influential allies and his acceptability to an influential allied group. In all the male establishments, stable alliances are found, and they are decisive in determining an individual's place in society, for the combined establishment outranks any individual. In a band of cynocephalus baboons in Nairobi Park, the establishment consisted of three males, called Dano, Pua and Kovu, with Dano as president. On several occasions, Dano and another male called Kula happened to be together and some distance from the rest of the band. It could then be seen that Kula could drive Dano away from food supplied by the observers. But whenever a quarrel arose in the ordinary daily life of the band, Dano's authority was supreme, for he was always loyally supported by Pua and Kovu, whereas Kula and the other two subordinate males were incapable of combining. Very similar observations have been made on rhesus monkeys in India.

These *stable alliances* result automatically from two things, both first clearly observed in zoo communities. First, monkeys show to an unusual degree the principle of contagion observed in most higher social animals. The sight of one animal doing something provokes in others a mood in which they are likely to do the same. In his hamadryas baboons at the Zürich Zoo, Kummer found that the sight of one monkey threatening would cause a near-by monkey not only to threaten, but to threaten in the same direction (even if the second monkey could not see the object of the first one's threat). Second, as Chance observed at Regent's Park, the members of a monkey establishment have a certain mutual tolerance, and tend to remain close together in social space; presumably they normally develop this in the play-group. So if one of them is threatened, his neighbour automatically joins in against the less familiar and usually more distant opponent, who is infringing the social space of the whole establishment. Chance has since noticed that establishments in the wild (or in the zoo) never exceed six members, apparently an upper limit to the complexity of close social relations. Even in the hamadryas democracy, a given male only has close relations with five others; but apparently in that case a number of such groupings interlock to build up a whole troop.

When females are influential, as in Japanese monkeys, they are also found to be capable of forming stable combinations, ready to act together against a male, and are similarly clustered in social space. Hence the situation at Takahashi (p. 65), where a male potentially dominant over all four male leaders was never permitted by the females to enter the central court. On the other hand, when the females are of relatively low status, as in cynocephalus baboons, they are found to lack the capacity for combination with each other. Langur females form only temporary alliances, between any two or more who happen to be near together at a given time, but these serve effectively to keep males in their place.

Status in wild monkeys, therefore, is generally determined by influence and popularity, rather than by toughness and brute force. Monkeys tend to be divided, irrespective of individual rank, into classes (such as leaders and sub-leaders in Japanese monkeys) with different privileges in social space. Leadership requires high status, and since this depends on influence rather than strength, highly aggressive monkeys will not be selected as leaders. Among the sub-leaders at Mount Takasaki, the strongest, Achilles, was also highly aggressive. The central females, who liked firm leadership but not bullying, never submitted to his control, and he was definitely subordinate to two other subleaders, Uzen and Kuro, who were weaker but milder-mannered, fond of infants, popular with females and tolerated by the supreme leader Jupiter. A leader must, of course, be firm and able to assert himself, but this is quite different from, indeed quite the reverse of aggressiveness, which is a sign of edgy insecurity. The selection of the least aggressive monkeys as leaders is one of the rewards of the stable alliance system.

Another benefit is a remarkable social stability, so that

changes in the social order are smooth and free from violence.
We shall see later that an attempted revolution, occurring under
some degree of stress, may be defeated by the solidarity of the
leaders. Under greater stress, changes in the leadership may be
frequent. But in natural conditions the electoral system normally works too well for serious discontent to arise, and a leader's position is generally conferred for life. In the Taishakukyo
band of Japanese monkeys, the ageing president Bartollo
(nearly thirty years old) appears to have been demoted to
fourth rank, but he continued to be treated unmistakably as one
of the leader class, till finally he became too weak to follow the
band in its daily movements, and disappeared in the forest. At
Mount Takasaki, the dying president Jupiter eventually lost the
respect of the sub-leaders and cadets, but his leader colleagues
respected him to the last, and even protected him by driving
away the impertinent and aggressive sub-leader Achilles. Only
after Jupiter's death did the second leader, Titan, fully take
over the presidency. On the other hand, a leader cannot resign;
if he shirks his responsibilities, he has to accept exile from the
band. At Mount Takasaki, the third leader Pan, for unknown
reasons, lost interest in his duties and took to leaving the central
court and loafing about the outer circle. The cadets there began
to treat him as a solitary, and it is their custom to combine and
drive away solitaries, who, however personally tough, lack the
credentials of a central leader. Eventually they drove Pan out
altogether, and he was last seen living as a solitary in a wheat-
field over 300 yards from the band's feeding-ground.

A leader, then, is a monkey of high status, conferred for life if
he performs his functions in a responsible way. These functions
are important for the whole society. First, the leaders have to
guide and protect the band in its relations with its natural surroundings. They often find the most promising places for food
and rest, and they always decide the route to be taken on the
daily excursions, sometimes by a sit-down veto if the band
moves off in the wrong direction. An entire hamadryas band,
for instance, was seen to defer to the decision of a very old but
highly experienced male, who vetoed the usual route and chose

a detour past terrain altered by a flood. Female and juvenile stragglers are rounded up when it is time to move on; this is a routine assignment for Japanese monkey leaders and sub-leaders. Jupiter used to give the signal for leaving the feeding-ground by climbing a tree, shaking the branches and calling 'ga ga ga', after which the band was formed up by other leaders and followed him into the forest. Even among the roving, independent chimpanzees, the ranking leader takes charge of any temporary party he happens to have with him; when he leaves a tree, the rest generally follow, especially if he decides to 'let out a big "boom-boom" on a buttress' drum. 'Once, too,' writes Vernon Reynolds, 'a big male was in the lead of a party of 17 chimpanzees crossing the main road; after they had crossed he went back to the side they had come from for a minute, then recrossed, and the whole lot went hooting and drumming into the forest. Had he been checking up to see if anyone was still to come, a hesitant chimp, perhaps, too shy to cross the road near where we were standing?'

In two Japanese monkey bands, leaders have been seen to herd their subjects away from traps or baits, and actually attack foolhardy monkeys who went too near. Eternal vigilance is often the price of safety from predators in the wild. When a band of patas monkeys approaches a sleeping-ground, leading males explore the area for up to 600 yards around, and scale high trees, from which they scan the surroundings for up to thirty minutes, probably to make sure no leopards are about. Cadets are always scouting around a moving Japanese monkey band; those who do so most regularly are believed to get more rapid promotion in status. In these elaborate societies, there is a regular system of delegated duty. In the forest, the first outlying male (sub-leader or cadet), who sights a human observer, stands his ground and calls 'kwan kwan'. Very soon he is relieved by a leader, who takes up the call, while his junior can join the rest of the band in retreating to a safe distance.

When duty calls, or danger, monkey leaders are never wanting there. They earn their high status by fearless action in the face of natural dangers. Male patas monkeys are too small to take on their predators, but when a patas look-out sees a potential predator (such as a human observer) he draws attention to himself by shaking the branches of his tree, and then descends and dashes off in the opposite direction to the band, decoying the predator away. Leaders or teams capable of intimidating a predator attack without hesitation. On Cayo Santiago, rhesus presidents would charge furiously at humans handling cages of captive monkeys. Once a young captive began to call 'when his band was nearly 200 yards distant and out of sight. The leader charged all the way to the cage, and his entire band of more than 20 animals followed' (Koford). Washburn and DeVore once saw a couple of dogs run barking towards a band of cynocephalus baboons. 'The females and juveniles hurried, but the males continued to walk slowly. In a moment an irregular group of some 20 adult males was interposed between the dogs and the rest' of the band. Carpenter saw a flock of black vultures land among a howler band. 'As they did so a burst of howling roars was given; young monkeys dashed for their mothers which took them on their backs; and the males rushed towards the birds roaring furiously.' The vultures took off at once, one of them dropping in his flight the hind-leg of a dead sloth. Still more impressive, Carpenter once saw a juvenile howler attacked by a 'dark, cat-like form', which was probably an ocelot (a powerful and sizeable predator of the cat family). When he saw the male leaders of the band, who had been two tree tops away, 'they were rushing toward the place where I later located the juvenile and from which the cat-like animal was moving' (without waiting to kill or remove its prey). 'They were roaring as I have rarely heard howlers roar.' Young howlers might be in danger from predators when a branch breaks and they fall out of a tree; to guard against this, on hearing a cracking noise, howler leaders set up a roar, while mothers look for and retrieve fallen youngsters.

These activities, which keep the band (especially mothers and young) safe and well-fed, are only half the job of the monkey leaders. Their functions are social as well as economic. They are responsible for both home and foreign policy. Within the band,

they are concerned with repressing quarrels, by intervening before they become too violent, and with protecting the interests
of mothers and young. Anyone who molests mothers or young is
instantly punished by the nearest leader, not only among Japanese monkeys, where the females are so influential, but also
among cynocephalus baboons, where the low status of females
is alleviated by this kind of chivalry. Bonnet macaque leaders
punish not only delinquents who attack females and infants, but
also louts who press their sexual attentions on unwilling females,
and will not take a screech for an answer. No objection is taken,
however, to sex between consenting adults. In a contented wild
band, with plenty of room for manœuvre, these disciplinary
measures are not often needed, and, as we have seen, leaders are
not given to unprovoked aggression, or they would not have
been elected.

When two monkey bands meet, the smaller gives way (p. 69).
In gibbons and howlers, relative numbers are conveyed by relative volume of noise. In less vocal species, like rhesus, the leaders
are responsible for arriving at a peaceful settlement, and this is
their main function in foreign affairs. In face of predators, a
rhesus president is a hero, but in encounters between bands of
the same species he indulges no foolish heroics. Instead, he
shows all the realism of Falstaff ('the better part of valour is
discretion') or the Duke of Plaza-Toro (who 'led his regiment
from behind, he found it less exciting'). While excited young
males posture and exchange threats with the other band, the
president sits coolly in his rear H.Q., making his appreciation.
If he decides his band is the weaker, he is the first to give the
example of retreat. In this way, violence between bands is normally averted, and territorial disputes fairly settled on the basis
of numbers. Indeed, apart from defence against predators (no
longer of great significance in *human* affairs), the chief function,
almost the defining function of monkey leaders, is *the reduction of
violence, including their own*, to an absolute minimum, in well-fed
and otherwise contented bands at peace with one another.*

* The effects of good leadership in man are discussed in Appendix
Five.

The trouble with all these social arrangements, which produce such admirable results in wild monkey bands, is that they
are largely automatic, as will be clear from the descriptions we
have given: they lean heavily, for instance, on the automatic
device of stable alliance. We have seen the monkey societies at
ease and peace in their wild homes; we must now consider what
happens to all their social machinery, including the beautiful
mechanism of leadership, when it is exposed to the stresses of
captivity. These stresses, as we have noticed, do not include the
shortage of food; so we are now to come to grips with the problem of violence in the affluent society.

1

MONKEY bands in the wild live at peace, free from serious tensions. Monkey communities in the zoo, as Zuckerman showed at Regent's Park, present a spectacularly different picture. They are full of tensions, and capable of orgies of slaughter. Yet these communities are always kept amply supplied with food; they are unmistakably affluent societies. What pressures drive them to violence, and how does the violence develop? Answers to these questions have emerged from the detailed results of three recent intensive studies of monkey communities in the zoo.

The first of these studies was made, like Zuckerman's baboon study, at the 'large oval rock-work enclosure' at Regent's Park that came to be known as Monkey Hill. This time the occupants were rhesus monkeys. On 3 April 1952, 253 of these monkeys were installed at Monkey Hill. From then until the end of October, they were subjected to detailed observation by Michael Chance. The second detailed study was made in 1955–9, at the Zürich Zoo in Switzerland, where Hans Kummer made observations on 15 hamadryas baboons, kept in an enclosure 15 by 27 yards in area. Finally, in January to August 1960, Vernon Reynolds observed 24 rhesus monkeys in an octagonal enclosure with sides 10 yards long, at Whipsnade Park in the English county of Bedfordshire. The numbers of the animals and the size of the enclosures are more than mere details; as we shall see, they are highly relevant for the problems of the violent affluent society.

Zuckerman's baboon colony was not the only zoo community to indulge in orgies of slaughter. Hall, writing in 1963, reported, as a 'recent example' of lethal conflict, that 'fighting broke out in a group of 17 baboons at the Bloemfontein Zoo [in South

Africa] when an "alien" adult male and adult female were introduced into their midst, as a result of which most of the animals were killed or died of their injuries'. However, zoo directors have naturally tried to reduce the more extreme stresses
as more was learned about them. In the colonies studied by
Chance, Kummer and Reynolds, some of the extreme stresses
were absent, and no actual massacres occurred. This is convenient for our purpose. The finer details of tension and stress
are much easier to unravel in a context of uneasy peace broken
by frequent non-lethal quarrels, than they are in the middle of a
battlefield.

Even these three communities were unmistakably more violent than any in the wild. The rhesus monkeys of Regent's Park
were so ravaged by dysentery and tuberculosis that after seven
months only 110 of the original 253 were still alive. It is extremely likely that the monkeys were rendered more vulnerable to
disease by the stresses of their frequent quarrels; four of the
dead revealed no sign of infectious disease at post-mortem, and
may simply have died of stress or shock from fighting, as is
known to occur in mammals. Biting and wounds were common.
At Whipsnade, not only were many animals wounded (including an infant) but one female was hurt so badly she had to be
shot, and one male had his arm broken and would almost certainly have been killed if the keepers had not removed him. Although we shall be drawing on all three studies, we shall be
specially concerned with Whipsnade, where Vernon Reynolds
made a special investigation of the onset and spread of quarrels.
Out of 4616 'social interactions' at Whipsnade (i.e. occasions
when one animal was seen to do something in relation to
another), 2347 (more than half) were quarrels. At Zürich, bites
serious enough to cause nasty wounds were commonplace. Kummer made a detailed comparison of the frequencies of various
kinds of behaviour in the Zürich baboons and in the wild
bands (of the same species) he studied in Ethiopia. In the zoo
colony aggressive acts were 9 times as frequent in females
and 17·5 times as frequent in adult males as they were in the
wild bands. Even if no massacres occur, a monkey society

in the zoo is clearly very unlike a monkey society in the wild.

What are the differences between zoo conditions and those of the wild? Obviously when the zoo colonies were set up (and also the Cayo Santiago colony), the members were strangers to each other, who had not grown up together. It says much for monkey sociability that some at least were able to set up more or less workable societies at all (including, in Chance's colony, even a supervised play-group). But clearly we cannot expect the smooth development which is usual in the wild, particularly when (as in Zuckerman's colony and the one at Bloemfontein) new adults are suddenly introduced. However, lack of familiarity is by no means the only, or even the most important stress for the captive colonies. Monkeys brought up in total isolation and then put together can form no society (p. 72). All the zoo monkeys had presumably at least had early social experience, though not with the same companions. The Whipsnade colony had been going for over three years when Reynolds studied it; all but the adults and one nearly adult male had been born in the colony, and by this time all the members 'knew each other extremely well' as individuals. Yet it was no more peaceful than Chance's colony of strangers. Trouble can arise, as we shall see, even in the Japanese open zoos, in societies whose normal development through the generations has never been interrupted. Conversely, even in the wild, a solitary from outside may enter and even lead a band other than the one he was reared in (p. 68). This kind of stress, therefore, only appears serious when combined with other stresses, or when the interruption in normal social relations is specially traumatic (we shall see that this was true on Cayo Santiago).

A much more serious problem that could arise in zoos was a grossly disturbed ratio of males to females. This would be upsetting in any society ruled by a male establishment, but especially so for the democratic patriarchate of the hamadryas baboons, where every adult male in the prime of life normally has 1–9 females to follow him (p. 61). In 1929, Zuckerman's hamadryas colony contained 39 adult males and only 9 adult females; 1 male had 2 females, 7 had 1 each, and the other 31 went without. The great massacres always began as fights for the possession of females (who were often killed in the struggle, which continued over the corpses). Zuckerman himself suspected that the massacres were due to an 'unnatural' sex ratio, and suggested that 'the London Colony would have been more tranquil had there been five times as many females as there actually were'. Modern zoo directors have generally profited by his suggestion, and the absence of outright massacres in the three post-war colonies is explained by a better balance of the sexes. Of Chance's 253 rhesus monkeys, 3 were adult males, 10 adult females, the rest immature. In 1955, Kummer's 15 hamadryas baboons included only 1 adult male with 4 adult females, the rest being not fully adult; by 1959, there were 3 adult males, but by that time there were 7 adult females. Of Reynolds's 24 rhesus monkeys, 4 were adult males, 8 adult females, and the rest not fully adult. All three colonies were therefore free from this kind of stress.

Any excess of males in the wild can be drained off by the emigration of some of them to live as solitaries or sometimes (for instance, in hanuman langurs) in all-male bands. There is, of course, no room in a zoo enclosure for more than one band, however it is composed. And all the other stresses we can observe seem to be related more directly to the most obvious difference between the zoo and the wild: the limited *space* provided by the zoo enclosure, far smaller than the normal territory of a wild band. This normal territory area is several *square miles* in most species; for instance, 0·5–5·0 square miles in common langurs, and 2–15 square miles in cynocephalus baboons. The zoo enclosures were all of the order of *hundreds of square yards* in area. Evidently the most striking feature of zoo colonies is *crowding*; since there is no food shortage, they may fairly be described as *affluent crowds*.

To begin with, zoo monkeys, unlike the wild ones, cannot spend much of the day-time in long tours of an extensive territory. In the wild hamadryas baboons of Ethiopia, Kummer has established that no trace of tension ever appears during these travels (p. 67), and such tension as does appear in the wild is only seen at the sleeping-ground, where problems of individual territory or social space can arise (p. 57). To judge from the field reports, this may well be true of other species in the wild. The zoo colony lives all the time in an area comparable to a sleeping- or resting-ground, in just the situation where tension can develop. The enclosure is a feeding-ground too, and food, instead of being scattered through a forest, is generally supplied at a fixed point. Individual monkeys (and, in the hamadryas, families) are thus constantly liable to trespass on each other's social space, especially when they gather round the feeding-place. Because of the fixed limits of the enclosure, monkeys cannot dodge and evade as far as they normally can even at a sleeping-ground in the wild. Subordinate hamadryas baboons at Zürich, when persecuted by superiors, would flee downhill. In the wild, this would take them as far as they liked into the plain, away from the lofty sleeping-ledge on the cliffs; they could then sneak back later. But at Zürich, they could go no farther than the wall. As Zuckerman wrote in 1932, 'confined to a small area, animals cannot separate from one another as they would in a natural environment'. Social space is compressed for all; monkeys are confined by the walls of the enclosure much as steam molecules are confined by the sides and lid of a pressure cooker. It is no wonder that aggression is always on the boil.

When space is abundant, as we saw in Chapter Two, the life of a monkey band is peacefully regulated by an elaborate social machinery. Under crowding, all the components of this machinery begin to break down. In this context, the corruption of the best is decidedly the worst, and every item of social behaviour, that helps to make life peaceful in the wild, can become a source of violence in the crowded zoo enclosure. In the wild, as we have seen, leadership is the most important positive factor in the control of violence. In the zoo, this institution undergoes profound changes, sometimes out of all recognition.

When the monkeys are unfamiliar with each other, as well as being crowded, one possibility is the complete failure of the system of stable alliances. This is naturally most prominent among hamadryas baboons, for among these monkeys, in the

D

wild, leadership is not based on an establishment; all males are essentially equal, and alliance is only used against foreigners. Under the combined pressures of crowding and shortage of females, Zuckerman's baboons exhibited a brutal struggle for power, yielding a simple hierarchy of individual rank, unstable and constantly relapsing into violence. Since the only basis for status was strength or ferocity, leadership was replaced by a system of 'despotism moderated by assassination'.

Under the combined stresses of unfamiliarity and crowding, rhesus monkeys at the Bristol Zoo, observed briefly by Michael Chance, displayed another political perversion. One very important aspect of monkey social life, which Chance has emphasised, is the attention the monkeys pay each other (p. 73), which appears either in the actual direction of their eyes (and sometimes of their rather mobile ears) or in the devious routes they take to avoid trespassing on each other's social space. The special attention which is paid to leaders has a useful function in the wild, since it helps a band to keep together and act swiftly and appropriately in emergencies. In the zoo, where leaders are more brutal, the attention paid to them is full of fear. Among Reynolds's rhesus monkeys at Whipsnade, for instance, the deep-throated threat call of the leader always caused 'a stir to pass through the whole colony'. Both in the wild and in the zoo, monkey leaders have a way of doing conspicuous and noisy things, which focus the attention of the rest. High-ranking rhesus monkeys in the zoo, both at Regent's Park and Whipsnade, frequently did this 'jolting' activity, climbing a tree and shaking the branches, or stamping on the roof of a hut, or crashing down on a see-saw if one was available. At Whipsnade, the leader normally jolted only when there was some disturbing noise, which might indicate danger, such as that of a low-flying plane; he was still performing a potentially useful function. But other monkeys jolted when they failed to get somebody's attention; for instance, a female, who was trying to become the leader's consort, jolted when he sat with another female. Now at the Bristol Zoo, jolting was used as a political technique by a determined demagogue. When the males of the establishment were around, butter would not melt in this monkey's mouth. Whenever they were out of sight inside a hut, he rushed to a tree and jolted. In this way he became apparently familiar to the crowd. When the breeding season came round, this colony held a general election; the establishment was thrown out of office, and the demagogue was elected president by the crowd's support.

This trick of making oneself apparently familiar is well known, of course, in human mass politics. If a group of strangers meet to form a committee or delegation for some purpose, they generally elect those who have spoken at the meeting, who appear familiar to them. 'The common folks believe in their leaders', wrote an American economist in 1929, 'we no longer look upon the captains of industry as magnified crooks. Have we not heard their voices over the radio? Are we not familiar with their thoughts, ambitions and ideals as they have expressed them to us almost as a man talks to his friend?' This was written just before the great stock-market crash on Wall Street. The famous demagogues of human history, from Cleon in ancient Athens to Hitler in modern Germany, regularly used the technique of the monkey demagogue of Bristol.*

Among Kummer's baboons at Zürich, where there were plenty of females to go round, the structure of family units was preserved, but the two younger males, lacking the training normally available on the march, were inert and ineffectual leaders. As we have seen (p. 63), the oldest and most experienced wife of one of these do-nothing lords took over all his functions. This episode shows a certain resilience and flexibility in the

---

* Of course, like true monkey leaders in the wild, true human leaders have always had to secure the attention of their peoples, not for meaningless or destructive personal predominance, but as a necessary part of their constructive function, a means to enlist the co-operation of a whole society for constructive ends. Elizabeth I, whom we have used as our chief example of a great human leader (Appendix Five), well understood this legitimate showmanship, a matter of great oratory, sense of occasion and personal panache. The effect is not to deceive people, but to draw their attention to real and relevant issues.

society, which could call upon the normally latent talents of a female to ride out, to some extent, the stresses at Zürich, milder than in Zuckerman's colony. But we shall see that there were other more serious distortions of social life, and we have already seen that there was plenty of aggression (p. 82).

In the rhesus colonies at Whipsnade and Regent's Park, it appears that the top leaders were able monkeys, who might well have been selected in the wild. Henry, the top leader at Whipsnade, for instance, showed all the alertness of a true leader. In the wild, the survival of the band is promoted by the fact that everyone focuses his attention on the leaders, and the leaders focus their attention on the resources, opportunities and dangers of the natural surroundings (as well as on the slightest disturbance of the peace within the band). The leaders might be said to *represent* their band in dealing with nature. Henry of Whipsnade was exemplary in this respect.

Whenever something unusual happened in the Whipsnade colony's surroundings, the first monkey to notice it uttered a warning bark. Such unusual events were, for instance, a man cycling by the enclosure, a man with an Alsatian on a leash walking past, some people and a dog chasing goats some distance away, the appearance of a green Austin van usually driven by the overseer of the keepers (and hence associated with removal of monkeys for various purposes), a white car driven by the vet (but only if it stopped near the enclosure), zebras galloping in the distance. On hearing the bark, the other monkeys looked up at once and tried to locate the danger. They then usually ran to the roof of the hut in the middle of the enclosure, or, if the danger was imminent (for instance, a keeper entering the enclosure) climbed the dead tree which rose from the centre of the hut. In this situation, Henry was always quick to take up a position with a good view of the disturbance, 'from which he watched the source of danger most attentively, for much longer, and with a greater fixedness of interest than the other animals, which spend much time jostling about as animosities reasserted themselves in the cramped conditions on the hut-top or up the tree'. This long span of concentration on one object is evidently

typical of a truly competent leader. Conversely, a male called
Dopey, who held the lowest rank among males (with one exception we shall meet later), showed a kind of behaviour 'typified
by lassitude and incompleteness. He never seemed able to concentrate on anything for long.' He would start doing something,
and quickly break off. Such a monkey could hardly be a good
leader, and thus far the social arrangements at Whipsnade were
still sound.

But although he was the right monkey for the job, Henry
behaved very unlike a wild leader. The lack of a daily feeding
trip deprived all the monkeys of a great deal of fun, interest and
occupation, and left Henry in particular with no economic
responsibilities. Nor could he really *do* anything about the danger situations he watched with such concentration. He was
thrown back entirely on his social function of dealing with quarrels in the colony. But because of the lack of room for manœuvre, not only were quarrels more frequent than in the wild,
but Henry could not rely on keeping his own social space free
from intrusion. At the feeding-place, he actually had to push
the others aside to give himself ample space to sit and eat. With
continual irritation and nothing else to occupy him, he was
easily provoked by the slightest sign of either intrusion or quarrelling. Sometimes, at a slight disturbance in the colony, he
would promptly attack an innocent bystander. Sometimes, apparently with no provocation at all, he would suddenly jump at
near-by monkeys and scatter all those within some distance of
him. He was moody and unpredictable; occasionally, unexpec-
tedly, he would fail to intervene in a serious quarrel. On the
whole, however, he gave an impression of edgy aggressiveness.
Rhesus monkeys generally screech with fear when threatened or
attacked by a more dominant animal. In Chance's colony, this
screech rarely had any effect on others. But at Whipsnade this
shrill, piercing, long-drawn-out sound had become a stimulus
for Henry to take aggressive action. This was quite automatic;
the victim screeched even if Henry himself was the attacker (when
of course the screech would not help the victim), and Henry's
aggressiveness in the crowded and confused mêlée was somewhat

indiscriminate — he sometimes attacked the very monkey that had 'appealed' to him. The other monkeys, when fighting, somewhat restrained their attacks from fear of Henry's intervention, but when Henry himself attacked he pulled no punches and bit hard, drawing blood and breaking bones. This brutality was often evident, for, of course, Henry's victims did not have much room to escape him. He once chased a female, who dodged in and out of the hut doors for two minutes twenty seconds before he gave up; usually, of course, he caught his victim.

A monkey leader in the wild will always protect mothers and babies from others, and certainly not harm them himself. Henry, on the other hand, was quite capable of attacking one-year-olds, and when the mother of one of them, with exceptional courage, actually dared to intervene, he bit her severely in the tail. Sometimes, when he was thus engaged, all the other monkeys expressed their disapproval by giving a combined 'hough' (the rhesus threat sound). On one occasion, when Henry was attacking a mother who still carried her baby, the little monkey had her hands severely bitten and lost two fingers. For several days afterwards, her grip on her mother's fur was poor, her remaining fingers were swollen and bleeding, and she repeatedly squeaked with distress.

The top leader in Chance's colony had much in common with Henry. At Regent's Park, there was a definite establishment, including two males besides the top leader, with a combined social space of 3 to 4 feet radius, within which other monkeys were not allowed. At Whipsnade the second male, Dick, often sided with Henry in quarrels. But in both cases there was a big gap between the top leader and his companions, and at Whipsnade Henry frequently attacked Dick. Henry, indeed, was absolute master of his colony, and except for the courageous mother just mentioned, nobody ever dared to resist him. It appears that in the zoo, even if the right top leader is selected, he is by no means the constitutional president found in a wild monkey band; he is an absolute autocrat, an arbitrary dictator, responsible to none. This emergence of dictatorship is one of the most striking results of crowding.

While Henry would tolerate no male near him, and thus acted as a dictator, he did have a female consort, dependent upon him and thus intruding only with his permission. So also did the dictator of Regent's Park. The position of such a consort is a perfect example of dependent rank (p. 65). Because she is permitted within the dictator's social space, and thus generally moves around with him, she is feared by all other monkeys, irrespective of her personal rank before she became consort. At Regent's Park, Chance observed and filmed a graphic illustration of the consort's place in society. A group of young monkeys were huddled together in a clump (as monkeys tend to do in cold weather). The dictator's consort approached the clump and huddled against it. One by one, as if they had suddenly remembered pressing business elsewhere, the young monkeys hopped out of the clump and moved off; by the time the dictator joined his consort, she was sitting there all by herself.

The court of Henry of Whipsnade was the scene of an extraordinary drama, watched closely by Vernon Reynolds from January to August 1960. At the start of the period Henry had an elaborate entourage. To begin with, there was his consort, Anne. Much of the drama occurred before the breeding season (when Henry had sexual relations with his current consort, but with other females as well). At this stage, then, the relationship of Henry and his consort was essentially one of companionship; they sat together often and moved about together. Besides Anne, who alone could regularly occupy his social space, Henry was attended by three other females, Malvolia, Nanny and Blondie. These were, in effect, his ladies-in-waiting; they (as well as Anne) groomed his coat (which was always in perfect condition) and, less frequently, he groomed them. Malvolia had a double post; she was also lady-in-waiting to Anne, who generally groomed her. This kept her on the outskirts of the social space shared by Henry and Anne, and gave her the second highest rank after Anne among the females. Besides those already mentioned there were four other adult females, but they were not part of Henry's entourage, and made no attempt to become consort; they took no part in quarrels over Henry's attentions, but

when they did become involved in quarrels they ranked next
after Anne and Malvolia. At the bottom of the female hierarchy
came Nanny, a lively but unambitious monkey, with a great
interest in infants, and, lowest of all, Blondie, a big, buxom female with a 'yellowish coat', extremely timid and submissive.

Although Henry was absolutely faithful to her as a consort,
and always continued to seek her company and sit with her,
Anne was in a continual state of jealous fury. She was embol-
dened by her high dependent rank. Like all the monkeys, she
was under the stress of crowding, and she defended Henry's
social space as if it were her own, frequently and furiously attacking intruders (other than Malvolia, her own hanger-on).
The usual intruders were, of course, Nanny and Blondie, whom
Henry himself sought out as grooming-partners. Analysis of the
numerous quarrels in the colony showed that Anne was pursuing a regular vendetta against her two rivals.

However faithfully he might seek her company, Henry was
quite automatically provoked by Anne's repeated aggressions
against Nanny and Blondie. Anne was covered with scar marks,
the result of his merciless punishment. Being about the most
aggressive of his subjects, she was constantly in trouble, but she
could never moderate her aggressiveness. Finally, on 16 April,
Henry gave Anne such a vicious wound in her right leg that she
had to be shot and removed.

Scarcely had Anne paid the final penalty, when a new drama
began, not without elements of comedy. Presuming on her previous favoured position on the edge of Henry's court, Malvolia
began to give herself the airs of a new consort. Formerly a quiet
and unobtrusive monkey, she now 'moved about with a pre-
posterous swagger and stiffness of the legs', 'she narrowed her
eyes perpetually, she became ultra aggressive, threatening all
other adult females alike ... and made clear-cut advances to
[Henry], following him about and grooming him.' Unfortunately for Malvolia, she was living in a fool's paradise. Henry
made no response to her advances, and never groomed her back.
Even before Anne's death, he had shown signs of interest in the
humble Blondie. With more discrimination than he usually

showed, he had refrained from attacking her and specifically protected her from Anne. As a widower, he began to court Blondie in earnest, seeking her out for company, following her about and grooming her. For a long time she remained timid and embarrassed in his company, baring her teeth (a sign of fear) as he 'settled in beside her'. But as he patiently continued to share his social space with her, she gradually began to change her personality, becoming less and less timid, and, finally, as haughty and aggressive as Anne had been.

Meanwhile the continual aggressiveness of Malvolia had, of course, provoked Henry to attack her again and again, often drawing blood, till she at last began to lose her groundless confidence and to return to her old submissive quietness. It was in vain that, during the first weeks, she went and 'jolted' (p. 86) to attract Henry's attention whenever he paid court to Blondie. Thus, as Blondie became more aggressive, Malvolia became more timid. This reversal, entirely due to the preferences of Henry, took many weeks to complete (from 16 April to 1 August). During the transition period, there was continual quarrelling between the two rivals. For a long time Malvolia was the assailant and Blondie the victim. Gradually the tables were turned, with many vicissitudes. On 15 June Henry had sexual intercourse with Blondie (the first intercourse of the breeding season in the colony), but the new consort was still far from sure of herself. The real turning-point came on 30 June. Blondie, screeching, chased Malvolia, who was making the threatening 'hough' sound. At this stage their actual behaviour had reversed, but each still felt confused enough to make the sound appropriate to her mood in former encounters. But by 28 July, Blondie was biting a screeching Malvolia. Finally, by 1 August, Blondie was the established new consort, and Malvolia had accorded her full recognition, salvaging her old status by becoming Blondie's lady-in-waiting as she had once been Anne's. A thoroughly chastened monkey, she finally knew her place. By this time Blondie, haughty and jealous, was beginning to show enough aggressiveness towards female rivals to earn attacks from Henry. By 26 August when Reynolds stopped his

*

observations, it looked very much as if the whole drama was going to begin all over again, with the once humble Blondie in the role of Anne.

In fact, Reynolds suggested that in the conditions of this colony such a cycle could continue indefinitely. It seems to be a combined consequence of three things: the crowding stress that made all the monkeys so prone to quarrel over space, the absolute dictatorship of one monkey, and the high but purely dependent rank of the consort. With his touchiness about others' aggressions, Henry would naturally choose a quiet, submissive monkey for his consort. Inevitably, as she found herself within his social space and feared on that account, she would become less and less humble, until her aggressiveness provoked Henry to savage punishment and finally to execution. And then the whole cycle would begin again. Malvolia, misled by her special position as Anne's attendant, had begun to behave like a consort when she was not one in fact; her aggressiveness naturally lost her any chance of succeeding to the consortship, and Henry turned to his dumb blonde instead.

When all three factors have been present in human societies, very similar sequences have often occurred, quite irrespective of the sexes of autocrat and favourite. The first favourite of James I of England, Robert Carr, became involved in a poisoning case, but it was his increasing arrogance that probably induced the king to throw him to the wolves, in favour of George Villiers, who at this stage played dumb and flattered James for all he was worth. Madame de Montespan, the lively favourite of Louis XIV of France, was similarly replaced, when she became too aggressive, by her creeping protégée, Madame de Maintenon, who always took care to manipulate Louis into doing the aggression himself. Sarah Churchill, wife of the famous Duke of Marlborough, made her husband's fortune by her success as the favourite of Queen Anne of England; as she became more and more of an aggressive bully, she was undermined by the queen's lady of the bedchamber, Abigail Masham, who has been described as 'quiet, cool, self-effacing and a good listener'. When the aggressive favourite was in a position to make real trouble, with the support of an important faction, it was sometimes necessary to kill him or her. Elizabeth I was an incomparably greater leader than James, Louis or Anne. But Elizabeth, in her last stressful years, had no option but to execute her delinquent favourite, the Earl of Essex, when his aggressiveness got out of hand. When she had chosen him, he had still been relatively well-behaved, and less aggressive than the much more gifted Raleigh, who (like the monkey Malvolia) began to throw his weight about before he had got the job. At Whipsnade, too, it would probably not have been feasible for Henry simply to discard Anne, whose rank and rights in social space had become very definite in her own eyes and in those of the other monkeys, so that her aggressiveness could no longer be tamed.

A still more exact human analogue of Henry of Whipsnade is provided by Henry VIII, King of England. Like the monkey dictator, he was capable of all the great leader's concentration and vigilance, and in fact he brought England through its most dangerous social upheaval without actual civil war, achieving this *tour de force* by his capacity to sense (chiefly through movements in Parliament) the repeated changes in influential public opinion, and to respond to these changes at whatever cost to his own peace of mind and private life. But under the colossal pressures of his time, he was brutally, even monstrously aggressive, ready at all times to kill anyone without hesitation; including criminals, he is said to have executed something like 72,000 people.

When Anne Boleyn first became King Henry's mistress, she behaved with proper humility, not only to Henry but to others. She wrote to Cardinal Wolsey, thanking him for a present 'in my most humble wise that my poor heart can think'. As she became more secure, and particularly after she became queen, she acted with more and more open aggressiveness against more and more people (including, of course, Wolsey himself). She was indeed, as the poet Wyatt is said to have written of her, 'wild for to hold, though I seem tame'. On the death of her divorced predecessor, Catherine of Aragon, she appeared wearing yellow, and boasted in public 'Now I am indeed a queen!' Henry

became increasingly provoked by her tactlessness, quarrelsome-
ness and furious tempers. It is said that she found him with the
lady-in-waiting Jane Seymour on his knee, and did not hesitate
to shout abuse at the demure Jane (who became the next
queen). When it became clear that she was unlikely to produce a
son, Henry evidently decided to punish her aggressions for good
and all.

For all his brutality, Henry seems to have divorced his wives
when (as in the case of foreigners) they had no dangerous faction in England. Anne did have such a faction, and it obviously
had to be dealt with. Throughout history, this problem has often
been tackled by a controlled and carefully aimed witch-hunt.
Anne was therefore accused of adultery with her least amenable
supporters, including her brother, Lord Rochford. There is no
evidence whatever that she was guilty. With a last effort to
achieve his object without killing Anne, the king sent an agent
to her prison to offer her life in return for a full confession of her
alleged unfaithfulness. Anne replied in a letter of real human
dignity, asserting her innocence and pleading for the lives of her
alleged accomplices. No doubt with some hindsight, she put her
finger on the crucial fact of her dependent rank. '. . . I always
looked for such an alteration as now I find; for the ground of my
preferment being on no surer foundation than your grace's
fancy, the least alteration, I knew, was fit and sufficient to draw
that fancy to some other subject. You have chosen me from a
low estate to be your queen and companion. . . .' But if the
letter has its human qualities, it also makes clear that Anne's
aggressiveness was now beyond cure. She does not hesitate to
attack Henry himself, mentioning his 'unprincely and cruel
usage of me', and, above all, she simply cannot resist indirect
attacks on Jane Seymour, 'that party, for whose sake I am now
as I am, whose name I could some good while since have pointed
unto; your grace being not ignorant of my suspicion therein'.
On receiving this letter, Henry hesitated no longer, and Anne
was duly beheaded.

The combination of stress, autocracy and dependent rank is
seen at its most dramatic at the courts of kings and queens. But

of course it can make its appearance at all levels and in all spheres of a modern human society. In less drastic terms, the Whipsnade story could easily be re-scripted for an office setting, with Anne as the boss's secretary, Malvolia as her personal typist and Blondie as the Cinderella of the typing pool. And even in equally drastic terms, such a story is not confined to royal courts: kings are not the only men to murder their wives. For monkeys or man, the story may stand as a fine illustration of the viciously aggressive personal relations that can develop in a society under stress.

2

With such an able but brutal dictator at their head, the rhesus monkeys of Whipsnade lived in continual tension. They kept out of Henry's way only by crowding each other. They were constantly liable to jostle and push, and to pinch or clip at those who jostled them. Intense inequality was evident at all levels of the society, not only at the top. When grooming occurred, it was generally obvious which of the grooming partners was of higher rank. When an inferior animal invited a superior to groom, the superior would often make a few perfunctory movements of token grooming, and then at once get into one of the postures of invitation to be groomed. The subordinate had to groom with the greatest attention, carefully picking over the superior's fur for bits of dirt and debris, rarely stopping to nibble the bits it found, always ready to allow for movements by the animal groomed, so as not to pull his fur when he changed position. On the other hand, if a superior really felt like grooming, the subordinate had to take it as long as the superior liked. The high-ranking monkey would pick about at his leisure, pausing to eat any morsels it liked, and the subordinate had to lie or sit absolutely still, and move when the groomer chose, and submit to being pushed about, like the child of a harassed human mother in a bullying mood. The fact that a superior could make his rank felt in either role explains how, in grooming partnerships,

the monkey of higher rank was sometimes mainly the groomer
and sometimes mainly the groomee (for instance, Malvolia
groomed Henry but was groomed by Anne). Grooming
took a similar form at Regent's Park, and a film made by
Michael Chance shows the acute discomfort and uneasiness of a
subordinate getting the grooming treatment from the dictator
himself.

Under these tense conditions, acts which in the wild would
serve to control violence become liable to cause breaches of the
peace. Rhesus monkeys have many postures and gestures of
threat, such as staring, bobbing the head, opening the mouth
without exposing the teeth, raising the eyebrows and flattening
the ears, lowering the head and shoulders and bending the arms.
These threat movements would serve as warnings in the wild; in
crowded conditions, with no room to dodge, they become provocations to violence. Analysis of the quarrels at Whipsnade
shows a whole set of social processes, each harmless or useful in
spacious conditions, all interacting to promote, prolong and
amplify quarrels in the zoo. The first of these is the tendency of the
leader to intervene in quarrels. In the wild, he can stop an incipient quarrel by a warning threat. In the zoo, where quarrels
are so much more intense, he tends increasingly to intervene in
earnest, with real and sometimes bloody *punishment* (generally,
but not always, inflicted on the aggressor). There is no doubt
that the danger of punishment by the dictator has a considerable
effect on his subjects. At Whipsnade, where we have seen Henry
so ready to inflict punishment, the screech of the victim in a
quarrel was high-pitched and penetrating, designed to attract
his immediate attention. The threatening 'hough' call was a
series of staccato, low-pitched sounds often interspersed with
quick glances towards Henry to see if he had noticed the aggression. But either sound was liable to attract the attention of
Henry and also of other near-by monkeys. As soon as a victim
screeched, his pursuer stopped and looked at Henry, and thereafter his attack or chase would be punctuated by uneasy back-
ward glances. But though fear of punishment made aggressors
uneasy, it certainly did not deter them from their aggressions,

and besides being useless as a deterrent, punishment could become the source of further violence, on account of three further social processes.

We have seen that (as Shakespeare observed for man, p. 25) violence and threat, like other activities, are highly contagious in monkeys, and that (as Kummer discovered at Zürich) a threat by one monkey induces others to threaten in the same direction. In the wild, this interaction is put to constructive use in the formation of stable alliances, and hence of establishments and public pressure groups, which ultimately help to reduce violence. In the Whipsnade quarrels alliances were thoroughly unstable. Monkey A might unite with monkey B in attacking monkey C in one quarrel, and a few days later A might join D in attacking B. Hence in the zoo this automatic reaction gives rise to an indiscriminate *bandwagon* activity, a tendency for near-by monkeys to join in any fight on the side of the aggressor, who is likely to be the winner.

Kummer showed that threatening in the same direction was so automatic that it occurred even if the second monkey could not see the object of the first one's threat (p. 74). He also noticed that, as a result, the second monkey often made a 'mistake', and attacked some quite different victim from the first one's. As he put it, 'through a chain of such misunderstandings a quarrel can soon spread to individuals who at first had no part in it'. *Contagion*, therefore, became merely a means of spreading and amplifying quarrels. If A and B were having a fight, C and D near by might start one of their own.

The final link in the vicious cycle was provided by an extremely important activity, first discovered in birds by Martin Moynihan (who later observed the night monkeys, p. 50). He called it *redirection*. In a rough and general way, redirection has long been familiar to practical observers of human behaviour, especially in bureaucratic and commercial offices. For it simply means giving the office-boy hell after one has had a rough time from the boss. Sheridan gave a beautiful example in *The Rivals*, in the scene where the father abuses his son, the son bawls out his valet, and the valet finally takes it out on a lesser servant.

He might have made his observations at Whipsnade or Regent's Park. In fact, in these descriptive terms, the process had been noticed by Zuckerman in monkeys, who (as he put it) 'usually "hand down" the punishment they receive'. But the recent animal studies have made the idea precise, and shown what a pervasive part this homely process can play in the societies of monkeys and man. When a monkey is frustrated, threatened or attacked by a superior, he shows signs of both resentment and fear, an uncomfortable and disturbing complex of emotions. He cannot express resentment towards the aggressor, who is too frightening. He can, however, resolve his conflict in an automatic way, by redirecting his resentment to another, less formidable monkey. He may vent his feelings in this way either immediately, or after an interval of time.

In the wild, conflicts of this kind for the individual are transient and relatively rare. Redirection enables a threatened, jostled or frustrated monkey to work off his feelings by threatening somebody else at a distance, or at worst by chasing him: the victim can easily get away. The process is unlikely to do harm, and may even prevent the build-up of tension. It has been described in several monkey species in the wild, but appears to be infrequent there. In the course of their 2000 hours of observation of cynocephalus baboons, Hall and DeVore observed redirection activities on a number of occasions, but it appears from their account that it was at all common only in a particular band under special stress (thirty-three instances), or after experimental interference, such as releasing a tame male and protecting him from the wild leader, who redirected against his subjects. In the zoo, on the other hand, it is certainly very frequent, and may also take the form of serious attack, since the victim often cannot escape. Thus crowding increases both the frequency of redirection and also its aggressive intensity. Under the continual stress and tension, the mood of resentment may be sustained for some time, and thus delayed redirection becomes prominent in the zoo; this can lead to the start of a new quarrel some time after the previous one has been brought to an end.

A special combination of bandwagon and redirection activity

A crowded society: monkeys in a zoo

Above: *Dictator in the zoo: Henry of Whipsnade, threatening* (*p. 90*)

Opposite: *A quarrel produced in wild hamadryas baboons by throwing food on to a resting-ledge* (*p. 67*)

Upper: In approaching the food, families come too close together, causing disturbance

Lower: The quarrel ends with one band of families in retreat; skirmishing still continues (right of centre)

Sex and pseudosex at Whipsnade (*p. 127*)

Upper: A male mounting sexually grasps the partner's legs with his feet

Lower: A male mounting pseudosexually keeps his feet on the ground

Disturbance of parental behaviour: rhesus mothers with their young (p. 271)

Right: A 'motherless' mother

Below: A normal mother

High-density housing in the 'affluent' society (pp. 226 ff.): Stuyvesant Town, New York, with 393 people per acre

Opposite: Housing riots and war (p. 115); women and children in modern violence (pp. 170 ff.)

   Upper: Riot in Brooklyn, New York, July 1966

   Lower: Vietnam, 1965. This family was given fifteen minutes to cross the river away from their home before it was bombed

*The population crisis in art: sculpture by Gustav Vigeland
in Frogner Park, Oslo*

appears in the zoo, which Reynolds has called *diversion*. It works
out as 'if you can't beat 'em, get 'em to join you'. At Whipsnade
when a monkey was threatened by a superior, he sometimes
stood his ground but turned his head away and threatened a
neighbour, redirecting his own resentment. The superior would
often automatically turn to threaten in the same direction, and
the diverting animal would then be able, with a little bit of luck,
to join his persecutor in a joint attack on the third monkey. This
process naturally had the effect of involving more monkeys in
any given quarrel. A still more deplorable activity of this kind
could even be used to start a quarrel between two other monkeys. The *quarrel-monger* would go and sit near a superior, pointing his own head in the direction of a rival. Sometimes this risky
procedure led to trouble for the quarrel-monger, but sometimes
it came off, and the superior attacked the innocent party.

It will readily be appreciated that, with all this going on, the
quarrels at Whipsnade were generally *compound* quarrels, involving several *stages* (A attacks B, B attacks C, D attacks E,
etc.). In the course of thirty-eight days (about 150 hours) of observation between 18 January and 14 April 1960, Reynolds observed 158 such compound quarrels, or roughly one every hour.
He has drawn up a very useful catalogue for 118 of these im-
broglios, involving altogether 390 stages. To simplify this catalogue, he has simply indicated, for each stage, the winner (the
monkey that showed aggressive or threatening activities) and
the loser (the one that showed evasive or submissive activities).
This makes it possible to identify all the processes we have described. Thus if a third monkey joins the winner of the preceding
stage in an attack on the loser, it is *bandwagon* activity. If a monkey attacks the previous winner, it is *punishment*. If two other
monkeys begin to fight after one previous stage, it is *simple contagion*. If the previous loser attacks somebody else, it is *redirection*.
We therefore analysed Reynolds's catalogue, and the following
figures emerged.

Sixty of the quarrel-stages were punishments, 29 inflicted by
Henry and 31 by other high-ranking monkeys. Fifty-three were
cases of bandwagon activity. Forty-two were cases of simple

contagion. Finally, no less than 85 were redirections; 13 of the quarrels actually started as delayed redirection by the last loser in the previous compound quarrel. Sometimes the same stage came under more than one heading; for instance, a loser could redirect by jumping on the next winner's bandwagon. Most of the quarrels must have begun as disputes over social space, but once started they could evidently spread in a variety of ways. Sometimes a monkey would redirect again and again; in one quarrel, after being beaten by Henry, Dick attacked five other monkeys in succession. Contagion and bandwagon activity were constantly keeping the quarrels on the boil, but the most straightforward and prominent vicious cycle was that of punishment and redirection. A few examples will show how the quarrels developed:

Henry beats Malvolia; Malvolia beats Blondie (redirection); Anne beats Blondie (bandwagon); Henry beats Anne (punishment); Anne beats Blondie (redirection).
Dick beats an adult female; Henry beats Dick (punishment); Dick beats Tom (redirection; Tom was an ambitious nearly-adult male).
Henry beats a three-year-old female; Anne beats Blondie (contagion). Henry beats Anne (punishment); Anne beats Blondie (redirection).
Anne beats a three-year-old female; Henry beats Dick contagion); Dick beats Tom (redirection); Tom beats the three-year-old (redirection with a touch of bandwagon activity). The next quarrel began with the three-year-old finding an even less dominant victim for delayed redirection, only to be punished by Tom.

It will be clear from these examples that, quite apart from the indiscriminate processes we have discussed, there were some special enmities at work; Anne, for instance, certainly had it in for Blondie, and picked on her as a target whether she was acting by contagion, to get on the bandwagon, or to redirect her resentment. It is true that we chose these examples because they included few individual monkeys besides the personalities we have already introduced. But the existence of special hatreds is a fact. Reynolds established it by a detailed further analysis of the quarrels. It appears that Henry was specially liable to attack Dick and Anne, partly because they were the next most aggressive monkeys after Henry himself, and therefore constantly inviting punishment, and partly because they tended to be in his neighbourhood, and therefore in danger when he expressed his edginess about social space. Dick and Anne, being near Henry, were liable to quarrel contagiously when he did, and also of course to redirect after his attacks. When they did so, Dick picked on Tom and Anne picked on Nanny and Blondie. Tom may have suffered because he was the next most aggressive male, and also (being on the threshold of adulthood) liable to trespass on Dick's social space. Nanny and Blondie were victimised, as we have seen, because they were liable to be near Henry. In the case of Anne at least there may have been some tendency, after many such provocations, to hate them as individuals; the other special hostilities can largely be explained as automatic reactions to intrusion or aggressiveness by others.

With punishment, contagion, bandwagon and redirection at work under stress, tension reverberates round the zoo society. But there is obviously a certain asymmetry. Dick and Anne were undoubtedly picking on monkeys lower in their respective hierarchies, of whom they were not afraid, and this tendency is general. From the nature of all the processes, and especially redirection, stress is transmitted down the hierarchies, and those at the bottom are in trouble most of the time. At Whipsnade, during Anne's lifetime, Blondie was at the bottom of the female hierarchy, and constantly at the receiving end of bandwagon and/or redirection activity. In Kummer's hamadryas colony at Zürich 80 per cent of all redirected attacks were aimed at the lowest-ranking adult female; the female of next lowest rank was the victim next preferred. On one occasion, the principal victim was bullied by all and sundry for about fifteen minutes; half a minute later, the poor creature was seen standing in a corner, threatening the wall of the enclosure with raised eyebrows. (The office-boy, after all, has nobody left to redirect against: he can only kick the wastepaper-basket.) It is natural that the universal whipping-boys among hamadryas baboons should be whipping-girls. Among rhesus monkeys the status of females is substantially higher; at intermediate ranks, females often won over males in the compound quarrels. Blondie was in fact not the most unfortunate victim at Whipsnade; this distinction was reserved for a male, Bruce, and his sad story takes us a step further into the world of violence.

When Reynolds began his observations in January 1960, Bruce was 'an apparently healthy full-grown adult male, differing in no spectacular way from the other adult males'. He was occasionally being groomed by adult females, and was still recognisably a member of the community. But he was decidedly at the bottom of the male hierarchy, below Dopey (p. 89) and even young Tom (p. 102), and the pressures he was exposed to were too much for him. Gradually he withdrew from social contacts. He developed a habit of 'dashing to the food patch as soon as the keeper had dropped the food, seizing a large piece before the other animals arrived, and making off with it to a quiet spot to eat in peace while the other animals congregated on the food patch to feed'. Gradually, in turn, the other monkeys began to treat him as a complete outcast, as if he were a stranger from another band, no longer entitled to a place, however humble, within the hierarchies of the colony. On 15 March (and, as Reynolds notes, no doubt on other occasions not observed) he was violently attacked by Henry, Dick and Tom, and badly bitten. After this he spent more and more of his time inside the hut in the middle of the enclosure, peeping out and emerging from this ghetto only when no other monkeys were looking, to grab food, stuff it into his mouth and cheek pouches, take a spare piece in his hand, and bolt back to his refuge. In the wild, any monkey would leave and become a solitary (like the baboon Lone, for instance, p. 69) long before he was under this kind of pressure. Bruce did indeed escape, but England is not a kind environment for rhesus monkeys, and he despondently returned to the enclosure, to be greeted by a unanimous outburst of threatening 'hough' calls from the entire colony. On 5 May, the outcast was found to have a broken arm, and was removed. He was placed in a cage with a female (who had also been removed to have a disease cured). In his desperate ghetto existence, he had feared this female as much as any other member of the society that persecuted him, but in the cage he rapidly established dominance over her, and returned to the ordinary social behaviour of a rhesus monkey. This happy ending, as we shall consider later, is itself an instructive part of the story of Bruce.

It is clear that under the stress of crowding monkeys are even crueller to anyone they consider an outcast or foreigner than they are to those who are still treated as members of the band. Bruce had lost his social birthright, he had ceased to be familiar to his fellows. When such an outcast is available for persecution, he or she becomes a universal object for redirection. The band-wagon tendency then has the effect of polarising redirection, so that all the monkeys turn their resentment towards the same victim. This sustained *mass redirection* against a pariah is the most extreme form of violence observed in the zoo, short of the outright massacres seen in Zuckerman's colony.

In a single society confined in a zoo, redirection distributes and amplifies the stresses within, and mass redirection can only be turned against pariah individuals. What would happen if a monkey society under stress were not so confined? We have one important observation which suggests an answer to this question. In 1938, when Carpenter shipped his rhesus monkeys from India to Cayo Santiago (p. 43), the land and sea transport of monkeys was carried out under frightful conditions. Monkeys for export were packed in bamboo cages for rail shipment to the coast, and during these journeys 10–20 per cent of them died of thirst, suffocation or the fierce fighting that occurred *en route*. On the freighters that carried them by sea, where no adequate facilities were available, deaths amounted to a further 6–40 per cent. It was partly through Carpenter's efforts that conditions began to improve; the same problems arose later in air transport, and again took much time and effort to overcome.

Thus it happened that the monkeys for Cayo Santiago were transported there under terrible conditions. On the voyage the females were confined, each with her young, in separate cages.

We shall see later (pp. 270–1) that it is socially disastrous for young monkeys to be reared by their mothers alone, without the precious experience of the play-group; that such isolation with their young has a stressful effect on the mothers themselves; and that defect in the behaviour of mothers can cause havoc (and, in particular, serious aggressiveness) for generations. There was food shortage on the voyage, and the mothers were under such stress that most of them fought their young for food, and at least eight mothers killed their babies. Family life thus suffered a severe blow, and the normal opportunities for peaceful social integration in the play-groups were utterly disrupted.

On arrival at the pleasant islet of Cayo Santiago, the new monkey societies were free to roam at large, but they were suffering from the *after-effects* of very severe stress. During their first year on the islet, there was heavy mortality from lethal fighting, and indeed they seem to have remained unstable and relatively aggressive long afterwards. In particular, the social machinery of leadership selection had been grievously upset. Hence in one of the bands that now formed there arose an aggressive dictator called Diablo, more autocratic and bad-tempered than even those of the zoo colonies. In terms of the number of quarrels he engaged in and won, he was about five times as aggressively dominant as the second ranking male in the band. (Using similar criteria, we can estimate that Henry of Whipsnade was about one and a half times as aggressively dominant as Dick.) Diablo's subjects were therefore under even greater pressure than those in zoos, yet they were not restricted by the walls of an enclosure. Exactly as we might expect, the resulting mass redirection turned outwards. Kept at a distance by their dictator, constantly harried by him and too frightened to resist, they redirected against the other bands on the islet, in what amounted to a war of conquest; eventually they had the run of the whole islet. The normal band territorial system had completely broken down. At this point Carpenter performed a critical experiment. He removed Diablo and caged him. The band at once withdrew into a normal territorial range. For a while there was a certain amount of fighting within the band, as the monkeys worked off their remaining resentments. Eventually these post-war disturbances subsided, a moderate leader took over, the territorial rules were properly observed, and peace returned to the island. Such is the story of Diablo, the monkey warlord of Cayo Santiago, suggestive evidence that mass redirection can lead to war.

3

Though monkey bands can be as big as human food-gathering tribes (p. 59), it seems at first a far cry from these communities of (at most) several hundreds to the vast societies of millions that form the units of human history. So far as violence is concerned, it is clear that we can now bridge the gap. For the processes we have just considered, especially redirection, can operate under stress to amplify tension and distribute violence through a society of any size and complexity. Mass redirection, in particular, can readily produce violence on any imaginable scale. The story of Bruce shows that there is a critical difference between the treatment of low-ranking individuals and the treatment of those whose behaviour is sufficiently unfamiliar to appear foreign — whether persecuted minorities within or national enemies outside the society. A large human society can, of course, contain a number of different cultural groups (like separate bands of monkeys), which may differ *en bloc* in status as social classes, and the targets of mass direction in man, even within a society, can be large groups of people, not merely individual pariahs. Since the labour of such groups may be needed (a factor not applicable in monkeys), they may be treated ambiguously or alternately as the lowest-ranking members of society (as Bruce was at first) or as alien outcasts, fit only for lynching (as Bruce became). Fear of being outcast in this sense has been a potent factor in keeping subject classes docile, and lynching in the Southern States has often been promoted to prevent Negroes from using their economic bargaining powers (for instance, when their labour was in demand in the North).

Mass redirection has been a serious obstacle to human social progress, for it masks the real discontents in a society. Instead of asserting themselves in a constructive way, a grossly exploited group (like the Southern poor whites) has again and again expressed its discontent in violence redirected against outcasts (like the Southern Negroes). There were two occasions in the history of the South when the poor whites began momentarily to tackle their economic and social discontents by peaceful means. The first was the Populist movement of the 1890s, the second was the trade union movement of the 1920s. In both cases the less responsible members of the ruling groups (factory-owners, press, churches) succeeded in convincing the white masses that they were splitting white unity and the Democratic Party, and threatening to let in the Negro; in both cases the progressive movements collapsed, and the white masses turned upon Negro victims.

The fact of mass redirection has also provided specious arguments in favour of the innate aggressiveness of man. In the East Anglian riots of 1816 (pp. 21 ff.) the peasants, for all their confusion, were relating their not excessively violent protests to the real problems they faced; once the facts are known, the accusations of innate aggressiveness are seen to be absurd. But when Tudor Londoners attacked foreigners (p. 25), or Southerners lynched Negroes, they were injuring or killing people who had done them no harm and (in the case of the Negroes) were under even greater stress themselves. Such senseless cruelties appear at first sight the outcome of nothing but inherent aggressiveness. Yet the Londoners could not buy enough to eat, and the Southern whites were suffering the terrible economic stresses associated with low cotton prices (p. 20). The monkey observations show us with the utmost clarity that these senseless cruelties are not occurring in a vacuum. Resentment is redirected only when it exists, and when stress in the society is activating the vicious circle which includes punishment from those of higher rank. The Southern workers who left the unions and lynched Negroes had grounds for fear as well as resentment; in 1929 seven white strikers were murdered (and their murderers were acquitted) and seven white union organisers were framed and sent to prison for terms ranging from five to twenty years. The authorities who condoned these crimes were themselves driven by economic fears and pressures: many wealthy Southerners did in fact go bankrupt in the next few years. Anxious over fancied intrusion on their privileges, terrified of social upheaval, they displayed in more extreme form the same sensitivity about insubordination or disturbance that made a brutal autocrat out of Henry of Whipsnade.

Mass redirection provides the link which makes the problem of violence one coherent problem, for it connects individual violence, civil disturbance and war. The monkey results have provided ample support for the view of war put forward by the British sociologist Stanislav Andreski in a number of books since 1954. Andreski sees civil violence and foreign war as alternative results of stresses in a society. The factor of redirection must produce precisely this result. Under stress, violent crime is generally the first symptom. Contagion combines individual resentments into mass riots. Through further contagion, mass outbreaks follow each other in rapid succession in different places. The riots in East Anglia in 1816 were so contagious that the authorities were firmly convinced there must be a subversive organisation, though the careful modern researches of A. J. Peacock provided no evidence for this at all. Similar chain reactions were seen in the contagious spread of race riots and teenage battles in Britain in the 1950s, and in the serious riots in several American cities in the summer of 1966.* When stress is prolonged, this anarchic violence may develop into mass civil warfare between cultural groups of high and low status (class war). To avert such revolutions, governments and other authorities automatically seek, by the pressures of propaganda and terrorism, to promote mass redirection against alien minorities,

* As the still worse riots of 1967 developed (see footnote, p. 115), some American authorities, like those of England in 1816, began to suspect organised conspiracy. In a programme transmitted by satellite and televised in Britain on 26 July 1967, John Conyers, Congressman for Detroit, reported his own immediate on-the-spot enquiries both there and in Newark. He found no evidence in either city of organisation or systematic agitation from outside.

foreign peoples, or both. Thus there are indeed alternative outcomes of prolonged stress: civil conflict or international war.

Some of the more outspoken human rulers have admitted that human beings will only go to war under the pressure of fear. Frederick the Great, certainly an expert on this subject, laid down the rule that a soldier must fear his officers more than he does the enemy. Leon Trotsky, founder of the Red Army, declared that a soldier must be faced with the choice between a probable death if he advances and a certain death if he retreats. Almost every army in history has imposed the death penalty for desertion in the face of the enemy. But even these cynical experts omitted to mention the other necessary component — resentment against the authorities, redirected against the enemy out of fear. Understandably enough, there has always been extreme official reluctance (even on the part of highly capable governments) to let this become generally known. When Tilney was censoring the scene of the London riot against foreigners (p. 25), it was particularly the causes of the riot he wanted suppressed, for then the fact of redirection would be evident. Official uneasiness on this subject may be present even in modern democratic societies; there is a curious pressure in the academic world to separate the study of warfare from that of other forms of violence, and thus mask the connection between them. However, as we shall see, the promotion of mass redirection is a hazardous procedure for any government, and responsible modern authorities have everything to gain from letting this particular monkey out of the bag.

Apparent evidence for the absence of any relation between war and civil violence was presented in 1963 by the American scientist Rudolph J. Rummel. He carefully compiled measures of domestic and foreign conflict (including death-rates) for seventy-seven nations in the years 1955–7. As a result of a highly sophisticated statistical analysis, he concluded that 'foreign conflict behaviour is generally completely unrelated to domestic conflict behaviour'. But this may be an example of the pitfalls of highly sophisticated statistical analyses of rather coarse survey material (especially when taken over a short period). The redirection factor would tend to produce violence either at home *or* abroad, a negative correlation. But, on the other hand, the sheer absolute amount of violence, as a symptom or measure of the absolute stress in society, would give the contrary effect: the greater the stress, the greater the violence both at home *and* abroad, a positive correlation. In gross statistical surveys, the negative and positive correlations would cancel out, leaving the apparent absence of any relationship between violence at home and abroad. It may well be true (as appears from Rummel's tables and much other evidence) that 'foreign conflict is not a necessary and sufficient condition for domestic peace', but Rummel's more general conclusion does not follow. He has only disproved the oversimplified hypothesis that violence can *only* occur at home *or* abroad and not in both directions at once.

Considered over broad sweeps of time (rather than the three years of Rummel's study), human history affords ample indications that Andreski is right, and that civil and foreign violence are alternative outcomes of stress in society (not necessarily mutually exclusive outcomes). Rummel himself admits that 'if one were to take a longitudinal slice out of the history of many nations, a very close relation in the fluctuations of domestic and foreign conflict behaviour might be found'. In fact we can often see long-term *alternations* of mainly civil and mainly foreign violence. The religious wars in sixteenth-century France broke out soon after the final frustration of the attempted French conquest of Italy. Conversely, in sixteenth-century Japan, the end of a terrible century of civil war was marked by the dictator Hideyoshi's invasion of Korea. One striking long sequence is provided by the story of the Plantagenet kings of England:

Henry III	Civil war
Edward I	Foreign war
Edward II	Civil war
Edward III	Foreign war
Richard II, Henry IV	Civil war
Henry V	Foreign war
Henry VI	Civil war

This particular sequence, and its significance, were not lost on William Shakespeare, who made a very careful study of the English chronicles. He presented his findings in the longest and most impressive series of historical plays ever written. He saw clearly that the alternation was explained by mass redirection, promoted by the more energetic rulers, and this time he smuggled the message past the censors. In the last act of *Henry IV*, *Part II*, he expressed in one and a half lines the underlying mechanism of these seven plays. 'Be it thy course', says the dying king to his heir Prince Hal,

> 'Be it thy course to busy giddy minds
> With foreign quarrels. . . .'

The sequel, in the next play, is the Battle of Agincourt—for Henry V took his father's advice.

On the other hand, the reign of Elizabeth I shows that an outstandingly great leader, by taking positive action to reduce stress and diplomatic measures to ease tension, could reduce violence both at home *and* abroad, and how, when the problems became too great even for her abilities, violence both at home *and* abroad marked the closing years of her reign (pp. 27–8, and Appendix Five). Violence at home and abroad could therefore either alternate or synchronise, and the two relations would certainly cancel in any study such as Rummel's.

Although her censors might not like the subject discussed, it does not seem that Elizabeth herself was ever prepared to resort to promoting mass redirection, even under considerable stress. In this she differed from rulers of ordinary ability, who have rarely hesitated to use this device more or less automatically. In this, in fact, she showed her exceptional intelligence, for the techniques of diversion and quarrel-mongering, risky and uncertain even among individual monkeys (p. 101), are extremely risky and uncertain when employed on human masses. They must obviously lead to a vicious circle. The stresses that set up the original tension, far from being cured, are normally (in modern times always) increased by a war. One obvious danger-point for civil disturbance is the period just after the war comes to an end, when resentments can be turned back against the authorities at home. The 'post-war disturbances' in Diablo's band on Cayo Santiago (p. 107) have many parallels in human history. Francis Bacon did not fail to include 'disbanded soul-diers' in his list of the causes of sedition. Several of the East Anglian rioters of 1816 were ex-soldiers, demobilised at the end of the Napoleonic Wars in the previous year. The more intelli-gent contemporary writers noticed this factor as contributing to the many riots of the time. 'Many military have returned to us of late,' reported one East Anglian clergyman, 'who have neces-sarily increased the great want of labour.' The end of the First World War saw a whole series of mutinies and riots in Britain, following each other in a wave of contagion. At Calais, 2000 British troops set up a 'Soviet'. In England itself, 10,000 troops mutinied at Folkestone, 2000 at Dover and some 60,000 at camps elsewhere, all on the same day (6 January 1919). Later in the year, in a mutiny and riot at Kinmel Park, where the Red Flag was raised, five people were killed and twenty-one wounded; meanwhile civilian strikers were fighting pitched battles with the police in Glasgow.

This kind of backfire can occur on a much greater scale. The end of the Franco-German war of 1870 was followed by the extremely bloody and vicious civil war between the Paris Com-mune and the rest of France. And, of course, if the stresses be-come serious enough, the backfire can occur before the war is officially over. The most spectacular backfire in history occurred in Russia in 1917. The Tsarist Government had attempted to divert the resentments of the Russian people into the war against Germany. The war caused such frightful suffering to the Russian armies and civilians (chiefly through food shortages and epi-demics) that the soldiers simply marched back to launch the Russian Revolution and the appalling civil wars that persisted for years afterwards.

When soldiers are fighting at a distance from home (and when the navy is loyal to the government), a backfire of this kind is obviously less likely. But the effect of a war on the civilian population may have the same results. A vicious cycle of this

kind began to develop in the 1960s in the United States. We
have seen that a large fraction of the American people are living
in serious poverty (p. 35), and we shall see later that the most
severe stress in the United States is the shortage of decent housing (Chapter Six). In proportion to their numbers, the American Negroes are certainly the chief sufferers from both bad
housing and other forms of poverty. The increasingly violent
war in Vietnam, in which more and more troops have been engaged, may be seen as an attempt to export the violence which
might otherwise break out at home. It has been noted that 16
per cent of the troops sent to Vietnam are Negroes (who made
up less than 11 per cent of the American population in the
Census of 1960), and that 22 per cent of the fatal casualties (a
good indication of front-line postings) are Negroes or Puerto
Ricans (another depressed group). These percentages alone
could result partly from the fact that Negroes and Puerto Ricans,
because of low educational opportunities, are less likely to obtain the kind of skilled jobs offering exemption from military
service or employment in safer rear positions. But there are
other indications that the policy of diversion is being more or
less consciously adopted. An official publication, circulated to
American officers in Vietnam, expresses this policy with a naïve
simplicity which makes remarkable reading in 1966: 'It [the
Vietnam war] is building a new type of youth. They are becoming filled with a sense of duty and patriotism and there is little
doubt the war will do much to reduce juvenile delinquency in
America.' There can rarely have been so open an admission that
mass redirection is being brought about. The publication is not
a propaganda leaflet, but a collection of informative medical
statistics, arranged as 177 lessons on how to fight the Vietnam
war. It closes with an extract from a letter to President Johnson
from a soldier's wife in Milwaukee: 'I pray that when my little
boys grow up they will be able to fight for the American cause in
Vietnam.'

The vicious cycle, however, is being closed by the enormous
and mounting *cost* of the Vietnam war. By 1966 this was causing
drastic increases in the cost of living in the United States (p. 14).

In an attempt to control the economic upheaval, the government attempted a credit squeeze, but it seems that the only sector of the economy seriously affected by the squeeze in 1966 was housing. As a result, house-building reached its lowest level since 1960. Since bad housing is perhaps the most important of the stresses in America, a whole series of riots, generally connected with protests about housing, broke out in the summer of 1966. The cycle can therefore be summarised thus: poverty and bad housing lead to increases in violent crime (p. 31); a war is fought and intensified to redirect the violence abroad; the cost of the war leads to greater poverty and a more intense housing crisis; housing riots break out on an alarming scale. The story is the more tragic in that the American Administration of this period had prepared a most imaginative series of reforms designed to reduce poverty (drastically axed to pay for the war — p. 14). These reforms, tackling the problem at its roots, might have gone far to reduce stresses and violence in the United States.* It is in this sort of connection that the results of the study of monkey societies may be of the greatest assistance to responsible governments, alike in the United States and in the rest of the world. For they can use this information to free themselves from the tragic consequences of indulging the automatisms of a monkey colony under stress, and to substitute the rational solutions of human applied science.

The increase in stress caused by warfare, which eventually makes resentment override fear of the home authorities, provides some explanation for the grand oscillations of history between civil disturbance and war. There is no doubt that under

---

* The vicious spiral continued in 1967. The cost of the war continued to erode the sums which might have been spent on reducing poverty in the U.S.A. Congress refused a bill to introduce effective rat control in the slums. As the summer began (bringing irritating heat and the serious seasonal water shortage in many American cities), another series of riots broke out, worse than those of 1966. Between April and the end of July riots had occurred in Nashville, Houston, Tampa, Cincinnati and Newark, culminating in the very serious riot in Detroit, in which more than thirty people died and more than 1500 were injured.

certain conditions, and especially after one or more costly or destructive wars, people are not prepared to redirect against foreigners. After the First World War the British Government (alarmed by the mutinies of 1919) was contemplating new wars, such as the invasion of Russia and the annihilation of Turkey. Both wars were stopped by the absolute refusal of the British people to support them. In July 1920 the British Government sent an ultimatum to the Bolshevik Government of Russia, which was driving an army of invading Poles back into Poland. The Labour Party Executive and the Parliamentary Committee of the Trades Union Congress promptly began to arrange for an immediate General Strike, and it was evident that this strike (unlike the one that occurred later for domestic reasons) would have overwhelming public support. The government at once denied any intention of a war, and soon afterwards withdrew the small British invasion force in northern Russia.

This was not the first time in its history that the English people had refused to be stampeded into mass redirection. One of the more agreeable episodes in the history of human violence occurred in the last years of the dictatorship of Cardinal Wolsey. The career of this man illustrates both the realism and the ruthlessness of Henry VIII (p. 95). From about 1515 to 1529, Henry allowed the Cardinal to govern England as absolute dictator of Church and State, eventually combining the offices of Lord Chancellor, first minister of the King, and permanent representative (legate) of the Pope in England. In the course of his dictatorship, Wolsey virtually destroyed the many local and special privileges and powers of the medieval nobles and churchmen. In 1529 Henry coolly discarded the Cardinal and took over a modern national state, having the good sense to share his almost absolute powers with Parliament, where the rising new social classes were already well represented. Wolsey incurred all the passionate hatreds aroused in the process of modernising the English state; Henry obtained the universal gratitude of his subjects for dismissing the dictator and taking his place.

The job Wolsey was doing for him meant so much to Henry that he gave the Cardinal an almost completely free hand. Wol-

sey was a single-minded, or at most a double-minded man. He
was interested in money, and in his own prestige. (As long as
people did not interfere with these pursuits, he did not mind
what they believed, so no heretics were burned during his rule,
much to the annoyance of the bishops.) Though never satisfied,
he did not do too badly in acquiring money; his income on the
eve of his fall has been estimated as £50,000 a year, the equivalent of several millions today. He was equally insatiable in his
quest for prestige. When the King made his bastard son a duke,
Wolsey made his own bastard a dean (with fourteen other miscellaneous ecclesiastical offices), but even Henry drew the line
when the Cardinal asked for a bishopric for this teenager. The
main object of all Wolsey's efforts, however, was to become
Pope. In pursuit of this object, he involved England in a long
succession of extremely costly and otherwise completely point-
less wars. By 1525 the English had had enough.

In this year Wolsey began to prepare an invasion of France.
This required a perfectly enormous special tax. It was at this
point that resentment began to outweigh fear of the authorities:
'the poor cursed, the rich repugned, the light wittes railed', the
people were 'not greatly caring what they doo or what become
of thayme'. The result was a surprisingly unanimous tax strike
in all the counties, each convinced (or at least saying so) that
the others were paying less, or nothing. In Norfolk, for instance,
'many have been put in hope to pay nothing by rumors that
those of London nor the other shires will consent to the first
rates'. There were numerous protest meetings (1000 people in
Essex, 20,000 at Cambridge), and in Huntingdonshire the tax
commissioners were forcibly prevented from sitting. Within a
couple of months, Wolsey was sadly writing to his foreign allies
that 'the king's coffers are not furnished for a continuance of
war, and his subjects cannot help him'; the war was off.

Wolsey, however, was incapable of learning the obvious
lesson. In January 1528 he declared war on the Habsburg Empire, among other things because the Emperor had twice pro-
mised him the papacy and secured the election of somebody
else. The Habsburg Empire included the Netherlands (then

E

including Belgium), and the economy of England (and to some extent that of the Empire) was absolutely dependent on the export of wool to the textile manufacturers in the Netherlands. It was said a few years later that half the English population depended for their livelihood on this trade. The declaration of war at once threw thousands in England out of work. Wolsey plodded gamely on with the old technique of diversion; he blamed the unemployment on the presence of German merchants and apprentices in London. On this occasion, nobody believed him. Riots broke out throughout East Anglia and in Wiltshire and Somerset, and the justices of the peace, who reported the Somerset rising, glumly remarked that 'it is expected that other parts will rise'. In Kent the people were proposing to solve the war problem by sending Wolsey to sea in a boat with holes bored in it. Again within two months, Wolsey had to negotiate with the Emperor; on 15 June, an outright truce was concluded. In the following year, Wolsey was disgraced and the King took over nearly all his financial assets (and also his debts, which Henry was annoyed to discover were eight times as big as the Cardinal had claimed). Within three years the English people had averted two wars.

Four/Pseudosex

1

THE tensions of the crowded zoo colony of monkeys, amply expressed in the various processes by which quarrels persist and spread, have other, more complicated effects, by no means irrelevant to the problem of violence. One of the most striking characteristics of the zoo colony is the presence of extreme inequality between its members. In the wild, status hierarchies and classes are a matter of public convenience and order; they do not seriously affect any monkey's life, liberty or pursuit of happiness. There is no inequality of health or well-being between the highest and the lowest in the band. In the zoo, inequality becomes a serious matter for the underprivileged. Monkeys at the bottom of the hierarchies are often thin, not because there is any real food shortage, but because they are harried about and given no adequate opportunities to collect their share of food. Those of high rank are sleek and well-fed. From the nature of grooming in the zoo (p. 97), top monkeys, especially the dictator, are always beautifully groomed, with fine, healthy fur. Under-monkeys get either no grooming or perfunctory grooming or grooming shaped by the whims of their masters; they are therefore generally unkempt and uncomfortable. At Zürich, Kummer found that having to groom oneself was a criterion of low rank. This connection between status and skin comfort is sometimes almost as simply expressed in man. According to the Australian anthropologist Lester Hiatt, there is a tribe in the New Guinea highlands who describe an important man by saying that 'skin bilong im strong feller too much'; describing someone of no account, they say 'skin bilong im dirty, all same pukpuk' (crocodile). In modern civilised societies too, the connection between grooming and status is sufficiently obvious, and made much of in commercial advertising.

All observers of monkey colonies in the zoo stress the perfectly relaxed, smooth movements, postures and gait of the upper
monkeys, especially the dictator, and the tense, jerky manner
of the underlings. This constant tension, together with their
hurried meals and ill-kept coats, must undoubtedly affect
their health. At Zürich, Kummer observed four adult females in
their sleep, over one hour a night for eight nights, and counted
the movements they made. The highest-ranking female moved
27 times in her sleep, the second one 45 times, the third one 70
times, the lowest-ranking female 94 times. Thus constant tensions and fear by day was expressed in disturbed, restless sleep
at night. The fear was not, of course, groundless. Because they
are more often the victims of bandwagon and redirection (p.
103), the under-monkeys are more often wounded, and Kummer could also measure the rank of his baboons by the number
of scars and wounds (obviously greater the lower the rank). It is
no wonder that, under sufficient persecution, a zoo monkey like
Bruce can withdraw completely from social relations. Towards
the end, he was, in Reynolds's words, 'a pitiable sight, with one
fore-limb broken, an expression of the deepest melancholy, all
his ribs showing through his lean and bite-scarred flanks, and a
nervous agitated air'. In our own stress-laden societies, sociologists have long been using the 'incidence of psychosis and nervous disorders' as a measure of low status. It yields reliable
charts of human hierarchies. Thus, in a recent study of admissions to mental hospitals in Pennyslvania, this criterion showed
up a neat picture of status determined by colour, religion and
sex, in that order. White Protestant men had the least mental
illness, white Protestant women came next, then white Catholic
men, and so on down to the unfortunate coloured Catholic
women, who suffered most. Material affluence, it appeared, did
not affect status, or help to relieve stress at the bottom of the
hierarchy. In the days of the tough and callous captains of early
nineteenth-century industry, it was widely believed (by those
on top) that underlings were underlings because they were
weak-minded and prone to nervous disorders. It is now sufficiently obvious that cause and effect are the other way round —

the pressures at the bottom of a status hierarchy are enough to upset anyone's mental balance. The point was beautifully made in the case of Bruce, for as soon as he was removed from the community that made him an outcast (p. 105), he showed himself in full command of his monkey faculties, and quite capable of acquiring higher status than one of his persecutors.

In the crowded zoo colony, then, hierarchies are absolute (p. 56) and brutal, and gross inequality prevails. Subordinate monkeys are liable to varying amounts of bullying and frustration, all the way to the danger of becoming complete outcasts, like Bruce, with the extreme persecution that results. Grooming (or being groomed), an expression of personal service or equitable friendship in the wild, becomes only a means of currying favour, and a symptom of the gross inequality (p. 97). Meanwhile monkeys of all ranks are constantly forced into close proximity with each other (the source of all the trouble). For monkeys of all ranks below the dictator,* life is full of personal conflicts, when situations in their surroundings evoke conflicting emotions — fear, resentment, the desire to approach or remain near attractive things like food. Such conflict situations for the individual can of course occur in the wild, in monkeys and other social animals, but they are then momentary, easily resolved, and not a common or prominent feature of social life. Monkeys, like other social animals, have developed several ways of resolving these momentary conflicts. These devices appear occasionally in the wild; but in the zoo, where the conflicts are frequent, prolonged and intense, conflict activities become acute and pervasive, and on the whole they fail to reduce—and may indeed considerably increase—violence in the community.

One of these conflict activities is redirection, which we have already considered at length (pp. 99 ff.). Another was discovered by Michael Chance and Ewan Grant in caged white rats, shown by Chance to be widespread in animal behaviour, and called by him *cut-off*. A subordinate animal can avoid

---

* As we have seen, the dictator himself is under tension, but since he is not seriously afraid of anybody, he expresses the tension in frequent and somewhat indiscriminate attacks on others (p. 89).

provoking a superior by averting his eyes or by otherwise cutting off the sight of anything that would tempt him to do so, by arousing resentment or some desire that would bring him into the superior's social space. Like a wise monkey, he sees no evil. Cut-off activities have not often been reported in wild monkeys, but they are easily elicited by artificially provoking a conflict situation. If an orange is thrown between two Japanese monkeys in an open zoo, the superior behaves as if the food is his own and takes it; the subordinate simply looks away. In zoo or other captive conditions, cut-off becomes extremely common. The American psychologist A. H. Maslow has described what happens when two rhesus monkeys are caged together for the first time. Ranks are settled very quickly; if the sizes are markedly different, the bigger animal becomes dominant, irrespective of sex, if the sizes are roughly equal the issue is decided in favour of the one with the more self-assured posture. 'Characteristically,' writes Maslow, the one that will be dominant 'maintains a level stare and the other drops his eyes or looks off to a corner.' At Whipsnade, Reynolds often saw an activity he called 'looking away'. A monkey, threatened by a superior, would turn his head away and look in another direction (upwards, downwards or to one side). As he looked away, he would sometimes bare his teeth (a sign of fear). In this way the monkey would avoid any temptation to respond to his superior with a counter-threat, and the aggressor might calm down.

From the amount of violence that occurs in zoos, it is clear that cut-off does little to reduce it effectively. There is some indication that the mere sight of a monkey face near by may be provoking, so that when the subordinate turns his face away he is removing a provocation. But if the superior is of very high rank and especially easily provoked, he may actually be offended by the head-movement. At Whipsnade, the monkeys never dared to look away when threatened by Henry himself. At Regent's Park, when near the dictator, they would uneasily look away and back again repeatedly. Moreover it is easy to see how this kind of cut-off can develop into diversion — the subordinate monkey, looking away towards a third one, need only threaten in that direction and the superior may join in. A quarrel-mon-ger (p. 101) will even enter the danger situation to achieve his nefarious purposes, going or staying near a high-ranking mon-key and pointing at a rival. In this way quarrels are spread, or even incited among monkeys at peace. Finally, evidence from animals other than monkeys suggests that an animal may some-times avert his head or eyes not to reduce his own resentment or appetites, but to reduce his own fear and give free play to his own desperate resentment — a very dangerous mechanism in-deed.

Besides redirection and cut-off, there is a third kind of con-flict activity, discovered in birds by Niko Tinbergen and Adriaan Kortlandt, widely studied in animals by Tinbergen, and called by him *displacement* activity. An animal torn between fear and resentment may solve the conflict by redirecting the re-sentment to another object or by shutting his eyes to the disturb-ing situation; but, alternatively, he may avoid either fleeing or attacking by doing some third, quite irrelevant thing. A herring gull, for instance, when in a conflict between the urge to attack another gull and the urge to escape, may pull up some grass, as if to build a nest. Displacement activities such as this are often mixed with cut-off and redirection: thus the grass-pulling gull will automatically be looking down, away from his rival, and he may also pull rather fiercely, redirecting some of his urge to attack. In general, displacement activities usually differ in form from the same acts when performed in their normal context (for instance, grass-pulling in the course of actually building a nest), for they are not being carried out in the usual mood. Dis-placement acts are generally disoriented, disorganised, and in-complete.

In animals other than mammals, sexual acts are rarely used as displacement activities, probably because they are usually tightly controlled and timed by chemical mechanisms. But in mammals, and especially monkeys, sexual acts are often seen in non-sexual contexts. In most monkey species and societies, the female invites intercourse by *presenting* the rear of her body to the male. But this act of presenting is often done by a male or female who is frightened of a superior (male or female) but wants to stay where it is or approach within the superior's social space without being attacked.

It has been shown in many animals, by Sir Julian Huxley, Konrad Lorenz and Niko Tinbergen, that conflict activities are often modified and standardised, or *ritualised* (as Huxley called it) to serve as automatic social signals. In the restricted lives of lower animals, the same conflicts (however mild and momentary) are liable to recur on the same occasions again and again through the generations. So redirection, cut-off and displacement activities can become regular features of social interactions such as those of threat and courtship. It is a logical step to make them eventually into signals which produce automatic effects on other individuals, which will help to reduce the conflict for the signaller. Most obviously, they can become appeasement signals, which serve to reduce (or at least divert) the aggression of the animal that frightened the signaller. These developments can occur by organic evolution, or by change in social rules transmitted 'culturally' — that is, by the training provided by parents and leaders, who punish those who break the rules.

It is easy to understand how the displacement activity of presenting can become a signal of appeasement. Except for grooming and huddling against the cold, sexual behaviour is virtually the only context in which adult monkeys normally tolerate close proximity, indeed close contact with each other. And so the usual reaction of a superior, when a subordinate monkey presents, is to accept him within his own social space, and suspend any intention of attacking him. The superior may simply stop threatening the presenting monkey, or he may stop threatening and *mount* the subordinate instead.

The presenting and mounting that occur in these situations look superficially very like ordinary sexual behaviour, and were regarded as such by human observers for centuries. Frightened monkeys may naturally present to human beings, and this earned them an unenviable reputation. When the French naturalist Buffon published his account of monkeys in 1766, he referred to a baboon he had seen, which was 'insolently lascivious,

and satisfied its strong desires in public. It seemed to make a
parade of its nakedness, presenting its posteriors oftener to the
spectators than its head': the wretched animal must have been
terrified. The German biologist T. Knotterus-Meyer, who observed presenting in macaques and baboons at the Hanover
Zoo, was the first (in 1901) to notice that subordinates presented
to dominant animals when frightened. He described presenting
as a 'sign of deep devotion', which 'flatters' the superior.
Zuckerman saw a great deal of mounting and presenting on
Monkey Hill, and realised that the presenting animals were
often not acting from sexual desire; he compared them with
human prostitutes (1932). Displacement activities were described in birds in 1940, and this prepared the way for a new
approach to the subject.

In the course of the 1950s, Claire Russell in England and
A. H. Maslow in the United States independently decided that
much apparent sexual behaviour in monkeys and man was not
true sexual behaviour at all, but something else, related to fear,
resentment, dominance and submission, which they both independently called *pseudosex*. Claire Russell went on to inter-
pret submissive presenting in monkeys as a displacement activity, which must therefore become more frequent under stress.
In fact, pseudosexual activity is far more commonly reported in
zoo and laboratory monkey communities than in those observed in the wild.

In most monkey societies, the differences between sexual and
pseudosexual presenting and mounting are not very clear cut,
and it is not always easy to distinguish between them; indeed
there must often be mixtures, when true sexual behaviour is performed under conditions of stress and dominance tension. Maslow pointed out that pseudosexual mounting is 'often' incom-
plete, with no erection, and pelvic thrusts either absent or 'weak
and nominal'. But at the time Claire Russell and Maslow developed their ideas, the evidence was still somewhat confused.
Now monkey societies, whether in the wild or in the zoo, differ
considerably (within the same species) in their 'cultures' — the
traditional rules, taboos and signal codes which the monkeys are

*

conditioned to observe. At Regent's Park, for instance, Chance's rhesus monkeys would smack their lips as a friendly gesture; this was never seen among the rhesus monkeys at Whipsnade. At Whipsnade, the monkeys often made an 'intention' movement, flexing their fore-arms and lowering their heads as if about to spring at an opponent: this might or might not develop into an attack. At Regent's Park, this had been ritualised into a threat movement: the monkey would lower and raise its head in this way a number of times in quick succession. At Regent's Park the screech of a victim rarely had any effects; at Whipsnade it regularly brought Henry on the scene to inflict punishment. It happens that in the Whipsnade 'culture' sexual and pseudosexual behaviour were absolutely distinct and recognisably different. This provided complete verification of the concept of pseudosex. When Vernon Reynolds observed the Whipsnade colony, he was unaware of the theories of Claire Russell and Maslow, and it was not until after he had written up his observations (and himself interpreted presenting as a displacement activity, ritualised as an appeasement gesture) that Michael Chance told him of Claire Russell's work.

At Whipsnade, presenting by the female *never* occurred in true sexual behaviour among adults. Instead, the male normally initiated mating by prodding or patting the female's rear, or gently pulling it upwards; if she was willing to respond, the female would then raise her hindquarters and the male would mount. At Regent's Park, where the female initiated mating (as is far more usual) by presenting her uplifted rear, these prods and pats by the male never occurred. Whenever a Whipsnade monkey (male or female) presented to another (male or female), the act was pseudosexual, and motivated by fear of a superior. The two situations were thus clearly distinguished. As a further refinement, when true sexual intercourse was taking place, the female often looked back at the male in a friendly way. Any monkey engaged in pseudosexual presenting, and afterwards when being pseudosexually mounted, would look away, and was obviously engaging in cut-off activity.

The sexual and pseudosexual mounts were almost as sharply

distinct. Pseudosexual mounting always occurred as a reaction
to presenting, in tense situations, and was completely promiscuous. Sexual mounting only rarely occurred in this context,
and then only if the two animals were already 'associating
closely in a sexual partnership'. The other differences show
clearly that a monkey that mounts pseudosexually is *not* in a
sexual mood, but reacting automatically to a compelling signal.
A male engaged in true sexual mounting would be, so to speak,
swept off his feet: he would grasp the female's hocks with his
own hind-legs, bringing himself into position for complete intercourse. A monkey (male or female) mounting pseudosexually
almost always kept his or her feet on the ground, and the male
was thus often actually incapable of penetration. A male engaged in sexual mounting would show an erection, penetrate
and perform a series of vigorous pelvic thrusts before dismount-
ing (the whole sequence would normally happen several times
before ejaculation). A male mounting pseudosexually normally
had no erection; in one case the male was seen to develop an
erection in the course of pseudosexual mounting, but as soon as
it occurred he 'finished the mount without making any attempt
to penetrate'. Monkeys mounting pseudosexually might make
rhythmic movements and pelvic thrusts (even if they were females), but these were rarely vigorous and often omitted. Finally, true sexual mounting naturally occurred only in males, while
pseudosexual mounting was done by both sexes. With all these
criteria, there was virtually no doubt whether sex or pseudosex
was going on; and, as might be expected in a crowded zoo
colony, pseudosexual activities were extremely frequent and
closely related to inequality and tension.

2

Thanks to the exceptional 'culture' of Whipsnade, we need have
no doubt of the nature of pseudosex, as a conflict activity occurring frequently under social tension and stress. It is indeed
very common in all zoo communities, and takes a number of

forms besides those described so far. It may get mixed up in
sexual episodes when these take place under tension, but, even
in cultures where it does not differ so clearly from true sexual
behaviour, it can now readily be spotted from the context and
from its compulsiveness. Not all the forms of pesudosex have
been analysed as completely as the activities of mounting and
presenting at Whipsnade; but all certainly have in common a
close relationship to inequality, enforced proximity and
stress.

While pseudosex always reflects inequality, it need not take
the form of mounting by the superior. Dominance can be expressed in grooming as well as in being groomed (p. 97); similarly, it can be expressed in being mounted as well as in mounting. At Whipsnade this was rare, though Henry was once or
twice mounted by Tom. At Regent's Park it seems to have been
more frequent; Chance noticed that the dictator sometimes
'presented to his colleagues' of the establishment. 'This was
with as much ease of movement as with any other gesture. At
no time were his movements jerky', unlike those of his colleagues
when they approached and presented to him. Among Simonds's bonnet macaque bands in southern India (which were
under some stress of crowding, p. 49), superior males were seen
to mount subordinate males twenty-three times, and subordinates to mount superiors eleven times. On about half of these
latter occasions, the superiors had presented; in the other cases,
the superior had forced the subordinate to mount 'by backing
into it and reaching back to grab it . . . the subordinate monkey
might try to avoid mounting, but the dominant monkey would
continue backing into it until it did mount, lip-smacking while
mounting' (in these communities, lip-smacking was a sign of
fear). Among caged white rats, Chance and Grant actually
found a greater tendency for pseudosexual mounting by subordinates; among monkeys, there are evidently considerable
cultural differences, but the bonnet monkeys show conclusively
that the inequality may be expressed either way. Maslow and
his colleagues quote American army slang which illustrates the
similar reversibility in man: a subordinate appeasing a superior

'is called "brownnose", "being cornholed", "asskisser", "ass-licker", "being browned"'. The British slang phrase 'arse-hole crawling' makes an obvious reference to the situation of subordinate mounting superior.

At Whipsnade, Reynolds recorded a peculiar call, made by both males and females, which he called 'girning', and described as 'a straining sound much like that of a terrier which wants to go out for a walk'. It seems only to be uttered in pseudosexual situations. Tom, for instance, girned when presenting to Henry. On another occasion, after some aggressive behaviour by Henry, Tom 'moved up to him from behind making the girning sound'. At this, Henry moved into a position for Tom to mount, and Tom mounted him.

When a Whipsnade monkey presented, the superior might do one of three things. He might simply accept the subordinate's presence near by, and suspend any threats; or he might mount the subordinate; or, thirdly, he might *inspect* the subordinate's ano-genital region, using his eyes, hand, nose and/or mouth. This kind of voyeuristic behaviour might be done by either male or female to either male or female, and would sometimes be followed (irrespective of sex) by (pseudosexual) mounting. This, too, appeared to be an expression of dominance. Among the bonnet monkeys, a superior would sometimes sniff the face of a subordinate; this was certainly an expression of dominance (subordinates never sniffed superiors), and may be a cultural variation on the theme of pseudosexual inspection.

If some monkeys under stress are peeping Toms, others are *exhibitionists*. Among caged squirrel monkeys, a superior will frequently approach a subordinate, spread his legs apart, and thrust his erected penis in front of the weaker animal's face. Detlev Ploog and Paul Maclean, who have studied these monkeys in captivity, report that this particular pseudosexual act is an unfailing indication of higher rank. With presenting, mounting, forcing others to mount, the seductive girning call, inspection and exhibition, it seems that monkeys under stress develop a considerable repertoire of pseudosexual activities.

Whatever its forms, pseudosex is clearly a device to enable

two monkeys, extremely unequal in status, to remain in bodily
contact for a few seconds and near together in space for longer
periods. As such it might in theory serve to reduce the tensions
of inequality and close proximity, both inevitable under crowding. In this case, it would reduce violence. Conceivably this
might be true under mild and/or temporary stress. But in the
highly crowded communities we have been considering, its role
seems to be, at best, ambiguous. Like all the other social devices
we have examined, it can actually promote or complicate violence under certain conditions.

This positive connection between pseudosex and aggression
appears in two ways. First, there is often reason to believe that a
pseudosexual act by a superior is itself expressing direct aggression: this we may call *sadism*. The victim is often plainly unwilling, frightened and unhappy. The subordinate bonnet monkeys,
as we have seen, were often definitely reluctant to mount a
superior, and were forced to do it, lip-smacking with fear. A
subordinate squirrel monkey, when the erect penis of the
superior is thrust into his face, 'sits in a cowering position while
ducking its head as though dodging a blow . . . if it does not remain quiet during the display, it may be viciously attacked'.
Sometimes it is certain that a pseudosexual act arouses both fear
and resentment in the victim, for sometimes the victim redirects
his resentment afterwards. One Whipsnade female, after being
inspected by Henry, 'chased another female around the enclosure'. In Reynolds's catalogue of quarrels (p. 101), there
were four clear cases of a victim making a redirected attack
after being mounted — for instance, on one occasion Henry
mounted Anne and she immediately attacked Nanny. Although
he did label them separately, Reynolds included mounting and
presenting in his catalogue of the compound quarrels, exactly
as if they were aggressive interactions. This seems fully justified,
for they fit perfectly into the sequences and follow all the principles observed for the other aggressive and submissive activities (pp. 98 ff.). Thus on seven occasions, mounting was actually done as a punishment, inflicted by a superior on the winner
of a previous quarrel-stage. On two occasions, a monkey mount-

ing another was punished exactly as if he had been aggressive. On at least two occasions, mounting occurred contagiously, just like any other form of aggression. All these cases fit in with the conception of directly aggressive pseudosex, or sadism.

Altogether, in the course of the 118 quarrels in the catalogue, there were twenty-two cases of presenting and twenty-seven cases of mounting (including two submissive mounts by sub-ordinates). Some of these were accounted for by the kinds of interaction just mentioned. Others were the outcome of yet another development of pseudosex under stress. For pseudosex may be linked, not only with direct aggression (when it becomes sadism), but also with provocation to violence, when we may call it *masochism*.

Diversion and quarrel-mongering are used to provoke violence between two monkeys other than the provoker (p. 101). When these are combined with pseudosex, the result is a masochistic activity called *protected threat*. This was first named and described in detail by Kummer, in his hamadryas baboons at Zürich. Pseudosex of any kind is rare in the wild, and would hardly have been discovered there. Protected threat provides an even sharper contrast; fairly common at Zürich, it was *never* observed in the wild hamadryas baboons of Ethiopia. At Zürich the normal hamadryas family unit persisted, and this made life particularly complicated for the females. On the one hand, they must not, without his special approval, invade the social space of their male overlord to the extent of actually touching him. On the other hand, any tendency to stray far away might invite punishment. On the whole, it was safer to be near him, and females tried to get as near him as possible, especially when they were frightened. Just as earlier in life they had run to their mothers when alarmed, so as adults they would run to the over-lord — even if he was the one who frightened them, for the process was quite automatic. From this there developed the device of protected threat. If one female wanted to get another into trouble, she would go near the male, present to him with her rear, and threaten her rival at the same time with her face and the front part of her body. If the rival did not react, nothing

happened. Sometimes, to ensure that she did react, the provoker would tug at her tail, and then hurry back near the over-
lord. The rival would now be frightened and hurry towards the
male herself, only to find the provoker in her way. She would
now bend her body grotesquely, in such a way as to present her
rear in the male's direction, while threatening the provoker
with her face (in the same direction). The male would ignore or
mount the provoking female (who was nearer him and facing
away), and would permit her to go and attack her rival with
impunity, returning hurriedly to him and again presenting; or,
often, he himself joined in threatening or even attacking the
rival (who was farther away and showing a threatening face in
his direction). The masochist could thus enlist protection and
even aggression against her victim.

It is obvious that this technique of protected threat can be
used to start quarrels and can lead to considerable violence. On
Monkey Hill, Zuckerman had often observed a 'sexual' approach 'that seems to precede the enlistment of allies before a
scuffle takes place. One baboon approaches another, smacks its
lips, presents, and, having evoked a reciprocal response from the
other animal, immediately turns round and threatens, by gesture, some animal who, previous to this performance, did not
seem to be in any way involved in the situation. Its threatening
attitude is immediately reflected in its new friend's behaviour,
and both become aggressive towards the third animal.'

Protected threat, in various forms, was fairly common in the
quarrels at Whipsnade. Given the different social structure of
the rhesus community, it is natural that the technique was here
used by males as well as females. For both sexes, it was generally
more dangerous to be near a superior, but presenting elimi-
nated the danger for the masochist. On six occasions, a monkey
presented to a superior (usually Henry) and then went and
attacked another monkey with impunity. On most of the other
occasions when presenting took place, a monkey was claiming
immunity from punishment by presenting hurriedly after its
delinquent action. There is no doubt that this masochistic technique makes possible acts of violence which the masochist

would not risk otherwise; and sometimes, as at Zürich, the superior joined in the attack on the innocent party. With all the other processes available to prolong and spread quarrels, pseudosex in both its sadistic and masochistic forms undoubtedly contributed to swell the sum total of violence in the quarrels at Whipsnade.

The combination of pseudosex and aggression can indeed result in particularly rigid and compulsive sequences of actions. Michael Chance has vividly described what was certainly in part pseudosexual behaviour between rhesus consorts at Regent's Park: 'Threat on the part of either animal is . . . immediately followed by threat in the same direction by the partner. Typically, when close to the male, the female, after threatening away from the male, threw her body across in front of him, moving the hind-feet up and down sharply in short bursts as she brought her hindquarters towards the male, or, if she were far away, her threatening behaviour was followed by a presentation stance, and he moved over to her and copulation took place.' 'This was frequently repeated and both animals appeared to be in the grip of a ritualized sequence of acts forming a "reaction chain". This behaviour always developed whenever the female or the male threatened a third party, or threatened apparently indiscriminately in a direction away from the partner.' Since these were consorts, there may have been some true sexual behaviour under tension mixed up in this (in one case there was ejaculation), but there is clearly also protected threat in a highly compulsive form. Such automatic sequences can, of course, involve more than two individuals. In one of the Whipsnade quarrels, Henry and Dick made a general aggressive move against all the others, a one-year-old presented to Henry, Henry mounted him, Tom mounted two three-year-old females in turn, Henry mounted Tom, Henry attacked Tom, Tom mounted Henry, Henry mounted Malvolia, in a regular orgy of pseudosex and aggression. More commonly, pseudosexual episodes occurred in isolation amidst long sequences of straightforward aggression. But they always seemed to inflame the disturbance further, rather than bring it to a close. In monkeys at least, the pseudosexual consequences of stress and inequality seem to be one more factor making for protracted violence under crowding.

3

During the troubled history of mankind, human societies have been exposed to far more complex sequences of stress and social inequality than the disturbed monkey communities we have discussed. It is, therefore, no wonder that pseudosex plays a more important and pervasive part in human social life than in that of the crowded colonies of monkeys. When the idea of pseudosex was independently put forward by Claire Russell and Maslow, both were relying as heavily on human as on monkey evidence. It is, indeed, abundantly clear that many human fantasies and practices hitherto called 'sexual' are permeated with elements of flight, attack, dominance or submission, as well as other inappropriate components, such as disgust. It was one of the greatest contributions of Sigmund Freud to show the very wide ramifications in human automatic behaviour of what he took to be sexual mechanisms. The evidence from monkey behaviour has made it easy to see that what he was really dealing with was pseudosex. Since this is always a reaction to social stress, particular patterns are readily transmitted from parent to child in the social context of the family, and may be further reinforced, distorted or intensified by social stresses and biases operating in adolescence (such as the initiation ceremonies of tribal societies) or later in life. Human language, which offers such enormous scope for creative communication, also offers new scope for social sickness, and permits the intrusion of automatic pseudosexual processes (which cut off communication) into the most subtle and complex aspects of human social behaviour. Here, however, we shall only consider some of the more obvious manifestations of human pseudosex, and their relation to social inequality and violence.

In an age when films and fashions are actually *advertised* as 'kinky', it can hardly be necessary to catalogue the more bizarre forms of human pseudosex. A glance around even the legally sold pulp literature on any legitimate bookstall will provide a rough guide to its scope and diversity, allowing for the restraints and sentimentalisations imposed by censorship. The various forms have been fairly comprehensively listed by Havelock Ellis and Krafft-Ebing and more recent experts, and (much more entertainingly) by Brantôme back in sixteenth-century France. This observant and intelligent courtier-journalist wrote two famous books — *Lives of Illustrious Ladies* (all named, and all 'chaste and virtuous') and *Lives of Gallant Ladies* (all anonymous, and all quite the reverse, though some ladies undoubtedly figure in both works). The second book is a kind of sixteenth-century Kinsey Report, not seriously dated, for the main varieties of pseudosex have not changed during recorded history.

Although a very large number of permutations are possible, dictated by the detailed experience of the individual and/or the special fashions of periods and societies, the main components of human pseudosex are not much more diversified than those found in monkeys: that is why large commercial markets are available for pornography and semi-pornography falling into a few broad categories. The five main themes have already appeared in our account of pseudosex in monkeys. Another human being may be used to provide automatic visual and other stimuli, as in monkey inspection or voyeurism. Such stimuli may be forced upon another person, as in monkey exhibitionism. Another person may be seduced into participation in pseudosex: this may already be the function of the 'girning' call heard at Whipsnade. Finally, pseudosex may be linked with direct aggression (sadism), or with the provocation of violence in others (masochism). These elements may be mixed in varying proportions. The somewhat greater diversity of human pseudosex is a by-product of the great capacities developed by mankind for making tools and appliances. In human voyeurism and exhibitionism, clothes obviously play an important part, producing compulsive involvements with wearing particular articles of dress (as in transvestism) or with having them worn by others (as in fetishism). In human sadomasochism, likewise, fetters, weapons and instruments of torture make their appearance.

As a result of the prolonged and extreme inequalities in human societies, and the tensions associated with their frequent changes (under the impact of technical and economic changes), human pseudosex is much more intense than that of the monkeys. The more bizarre activities (commonly called 'perversions') are more persistent and highly organised, and the same applies to the simpler forms of pseudosex. When male monkeys mount females pseudosexually, the activity is probably never fertile; in man it undoubtedly can be. When male monkeys mount males, they do not normally penetrate; anal penetration has been claimed in two reports only, some time ago (1914 and 1917), and has never been confirmed in all the subsequent studies of monkeys in captivity. It has never been reported in mammals other than monkeys, though pseudosexual mounting is found in a number of species (such as rats and mice). We have already mentioned the male at Whipsnade who desisted from a pseudosexual mount when he developed an erection (p. 127). In contrast, anal penetration occurs with appreciable frequency in man. As a heterosexual practice, it comes to light in divorce courts and in police proceedings in states where it is illegal. As a homosexual practice, its frequency has been estimated; A. C. Kinsey and his colleagues in the United States reported its occurrence in 16 per cent of a group of adolescent boys engaging in homosexual relations. Homosexual anal intercourse is moderately frequent in all tribal societies, and enforced on all males among the Siwa tribe in North Africa and the Keraki in New Guinea.

Since pseudosex is completely promiscuous (p. 127), it may be either homosexual or heterosexual in man. When it is heterosexual and by mutual consent, it is superficially like true sexual behaviour (as in monkeys). The presence of dominance involvements in straightforward heterosexual intercourse has been evident in many societies. In Brantôme's day there were discussions about whether the dominant partner was the one who lay on top, the one who was more active, or the one who made the other do the 'work'. Similar preoccupations appear in modern societies; Maslow and his colleagues, for instance, quote one female patient who felt she was dominant if on top, and another who felt she was dominant if the man was doing the 'work'. In man, it is less easy than among the Whipsnade monkeys to give simple criteria distinguishing sex and pseudosex. One criterion of pseudosexual involvement is the occurrence of convulsion at orgasm; the compilers of the Kinsey Reports found this to be fairly frequent in 'normal' intercourse, but it has since become clear, from the work of Michael Chance on several animal species, that convulsion at orgasm is associated with conflicts involving the urges to attack and escape. Though fundamentally promiscuous, pseudosex can certainly occur persistently between married couples; though always involving a free mutual attraction (in man as in monkeys, and even in birds), sex can certainly occur between strangers in transient encounters. Pseudosex generally involves a measure of obvious cut-off (such as closing the eyes), though this may be masked if it takes a voyeuristic form (compulsive concern with particular automatic stimuli combined with cut-off of all other awareness); it always involves a lack of emotional response to the partner. The two activities can be mixed, in varying proportions, as in the pair of monkey consorts at Regent's Park (p. 133), and of course the same couple can have predominantly sexual and predominantly pseudosexual relations at different times; a pair of lovers may begin with sexual relations, and gradually succumb to the economic and social pressures that make tension and inequality so hard to escape in human societies. Although the labelling of all *other* forms of pseudosex as 'perversions' has led to cruel persecutions, it is probably not without an element of common sense; the more perverse forms are probably the outcome of more severe stress, and the more extreme ones (especially, of course, sadomasochism) are more liable to pass into violence.

The connection between pseudosex and inequality in man is complex and still requires much investigation. However, it is not hard to see that the connection exists when we consider, for instance, the matter of prostitution and organised vice, which cater exclusively for pseudosexual activity. (Courtesans, such

as the Japanese geishas, are permitted some freedom of choice
and response, and may therefore engage in sexual activities; but
this kind of enterprise is not commercially important in modern
Western societies.) In 1859 Dr William Sanger wrote a report
on New York prostitution for the Board of Governors of the city
pauper institutions, who were worried by the incidence of
venereal diseases. Out of 2000 prostitutes, asked their reason for
adopting the profession, more than one-quarter said they were
driven by poverty. However corny, the old folk-song, about the
rich that get the 'pleasure' and the poor that get the blame, is
pretty near the mark as a comment on organised vice, though of
course the poor or otherwise underprivileged male can redirect
his resentments on to the prostitute, always in some way a social
outcast. Prostitution shows a mushroom growth in response to
flagrant economic inequalities. The exchange rate of the dollar
provides recent examples. By 1965, rising population, food
shortages due to the war, and the inflow of American troops and
American dollars had produced a shattering inflation in South
Vietnam. The war, meanwhile, was producing its crop of home-
less orphans. By 1966 it was estimated that at least 30,000 children under the age of sixteen were 'surviving by crime and vice',
the boys as thieves, the girls as prostitutes in garrison towns
(earning up to £100 a month at fourteen). Actual slavery is prevalent today in parts of Africa, Arabia and India; and it is interesting that most victims of modern slavery (the most extreme
form of inequality known) are used for pseudosexual purposes
(like the estimated several thousand slave-prostitutes, male and
female, in Bombay).

When a rising social class is attempting to secure equality
with its former masters, and emphasises equality in its political
programmes, it has generally favoured puritanical measures.
Examples are the gentry and merchants who made the English
Puritan Revolution, the lawyers who made the French Revolution, the industrialists who made Victorian England. It is no
accident that William Wilberforce campaigned with equal enthusiasm for the suppression of the slave trade and the suppression of vice. The effect, in all these cases, was not, of course, to

eliminate organised vice, but to separate it off from ordinary
social life, and pretend it no longer existed. This is clear from
the puritanical laws nominally in force in the various States of
the United States. The American Institute for Sex Research has
estimated that 95 per cent of male Americans could at some time
be prosecuted for breaking one of these vice laws. Hence the
laws have little effect in discouraging the practices against which
they are apparently directed. What they did achieve for some
time was to prevent people from comparing notes about their
sexual and pseudosexual behaviour, for anyone talking about
these matters was likely to be confessing to some technical
crime. In this instance the Kinsey Reports, based on confiden-
tial information, broke the implicit censorship. Since the distinction between sex and pseudosex is extremely recent and still
difficult, it is not surprising that puritanical law codes have
often penalised some forms of true sexual behaviour, which did
not conform to rules about marital relations.

Conversely, when a group is attempting to increase *inequality*,
and is even ready to assert this explicitly, it is likely to unleash
organised vice and make it a prominent part of the social life of
a country. The Nazis were prepared to use puritanical attitudes
for tactical purposes (such as bringing a false charge of homo-
sexuality to get rid of an inconvenient army leader), but the
Nazis grew out of, and greatly promoted, organised vice of a
scale and perversity rare in history. While the *Gauleiters* grew
rich on the proceeds of the local vice rackets, the Nazi Government officially urged the youth of the nation to engage in
promiscuous and unenjoyable — in fact pseudosexual — intercourse, to breed more supermen for the German Reich. There
is a marked contrast here with the puritanism of the English and
French Revolutionaries, the British industrialists and the Stalin-
ist régime in the Soviet Union.

The formal and informal censorships prevalent in human
societies have shown interesting changes. In Victorian England
the industrialists had achieved their desired equality with the
land-owners; between the new combined upper class and the
poor yawned the enormous gap which impressed Disraeli, and

made him call them 'two nations'. Victorians such as Disraeli
were relatively free to call attention to extreme class inequality,
which many still regarded as a perfectly proper state of affairs.
Meanwhile an extraordinary, perhaps unparalleled, prudery
reigned over the discussion of sex (and therefore of pseudosex).
Yet there is no doubt that organised vice was flourishing on a
considerable scale. When Dostoevsky paid his brief visits to
Paris and London, he was chiefly impressed by the bourgeois
propriety of the French capital and the Babylonian vice of the
English one. In 1833 a magistrate told a Parliamentary Committee that he had to deal with prostitutes of twelve or thirteen
years of age who haunted the drinking dens and were rarely
sober. Although prostitution was licensed in several garrison and
seaport towns, figures are hard to come by. A police report in
1857 gave an estimate of 8600 prostitutes in London, but two
years later W. Acton wrote, probably correctly, 'the return
gives, after all, but a faint idea of the grand total of prostitution'. In New York, where similar prudery prevailed and perhaps even greater inequality between rich and poor (especially
poor immigrants), the State Senate at the turn of the century
was prepared to accept an estimate of 50,000 — or one prostitute
for every thirty-six inhabitants of the city.

In the course of the twentieth century, partly through the
work of Freud, the curtain of secrecy surrounding sex (and
therefore pseudosex) was gradually lifted. In modern Britain
and the United States, patches of Victorian prudery undoubtedly survive; but the age of bikinis and mini-skirts and kitchen-
sink drama can hardly be called prudish in the same sense, and
amidst the flurry of commercialised pseudosexual stimuli it is
genuinely easier to discuss sexual and pseudosexual behaviour.
But the informal censor that governs the dreams of the individual and the topics of society has only changed ground. In
Victorian England and the United States of the same period
(and in the Soviet Union today, which has reached about the
same stage of industrialisation), prudery about sex was balanced
by a considerable readiness to examine and discuss social inequality: in the Soviet Union (where a girl is still considered to

be 'ruined' if she loses her virginity before marriage), an anxious eye is constantly kept on income inequalities. In our own societies there is a curious pressure to believe that everybody is affluent, and more or less equally affluent, and that poverty and inequality are things of the past. We have seen that this is far from being the case (pp. 34 ff.). In the United States, in 1959, the poorest 30 per cent of the population were actually getting a *lower* share of the national personal income than they did in 1910 (even if no account is taken of between five and ten billion dollars spent by the rich on their expense accounts). The American sociologist A. B. Hollingsworth recently made an informative study of the attitudes of psychiatrists. He found them all perfectly ready to talk about sex, but they sometimes tended 'to react with embarrassment when the question of social class is raised'. It is clear that we shall have to look both inequality and pseudosex in the face at the same time, if we are to unravel the relations between them in human societies.

When we consider the relations between pseudosex and violence in man, we are faced with an extremely complex situation, which still requires a great deal of research. In theory at least, we might conclude that, as in monkeys, pseudosex in man plays an ambiguous part, relieving or increasing tension, but on the whole, at least under severe stress, tending to promote violence. In its simpler forms, pseudosex must evidently make it possible for human beings to tolerate the close proximity and large inequalities to which they have been exposed for so long. But this will evidently also permit the build-up of tensions on a scale unknown in monkeys; as the stress increases, pseudosex must become more and more tinged with aggression, and sadomasochism, once it gets a grip, can produce the most frightful violence of all. Prohibition of the simpler pseudosexual outlets may well hasten this process; but so will any large-scale penetration of commercially organised vice into the social life of the community.

In human societies, territorial and hierarchical relations have become greatly complicated by the institution of property, which has often involved a greater or lesser degree of more or

less explicit 'ownership' of human beings. Moreover, the kinds
and gradations of social inequality are extremely complex;
hence when two people are closely associated, as in a marriage,
it is almost inevitable that one (or perhaps each in different contexts) will feel, consciously or unconsciously, socially inferior to
the other. So in all close human relationships it is difficult to
avoid the tensions which produce pseudosex. Human interpersonal relations, though obviously they can and must involve
much genuine sharing of 'social space' and its human refine-
ments, are constantly liable to complexes which involve, in
varying proportions, concerns about property, humiliations
arising out of social or economic inequality, and pseudosexual
interactions. Of such a nature is the complex conflict of emo-
tion called *jealousy*, in which the three components of tension are
always to be found; it is no accident that the greatest play on
the subject concerns the elopement of the Moor Othello with the
daughter of a wealthy Venetian noble, or that the Moor begins
to succumb to jealousy when his services are no longer needed
by the Venetians, who are quick to discard a general whom they
regard as anything but a social equal. In modern societies
jealousy finds widespread expression in divorce cases, which
(under most present laws) occasion great mental suffering and
stress, and which are explicitly concerned with property as well
as (usually) with 'unfaithfulness'. The crucial role of inequality
and humiliation in the jealousy complex is well illustrated by a
British appeal court case in 1966, in which three judges considered
an award of £7500 divorce damages made against a wealthy retired businessman, who allegedly used his money to seduce the
wife of a less wealthy professional man. The judges agreed in
reducing the damages to £2000. Mr Justice Scarman noted that
'our social mores have changed' since the days when 'a wife
was a piece of property whom her husband could not divorce
short of an Act of Parliament'. Evidently, as long as any
damages at all can be awarded in such cases, a wife is still 'a
piece of property' in the eyes of the law; the difference is that,
in the judge's words, today 'a man can divest himself easily . . .
of his adulterous wife'. The most interesting observations, how-

ever, were made by Lord Justice Diplock. He suggested that in the eighteenth and early nineteenth centuries 'it may have been plausible to hold that a poor man's resentment was justifiably increased if the adulterer used his superior wealth or station to deprive the poor man of his chattel-wife'. But he found it impossible to accept that in modern times 'the feelings and pride of a reasonable man are more affronted if his wife commits adultery with an opulent baronet rather than with an impoverished dustman, with a young Adonis rather than an elderly Caliban'. On the contrary, 'the lower the material and physical attributes of his supplanter, the more wounding the comparison and the greater the blow to his own self-esteem'. Coming from an appeal court judge, who must have wide experience of such cases, this pronouncement shows that social inequality (one way or the other) is an important component of jealousy.

Divorce is not all that easy, even now, and among the poorer members of the community there is a certain small proportion who are driven by jealousy to the crime of murder. Brief accounts of all the murder cases in England between March 1957 and December 1962 have been provided in *A Calendar of Murder*, a book written by the British sociologists Terence Morris and Louis Blom-Cooper, mainly to provide factual evidence relating to the problem of capital punishment. We have analysed some of these cases from several points of view. Here we may note that, out of *128* murders of wives by husbands, *35* were committed partly or wholly out of jealousy in its most familiar sense — that is, as a reaction to actual or suspected 'unfaithfulness'. The cases range from utter delusion on the husband's part to real provocation, in which the wife inflicted humiliation by taunting the husband with her 'infidelities'. Jealousy murders are not, of course, restricted to these cases. Wives murder husbands from the same motive, and so do unmarried lovers of either sex. Of all the murders in the United States in 1964, 22 per cent have been ascribed to 'romantic triangles or lovers' quarrels'.

In these cases, the 'unfaithfulness' motif was prominent; disputes over money often appear as well. In other murder cases, the pseudosexual theme may be less obvious. However it is noteworthy that murder is commonest between people who know each other well enough to become involved in dominance relations and therefore, at least latently, in pseudosex. In modern societies, more often than not, murder is a family affair. Out of *741* murders in England in 1957–62, the murderer was related to the victim in *388* cases. In the United States in 1964, such cases also made up just over 50 per cent of all murders; most of the remainder were murders of acquaintances. In England, during the period mentioned, only *147* murders were inflicted on strangers. Even in crimes of violence which stopped short of murder, in England and Wales in 1950, 1957 and 1960, less than half the cases involved people with slight or no acquaintance with each other.

Even without political terrors, murder is not always purely a matter of interpersonal relations. It may be related to organised crime. Partly because the attitude of society is so ambiguous, organised crime has always been closely connected with organised vice, and the prostitute has always been the most reliable and regular source of income for the gangster. The legal treatment of organised vice is an extremely difficult problem, for it is necessary to steer a balanced course between the Scylla of prohibition (which drives the system underground) and the Charybdis of promotion (which can give the system a large influence over society). The legislation in Britain that followed the Wolfenden Report was unwelcome to the police; driving the prostitutes off the street must certainly have increased the difficulty of dealing with the vice gangs. On the other hand, the open proliferation of every kind of vice in the Germany of the 1920s provided a breeding-ground for Nazism. The difficulty is to find a procedure which keeps organised vice under scrutiny while restricting its influence on society. The perils of prohibition and promotion may be illustrated by reference to human displacement activities other than (though in various ways related to) pseudosex. It is well known that the prohibition of alcohol in the United States gave rise (via the illicit trade in alcohol) to a monumental wave of violent crime. In the 1920s when Capone was consolidating his power in Chicago, there were more than

350 murders a year in Cook County, Illinois, alone; worse, it was in the prohibition era that the Mafia become entrenched in American society (p. 201). On the other hand, the recent legislation about gambling in England, which has made this a fantastically profitable legal enterprise, has almost certainly contributed to the rise of certain kinds of violent crime in England in 1965–6. The number of indictable offences involving firearms (a sure indication of organised crime) rose from 731 to 1140 in a single year (between 1964 and 1965); pressure began to be brought to bear on witnesses and juries in cases involving casinos; finally, on 12 August 1966, three policemen were shot dead in Braybrook Street, near Shepherd's Bush. Ironically enough, there are grounds for believing that the Mafia, which established itself in the United States under prohibition of alcohol, has finally been tempted to invade Britain by the irresistible profits of legal gambling. Hitherto, though individuals connected with the organisation (such as Eugenio Messina) have operated in the London vice rackets, the Mafia as such has scrupulously left Britain alone. From these two examples, it will be clear that the treatment of organised vice, as of other human displacement activities, is no easy problem. In the long run, however, it may help if we realise that all these activities, like violence itself, are products of stress in societies, and that pseudosex in particular is a reaction to serious inequality.

Five/The Natural History of Violence

1

IN the last two chapters, we have attempted to unravel a web of social inequality, perversion and violence. All these cruel distortions in monkeys, however, are clearly confined to the zoo. The ample evidence of the field observers has shown us the peaceful life of monkeys in the wild, and finally disposed of the view that aggressiveness, whatever the conditions, is an innate and inherent vice of monkeys and man. The question naturally arises, why should violence ever occur in any circumstances? What possible function could it serve, and why are monkeys and human beings capable of aggression at all? The question is far from academic, for if we can discover this function we may be able to perform it by humane and peaceful means, and one day eliminate violence for ever. In our search for an answer to the question, we have one important clue: the effect of crowding.

From our comparison of wild and zoo monkeys (pp. 83 ff.), it became clear that the most obvious source of monkey violence is crowding, the forcing of monkeys into closer proximity with each other than they normally tolerate.* That violence occurs only under crowding has now been established for a great many mammal species. In 1963 at a Symposium on Aggression held by the Institute of Biology, the then Scientific Director of the London Zoo, L. Harrison Matthews, surveyed the field literature and his own considerable field experience for instances of fight-

* Very recently, C. H. Southwick has reported experiments made at the Calcutta Zoo, which confirm the comparative evidence. Aggressive behaviour (threat, submission, attack, fighting) was studied and scored in 17 rhesus monkeys kept in a cage area of 1000 square feet. Partitioning the cage in two, with a door open between the two halves, had relatively little effect; but when the door was closed, restricting the monkeys to an area half as great (500 square feet), the amount of aggressive behaviour was roughly doubled.

ing in mammals. He could not find any cases of fighting to the
death, except under crowded conditions. The same principle
appears in birds (for instance, chickens and doves) and fishes
(for instance, sticklebacks).

Allowing for the simpler structure of their societies, mammals other than monkeys show the same tendency to brutal inequality under crowding. In the general terms of Paul Leyhausen (pp. 55 ff.), the privacies of territory and the courtesies
of relative hierarchy disappear, and absolute hierarchy prevails
in its most unrelieved form, as a natural consequence of shortage
of space. As the difference between ranks becomes steeper, subordinates eventually become desperate, and violence becomes
endemic, with mass redirection and the persecution of outcasts.
Leyhausen has vividly described the symptoms of a group of
cats caged together in a small space; the parallels with the zoo
monkey community are obvious. 'The more crowded the cage
is, the less relative hierarchy there is. Eventually a despot
emerges, "pariahs" appear, driven to frenzy and all kinds of
neurotic behaviour by continuous and pitiless attacks by all the
others; the community turns into a spiteful mob. They all seldom relax, they never look at ease, and there is continuous hiss-
ing, growling and even fighting.'

To produce this dangerous proximity, it is not always necessary to confine mammals in a cage or enclosure. If their food,
instead of being widely dispersed, is concentrated at a point, they
may be forced to invade each other's social space (pp. 67, 85), and
all the symptoms of crowding appear. In an area of woodland
near the Flag River in Bayfield County, Wisconsin, white-tailed
deer have gathered in winter for many years. They have seriously depleted the trees on which they depend for their food
supply. To keep them in the neighbourhood, hay has been supplied in recent years at fixed feeding-stations by the Wisconsin
Conservation Congress. In the winter of 1952 three American
scientists, C. Kabat, N. E. Collias and R. C. Guettinger, were
able to observe the behaviour of the deer as they clustered in the
small areas of the feeding-stations. They quickly established
absolute hierarchies, with bucks at the top, does in the middle

and fawns at the bottom. A high-ranking deer would approach a subordinate, and if he failed to retreat, would strike at him with his hooves. Sometimes the victim would redirect, attacking a still lower-ranking deer near by. The amount of quarrelling depended on the number of deer in the fixed area of the station, and hence on their *density*. When only 5–7 deer were present, only one quarrel was seen per deer per hour. When 23–30 deer were present, the rate was 4·4 quarrels per deer per hour. Aggressiveness was thus clearly related to the degree of crowding, though the deer were forced together only by their common need to use the artificial food supply. The fixed feeding-stations on Cayo Santiago are no doubt partly responsible for the relative aggressiveness of the rhesus monkey colony on the island (p. 106).*

Similar situations can arise without deliberate human intervention of this kind. The concentrated abundance of food in villages, towns and other human-occupied areas has led an estimated 88 per cent of the rhesus monkeys of northern India to congregate there. In or near the villages and towns, rhesus monkeys, and also bonnet macaque monkeys and langurs, live at much higher density than they do in the forest, and we have seen that these urban monkeys are correspondingly more aggressive (pp. 44, 49). On Barro Colorado populations of howler monkeys are much denser in some areas than others, because the former areas naturally yield more fruits or (for howlers are choosy) more of the fruits they specially prefer. In these densely populated areas, the volume of howling indicates a relatively high degree of tension between bands, though there is no definite evidence of lethal fighting. In the Upper Semliki region near Lake Edward the Belgian zoologist R. Verheyen counted the hippopotamus populations. He found they varied in density from one hippo per fifteen metres of river to one per five metres.

* In Southwick's experiments (see footnote, p. 146), aggressive behaviour of the rhesus monkeys was also significantly increased when food was provided in one basket, instead of on eight different feeding-boards. To feed from the basket, the monkeys obviously had to come close together.

He examined the corpses of five hippos killed in fights in the more densely populated part of the river. Hans Kummer made a comparison of wild bands of hamadryas baboons in an extensive strip of land in Ethiopia. As he went from east to west along this strip, he found an actual increase in the supply of food for the baboons, but a decrease in the number of sleeping-ledges. The western baboons were thus affluent but short of 'housing' (sleeping-space), and, as we might by now expect, they showed appreciably more aggression.

Clearly animals quarrel more and begin to fight fiercely when they are crowded at high population density. It is natural to wonder whether the resulting violence does anything to correct the conditions that brought it about: does it, in fact, reduce the local population? This suggestion has been experimentally verified in fast-breeding animals, which can be easily observed over several generations in time. The Australian zoologist John Clarke bred two populations of voles (small, mouse-like animals) in open-air cages, each 67 square metres in area, and observed them for eighteen months. One population was raised from a single Adam and Eve, the other from six males and five females. Both were supplied with 'a surplus of oats, available at all times'. The populations naturally increased, but not nearly up to their full breeding potential. The initially larger population began its second year with three times as many voles as it started with, but the maximum number it reached that year was only sixty-one, compared with fifty-eight in the first year, and at the end of the experiment it was declining. The demographic details suggested that something was limiting the growth of both populations, and that this something was hitting the initially larger population harder. Fighting was seen in both populations, including two lethal fights in the larger one, whose members also had far more scars, and the death-rate of infant voles was high. The evidence strongly suggested that violence, chiefly by its effects on the females and young, was checking the growth of both populations. The larger population developed a brutal absolute hierarchy, with a well-marked class structure. The upper-class males were heavy, healthy and had glossy coats;

F

their scars were only from small wounds on their heads, known to result from last-ditch retaliation by desperate subordinates. They moved freely around the enclosure. The middle-class males were almost as heavy and free-moving, but their fur was tattered and their rumps scarred from unprovoked attacks. The lower-class males weighed about half as much and cowered in corners; their fur was tattered and they had scars all over their bodies. The middle classes were liable to be chased and bitten on the rump, but the lower classes tended to be caught and bitten all over; though perhaps 'class' is hardly the appropriate term in so disordered and violent a society. Significantly, most of the females showed 'lower-class' symptoms; and the effect of the fighting on females and young was almost certainly the factor that kept the population down.

Equally impressive are the results of the American biologist J. B. Calhoun. He bred a colony from a few wild rats, in a pen of 10,000 square feet, and he also provided them with an ample food surplus at all times. During the twenty-eight months of the experiment, if the rats had bred all they theoretically could, they would have produced a population of 50,000. In fact the population stabilised at less than 200. The rats split into sub-colonies, with buffer zones between their territories. In each sub-colony, ranks were unstable and quarrels were frequent; the weaker rats were under such stress that they lost the normal rat capacity for hoarding food. Above all, the adult rats mercilessly attacked the young, causing such high juvenile and infant death-rates that the population was kept down throughout the experiment.

From these and similar observations it appears that violence breaks out in an animal society when the population density is high, and that it serves to bring down the population and spread the survivors out again. It begins to look as if we have found the function of violence in animals. It is a device for limiting the growth of populations, called into play only when it is needed for this function. But this is only a formula. We need to understand the function in greater detail, if we are to find a civilised substitute for what Leyhausen has called 'the old, cruel methods by which nature balanced our numbers'.

2

Just over two centuries ago, in 1766, a son was born to a wealthy land-owner of Surrey. The boy was called Thomas Robert Malthus. When he grew up he was encouraged to take Holy orders, but an active clergyman needed a good voice, and Malthus had a cleft palate. So he adopted an academic career, eventually becoming a professor of history and economics at Cambridge. Undergraduates, instead of church congregations, had to grapple with the professor's speech defects; but it must have been worth it, for Malthus produced, in his *Essay* of 1798 and his later works, the first really systematic treatment of the problem of population growth in its widest aspects. His work had a very wide influence, and it was the clear thinking expressed in the *Essay* that started both Darwin and Wallace, independently, on the train of thought that led them to the idea of evolution by natural selection.

Population is a complicated subject, but it has its simple aspects. Migration apart, the rise or fall of a population depends simply on the difference between birth-rate and death-rate, both usually reckoned as numbers per cent or per thousand per year. If the birth-rate is higher than the death-rate, the population rises. The trouble is that the rise is by compound interest, since the more people (or animals) there are, the more offspring they can breed. If a population increases by the same percentage every year, it increases by a constantly greater absolute number. A calculation has been made which shows the fantastic implications of this. If mankind had sprung from a single couple living about 12,000 years ago, shortly before the coming of agriculture, and if there had been one more birth than deaths per hundred per year (a one per cent increase per year), then today the world population would form a sphere of living flesh many thousand light years in diameter, expanding with a radial velocity many times faster than the alleged speed of light.

In real life, as opposed to the wonderland of mathematics, nothing of the kind can happen. So in real life the growth of a human or animal population is subject to checks or controls, and these were the subject of Malthus's exploration. He did not go into detail about animals, though he did remark, with characteristic insight, that 'the great check' to their increase is 'the want of *room* and nourishment' (our italics). But he made a systematic study of the controls limiting human population growth. The materials available to him were meagre, but he made brilliant use of them. For instance, he saw in the United States, where there was still unlimited food and land, the opportunity to measure the natural, uncontrolled increase of mankind. He decided that this natural increase should be a doubling of the population every twenty-five years, and he proceeded to test this hypothesis. Fortunately, by the 1820s, the results of three censuses were available; for the Americans, concerned with the fair representation of the States in Congress, were the first to count heads with modern completeness and accuracy. By ingenious methods Malthus estimated the increase in American population due to immigration from Europe, and, allowing for this, he concluded that the American population growth agreed with his hypothesis. He published his analysis in the *Encyclopaedia Britannica* in 1824. In 1965 the British economist J. Potter published a careful study of early American population growth. After similar allowances for immigration, he concluded that the natural rate of increase was only 'slightly below' the estimate of Malthus.

It was clear to Malthus that the controls on population growth could be classified into two groups. First, there were 'preventive checks', operating before birth. Such factors as late marriage, or a high proportion of people remaining single for life, would reduce the birth-rate. Second, there were 'positive checks', operating after birth, which Malthus summed up succinctly as the effects of 'misery and vice'. These would increase the death-rate. Malthus saw clearly that in the long run, if the preventive checks were not working, 'misery and vice' were inevitable. For, since indefinite uncontrolled natural increase is absurdly impossible, in the long run mankind must choose between low birth-rates and high death-rates. When he made a careful comparative study, he was surprised to find that the balance between the two kinds of control varied considerably between different countries and periods. Some had high death-rates and high birth-rates; others had low death-rates and low birth-rates. Malthus concluded that there was a real possibility of escape from 'misery and vice' by controlling the birth-rate of mankind. Among his preventive or 'prudential' checks, he did not explicitly include contraception: as we shall see, a possible reason for this reticence emerged only in 1966. But, in essence, he proposed control of birth-rates as a solution for the troubles of mankind; and he undoubtedly thought of violence as a population problem. Above all, he envisaged social behaviour as playing a key part in population control. His preventive checks were entirely social, and under 'misery and vice' he included not only famine and disease but the consequences of human violence.

In the two centuries since the birth of Malthus, much has been learned about populations of animals and their regulation, and, as usual, they provide relatively simple situations, which give us clues for unravelling the enormous complexity of human population growth and social behaviour. The year 1962 gave us a new look at the affluent societies (p. 34); it also saw the publication of a monumental book by the British zoologist V. C. Wynne-Edwards, called *Animal Dispersion in relation to Social Behaviour*. From an overwhelming mass of evidence, gathered over a period of seven years, Wynne-Edwards showed that much of animal social behaviour has been evolved as a means of avoiding overpopulation, which could irretrievably destroy the food supply of a species. Indeed his work suggests that the whole of animal social behaviour, while of course it has other functions, is geared to fit in with this vitally important requirement. The structure and ceremonies of animal societies are designed by natural selection to control birth-rates and/or death-rates, by affecting mating behaviour, care of the young and social relations in general. They are in turn closely geared to the actual abundance or scarcity of natural resources. Sometimes these arrangements have an elegant simplicity. A nice example of what Malthus would have called a prudential check can be found in the large, generally seafaring birds called skuas. The courtship ceremony of the Arctic skua, which lives around the Shetland Islands, includes a little ritual in which the male obtains a fish and presents it to the female. This is always repeated a number of times in the course of courtship, so it is probable that, unless a male skua takes his girl-friend out to dinner, he gets no joy, and no breeding occurs. In this case little is known about the changes in abundance of the fishes on which the birds feed. But in northern Sweden there lives another species of skua, which has abandoned the sea to breed on a mountain, preying upon small land animals. Their main food is a small rodent, the lemming, which has an elaborate population cycle of its own. On this mountain, lemmings are abundant in some years, and scarce or absent in others. It is known that the birds do not breed in the years of lemming scarcity. In 1965 the Dutch zoologist Piet Sevenster visited the mountain. That year there were no lemmings around at all, and Sevenster found only two pairs of birds, hanging about the mountain but showing no signs of breeding. Sevenster suspected that they might have a ceremony like that of the Arctic skua, with lemming instead of fish dinners, and that the trouble was, the males had no offerings that year. He tried to come to the rescue of one of the males by supplying ersatz lemmings, in the form of sausages. The sausages disappeared, there were marks of skuas at the spot where he had left them, and the pair concerned stayed on when the other pair gave up and left the mountain. Unfortunately, even sausages were scarce that year in the local store. If, as seems very likely, the remaining pair was engaged in courtship, Sevenster's supply of sausages gave out before the female had been dined often enough to overcome her resistance. So it was impossible to prove that the ceremony occurs and is necessary for breeding. But if we put the facts from the two species together, it is probable that the dinner-ceremony, so necessary for breeding, is only possible when there is actually plenty of food. Obviously this would be a perfectly designed control: the birds will only breed when there is plenty of food for their young.

There are many special devices of this kind, but by far the most important and general is the organisation of social space, and the tendency of higher social animals to fight when they are crowded. As Wynne-Edwards points out, unrestricted competition for food is liable to lead to irretrievable destruction of food resources. In the twentieth century the harpoon-gun and the factory ship opened up the Antarctic to the whaling fleets of mankind. In these extra-territorial waters, nations competed unsparingly for the whales, and as each stock was depleted there was even keener competition to get the lion's share of the last survivors. The formation of the International Whaling Commission in 1946 could not save the situation: the member nations could not even agree on the quota for 1964–5. As a result, the humpback whale had been drastically depleted by 1913, and the blue whale by 1931; by 1960, 80 per cent of the world catch consisted of fin whales, the last survivors, and in the same year survival curves already indicated that, at this rate of exploitation, the fin whales were dying out. Such is the result of unrestricted competition for natural resources.

Wynne-Edwards pointed out that this danger could be averted for an animal species if its members competed for space, which could in turn be made to respond very sensitively to change in the food supply. The whole competition would thus work *in advance*, giving the precious time necessary for a population of food plants or animals to recover. This is essentially what is achieved by the systems of individual territory, band territory and hierarchy within bands, all closely related to reproduction, and hence to the growth of the feeding population. The starting-point of the system, in mammals, birds and fishes, seems to be an intense resistance by the individual to close contact or near approach. This may be helped by the fact that, in all these highly social groups of animals, the surface of the body is liable to be disturbed by contact (disordering of fur or plumage, removal of scales). Anyway the fact of resistance is certain. The Swiss zoologist and zoo director H. Hediger discovered that most birds, when they congregate, maintain a definite 'individual distance' between them — as anyone can verify by looking at birds on a telegraph wire. Contact or close approach is only tolerated when necessary, chiefly in parental care and in mating. Mates, parents and young commonly develop special ceremonies to overcome the fear and/or rage that would otherwise be aroused by close proximity. These ceremonies are, in fact, ritualised conflict activities (pp. 121, 124). Mutual preening in birds (similar to mutual grooming in monkeys) is a case in point, studied recently by the British zoologist C. J. O. Harrison. He showed that it was in fact a ritualised conflict activity, and then examined its incidence in the different groups of birds. He found that it was present in species obliged for various reasons to tolerate prolonged close proximity — for instance, when pairs stay together for long periods, or when the nature of the terrain forces a pair to stay very close together at the nest-site, or neighbouring pairs to nest very close together.

This general intolerance of proximity is expressed in the formation of individual territories and band territories, and in the hierarchical structure of social space within a band, which is so acutely sensitive to crowding. These systems are closely related to natural resources on the one hand, and breeding on the other. In some oddly named Alaskan birds called pomarine jaegers, the territories of breeding pairs have been seen to fluctuate with the food supply, so that the breeding density varied from four to eighteen pairs per square mile, in years of scarce and abundant food respectively. Birds who had just become adult were able to breed in the 'dense' year, but in the 'sparse' year they were kept out by the competition for territory: so the production of young was geared in a sensitive way to the availability of food for them. In this case, some individuals in the 'sparse' year were forced to remain celibate. Sometimes they may merely be forced to spread into less lush areas, thus preventing exhaustion of the food resources on the more productive sites. Great tits and blue tits have been studied in two woods in the Netherlands, one more attractive, with more plentiful food, than the other. Territory size in the more attractive wood fluctuated; when the territories were large, only a few birds occupied the area, and others had to make do with the less happy hunting-ground. Hierarchy and social space in a band of monkeys may produce similar results in a different way. When natural resources begin to run short (but before there is serious danger of depletion), a band in its territory will begin to incur the tensions of crowding. Under tension, individuals are liable to leave and become solitaries (p. 68), or, as has been shown in langurs and other monkey species, males may leave and form all-male bands. In this way the breeding stock may be reduced; and this adjustment is reversible, for the emigrants may be able to rejoin the band later.

All these controls may be operated without violence as 'preventive checks', regulating the birth-rate in a smooth manner in each generation to cope with minor fluctuations in the food supply. If violence does break out, its effects are much more drastic, and it may be seen as an emergency measure. Not only does it raise the death-rate, but it reduces the birth-rate, and can produce effects over several generations. There is by now abundant evidence that the tensions of extreme overcrowding, accompanied by violence, produce physiological effects on the survivors, marked by the enlargement of certain glands and a disruption of normal mechanisms of physiological regulation. The effect on the females is not only to reduce their own fertility but to stunt the growth and impair the fertility of those of their young which survive at all. The evidence for these long-term effects was first assembled in 1962 by the British psychologist D. H. Stott, and further surveyed in 1964 by the American physiologist J. J. Christian. Evidence of this kind is available for mice, rats, voles, woodchucks, rabbits, dogs and Sika deer. Stress diseases and pregnancy stress in man are closely related to these stress effects in animals. Stott has studied in particular the incidence of births of malformed babies in human societies. As early as 1812 a doctor, Jacob Clesius, had noticed that these malformations are specially prevalent in times of war. They seem to have been widespread in the Thirty Years War in seventeenth-century Germany, and in Paris during the siege and revolution of 1870–71. In the maternity wards of fifty-five German hospitals, the malformation rate nearly doubled after Hitler's accession to power; it rose still further during the Second

World War and amidst the shambles of immediately-post-war
Germany. Monstrous conditions literally produce monsters. All
this suggests that violence is a key component of a complex
machinery for drastically reducing a population over an appreciable period of time.

The manner in which this emergency device is used varies between different animal species. Some of them accept crowding
and violence as a recurrent situation, and populations of these
animals have regular cycles of rise and decline, with crises that
cut them down to size every four or five generations. These
species include voles, studied by the Canadian zoologist Dennis
Chitty, and muskrats, studied by the American zoologist P. L.
Errington. At the beginning of the cycle, the population builds
up rapidly, in an uncontrolled way. When a certain density is
reached the animals become extremely aggressive. At the same
time the physiological effects of crowding increase their need
for salt, and each pair needs a larger territory from which to
obtain it. Each territory eventually becomes ten times as large,
so that many pairs are forced into poor feeding-grounds; but
this reduction in density is only attained at the cost of savage
fighting, including lethal attacks on the young. The stresses
affecting the mothers cause many of the surviving young to be
physiologically weak and susceptible to disease, so that many of
them die before the following breeding-season. The after-effects
of violence thus persist after the density has been lowered, and it
takes some time before the population recovers and begins a new
cycle of growth. During this interval, the food plants and animals can also recover, so that the population's natural resources
are never completely depleted.

Voles and musk-rats are highly territorial animals. When
forced into each other's company, like Clarke's voles (p. 149),
they evidently arrange themselves into ranks or classes. But,
equally evidently, from Clarke's experiment, there is no true
hierarchy, only a gradation of terror and scars in a community
constantly engaged in fighting. There are other animal species
which are territorial at low density, but react to a certain level
of crowding by forming true rank hierarchies, in which priori-

ties are allotted without this perpetual violence. These species include moles, studied by the British zoologists Gillian Godfrey and Peter Crowcroft and the German zoologist G. H. W. Stein, wild mice, also studied by Crowcroft, and laboratory mice, studied by the British zoologist John Mackintosh. In laboratory mice, Mackintosh found that caging individuals in isolation gradually switches them into the territorial phase, so that they are more aggressive when again caged with other mice. Isolation for eight days produces three times as much aggressive activity as isolation for one day. Once the hierarchical phase sets in, however, it can become stable. In wild mice, and probably moles, this two-phase system seems to work in the following way. Surrounding conditions may at times give rise to a shortage of space, while there is still plenty of food (for instance, mole tunnels may be temporarily flooded). The population is not immediately stampeded into reducing itself by violence, and this is useful, for when space conditions improve again there may still be plenty of food for a large population. In normal circumstances, family territories are large (10–20 square feet in mice, separate tunnel assemblies in moles). In crowded conditions, a hierarchy forms. Subordinate animals have no territories of their own, but they can use the foraging territory of a dominant animal in shifts while he sleeps off his meals, in the manner of Cox and Box. But this only works when there is plenty of food; otherwise the owner will spend most of his time foraging, and when he is awake trespassers will be prosecuted, and the schemes of other mice and moles gang aft agley. The result is immediate emigration, or, if that is impossible, violence. The hierarchical phase is set on a hair-trigger for an unusually rapid and sensitive response to a food crisis, with immediate reduction of the population. Moreover, if crowding itself becomes too extreme, the hierarchical phase will not work even if food is plentiful. The American zoologist C. H. Southwick used mice for an experiment like those of Clarke and Calhoun (p. 150). He let them breed in a pen of limited size, supplying them with unlimited food. When crowding reached a certain point through population increase, fighting became frequent and severe, and was accompanied by desertion, destruction or cannibalism of the young. By the time crowding reached the point where there was one fight per adult mouse per hour, survival of the young fell so low that population growth was slowed or ceased altogether. Mice, therefore (and probably moles), retain the emergency measure of crowding and violence; but, unlike the voles and musk-rats, they can adjust to a temporary crisis of *moderately* high density.

Monkeys, with their long generation span, their elaborate care of young, and their educative play-groups, have been able to make permanent use of a hierarchical system within each band, with enough regard for individual rights in social space to eliminate violence altogether in normal times. They owe much of their evolutionary success to their exceptionally low fertility (p. 54). Nevertheless, if the environment smiles upon them, wild monkey populations do grow. When a band becomes too big for the hierarchical system to work smoothly, it simply splits into two, by a process of peaceful fission. This process has been studied among Japanese monkeys, and in the rhesus bands of Cayo Santiago. In 1957 the rhesus colony on the island numbered 155, divided into two bands of 55 and 100 members respectively. By 1960 the total population was 420. The originally smaller band had reached 140 without splitting; the originally larger band had split, by successive fissions, into five bands, containing 140, 50, 40, 30 and 20 members. When a band divided, the current president usually continued to lead one part of it; the other fell to the leadership either of an originally second- or third-rank leader or of a former solitary. Once separated, the new bands adopt each its own territory, and relations between them are regulated in the usual way (p. 79).

It seems likely that monkey societies normally regulate the relations between population and resources in a peaceful way. Preventive checks and the basically low fertility keep population within bounds, and when a favourable environment permits population growth the monkeys maintain their normal band size, splitting repeatedly to allow 'daughter' bands or colonies to spread out, much as did the Danubian villages (p. 19) or the

ancient Greek cities that planted 'daughter' colonies all over
the Mediterranean and Black Sea. It is true that their generation span is much longer than that of voles or musk-rats, so that
a regular population cycle would be more difficult to observe.
But if they did have regular, periodic collapses into violence, at
least one of the wild populations studied by the field observers
would almost certainly have been in the 'violent' stage of the
cycle; whereas in fact all of them were found living in peace
(Chapter Two). Nevertheless, the zoo observations show unmistakably that monkeys have retained the whole system of violence under crowding as a means for drastic reduction in numbers. Changes in the environment of monkeys could occur even
before the activities of man, and such changes could result in
more or less sudden depletion or limitation of resources. A number of bands could be cut off in an isolated area by some change
in the terrain. When this happened, the bands would begin to
feel the space shortage before the food supply ran out. They
would then have the alternative of going to war with each other
for the remaining territories, or contracting their territories so
that each band became an affluent crowd. Despite the career of
Diablo (p. 106), the second alternative is probably more usual,
for whenever monkey populations have been seen to decline
(howlers on Barro Colorado, rhesus monkeys in parts of India)
the number of bands has remained constant but the number
within each has dropped, suggesting high mortality *within* each
band. Clearly, if each band began to behave like a crowded zoo
colony, violence would drastically reduce its numbers, before the
food resources were irretrievably depleted. If the population
continued to be cut off in a limited area, such outbreaks of violence might become recurrent. It is tantalising that we have
suggestive evidence that something like this has actually happened when no human observers were there to see it. On Barro
Colorado (cut off by the construction of the Panama Canal, p.
46), the howler population rose from 398 in 1932 to 489 in
1933, the number of bands rising from 23 to 28. By 1951, however, when the next census was taken, the population had sunk
to 239, divided among 30 bands: the average band size had

shrunk from about 17 to 8. It has been suggested that the howlers were hit by an epidemic. But even if this happened, crowding, violence and stress may well have made them more vulnerable to disease. In support of this, there is evidence of another
approaching crisis. By 1959 there were 814 howlers, divided between 44 bands of average size about 18. Between 1951 and
1959 the amount of howling had increased tenfold, and the din
could be heard throughout the day. This suggests (p. 69) that
howler bands were constantly coming into conflict on the edges
of their territories (which are larger than needed strictly for
food, because howlers like to have enough of their *favourite* foods
— p. 148). From all this, it seems likely that monkeys retain the
whole system of violence under crowding, not as a regular cycli-
cal procedure, but as a means of dealing with a *population crisis*,
caused originally by changes in the environment, in such a way
as to reduce the population enough to give the food resources
time to recover.

Any serious disturbance in the environment or the society
might well signal the onset of a population crisis. So we must
expect violence to result from severe stress of *any* kind. This in-
discriminateness of response becomes important in human societies, which have been subject to kinds of stress which hardly
arise in monkeys — for instance, the disturbances in social order
which result from technical change. Nevertheless, from the
nature of the whole system, the proper or natural stimulus for
the whole crisis complex would be *crowding*, either by itself or as
a by-product of food shortage. From all the animal evidence,
we can by now form a definite picture of the response as a whole.
There is a sharp increase in inequality, with insecurity among
the higher and real hardship among the lower ranks. Then a
whole series of switches is automatically thrown. Our study of
monkey societies in particular (Chapters Two to Four) showed
an extraordinary economy in social organisation. There is a
whole set of social devices which act to *reduce* violence in spacious
conditions, and to *increase* it under crowding. These include
threat, cut-off, pseudosex, intervention by leaders, contagion
and redirection, each of which relieves momentary tensions or

stops incipient disputes in the wild, and provokes or amplifies quarrels in the zoo (pp. 85, 98–100, 121–3, 130–4.) This curious double function at last makes sense in the light of population control. It secures all the benefits of peace (and hence progress) when population and resources are in balance, while providing a terrific boost for the complex of tension and violence once the switches are thrown by crowding, to ensure an immediate, drastic and prolonged fall in numbers.

A key part of the whole response to crisis is the switch in attitude and behaviour towards females and young, the crucial agents of population growth. Chivalrous protection of the females is transformed into brutal domination over them, the imposition of severe stress, and finally the kind of slaughter of females observed among the baboons of Monkey Hill. Even more dramatically, care and protection of the young is transformed into indifference, neglect, competition, domination and ultimately murder (sometimes followed by cannibalism). The fawns took the lowest ranks among the white-tailed deer at the feeding-stations (p. 148); in bad years, before the stations were installed, the fawns had 'suffered the greatest loss from starvation when food supplies were inadequate'. In all the mammal species studied under intense crowding, the young suffered most severely and showed the highest casualty rates from violence — in voles (p. 149), rats (p. 150), musk-rats (p. 158) and mice (p. 160), for instance. The reversal is most dramatic of all in monkeys, which show such elaborate care and education of the young in good conditions, and such brutal cruelty under crowding (pp. 41, 90). The young are both the innocent victims of heedless fighting between adults, and the object of deliberate (often redirected) attack and murder. Birds tell the same story as mammals; deliberate killing of young has been observed in gulls, terns, frigate-birds, pelicans, herons, wagtails, magpies, shrikes and white storks. Only the storks have been investigated in detail in this connection; it was found that they throw most nestlings out of their nests (to die) in years of population crisis. In short, when crowding spells that conditions are wrong for rearing them, mammals and birds neglect, desert, accidentally or deliberately kill their young. It is the extreme symptom of violence in the community, the last resort of redirection, and the most crucial device by which violence brings down the population.

We have now found a coherent explanation for the occurrence of violence under stress in higher animal societies. How far does all this apply to man? We might begin by considering individuals and families. We have just seen that the cornerstone of the whole system is the reversal from care and protection to neglect and ill-treatment of the young. Man has carried parental care even further than monkeys, and his children are normally cared for over a much longer period. This in itself may have somewhat distorted the system of population control; the reversal is more difficult in man. Cases are frequent of human mothers feeding their children at the expense of their own health in hard times (for instance, during the Depression in Britain), and of human parents making many other sacrifices under terrible conditions. In many an emergency, the principle of 'women and children first' has been genuinely practised. Nevertheless, there is equally no doubt that human adults are capable of neglecting, ill-treating and even killing their children; and this seems to be least infrequent when crowding and/or other stresses are affecting them, such as might impress on the individual the presence of a crisis and the unsuitability of conditions for rearing children. With a very large family, and without exceptional economic resources or help from other relatives, some measure of neglect is particularly likely. In modern societies, there is a close relationship between large families and poverty: they are responsible to a large extent for the number of British children — nearly a million in 1960 — living below the basic national assistance rates. Studies in 1966 by Abel-Smith and Townsend (p. 37) suggest that something like 25 per cent of all families with more than five children each may have incomes below the basic national assistance rates. Children of such families are small in weight and height and have lower educational opportunities than others; some of them eat little or no meat, and some have diets inadequate for health by the standards of the British Medical Association. Miss Maureen Canning has told us that she has visited large families in the North of England, in the course of social work, where the father cannot remember his children's names. In a court case in England in 1965 one couple counted on their fingers and finally worked out they had twelve children. The previous day they had told their defence counsel they had ten. The couple were convicted of neglecting their one-year-old daughter, who had been taken to hospital suffering from malnutrition and weighing as much as a three-month-old child. Along with ten other children, she had been left in charge of a sixteen-year-old daughter while the parents went to work. (The mother blamed this teenager for the disaster.) By the time the case came up, the father was unemployed and the family was threatened with eviction. Some of the children had been seen scavenging for food in dust-bins. This appalling situation seems a natural enough consequence for a poor family of having so many children literally to lose count of them. But neglect is by no means the only thing children have to fear in conditions of poverty and crowded housing.

The year 1962 was full of discoveries relevant to our theme. In July of that year five American doctors startled the medical profession with an article entitled 'The Battered Child Syndrome'. They had discovered that large numbers of small children (generally under three years old), taken to doctors for allegedly accidental bruises and bone fractures, had actually been savagely attacked by one or both parents. They were able to give detailed instructions for recognising this 'syndrome', or pattern of symptoms. They made a survey of seventy-one hospitals, which reported 302 such cases in one year; 33 children had died and 85 had suffered permanent brain injury. In only one-third of the 302 cases had there been legal action; the others were presumably diagnosed as accidents. They also circulated questions to seventy-seven district attorneys, who reported that 447 cases had come to their attention in the same year; 45 of these children had died, 29 had suffered permanent brain damage. Naturally enough, since district attorneys are more prone than doctors to suspect illegal activity, there had been court action in 46 per cent of these cases. In their article, the investigators described two cases as typical; in both cases the child had been unwanted. 'Not infrequently', they reported, 'the beaten infant is a product of unwanted pregnancy, a pregnancy which began before marriage, too soon after marriage, or *at some other time felt to be extremely inconvenient*' (our italics) — just the sort of unreasoned feeling that might afflict any mammal under conditions of population crisis. Surveying the medical literature for odd published cases of this kind, they found that most of them came from 'borderline socioeconomic groups', that is, from poor people at the bottom of the social hierarchy, always the first to feel all these pressures. The urgency of correctly diagnosing these cases was shown by a case where one battered child, discharged after treatment to the care of its parents, died of unexplained causes four weeks later. Since this discovery, cases of battered children have been found to be widespread in Britain. In April 1965 Home Office pathologists Francis Camps and Keith Simpson gave press interviews on the subject. They also emphasised the factor of unwanted pregnancies, and a London psychiatrist indicated that such cases were most likely when the parents had economic difficulties and were overworked and overtired.

In 1964 the British social scientists Terence Morris and Louis Blom-Cooper published a valuable summary of all the murder cases (involving 764 men and women) in England and Wales between 21 March 1957 and the end of 1962. Their book was written to provide evidence relevant to capital punishment, and their case-accounts sometimes lack the detail which would be relevant for our present purpose. However, we have analysed these cases, and the figures provide evidence that human beings are liable to kill their children in conditions when they feel incapable of rearing them, conditions which might indicate a population crisis. During this period, there were 118 cases of child-killing. Eighty-two of these cases involved killing by the child's own parent or parents; this is the usual proportion, though killing by strangers normally receives much greater publicity. In twenty-six of these cases, one or more of the following factors was present: unwanted child, large family, very young parents, unemployment, money troubles (such as hire-purchase debts), concern about the possibility of caring for the children. Thus nearly one-third of the child-killings were done under conditions where normal parental care seemed or was difficult, where the parents could not cope: this is certainly a much higher proportion than that of parents in the whole population (who do not kill their children) living under these conditions. In eleven cases, a father (in one case a mother) killed when feeling desperate about coping with a crying baby. In another eleven cases, the parent killed because of real, suspected or imaginary disease, deformity or suffering, as a kind of euthanasia. Some of these cases fell in more than one category; together they made up forty-one, or nearly half the total. Most of the remaining child-killers were severely mentally disturbed, sometimes echoing the same theme in insane terms (for instance, fear of bringing up children under the rule of invading Russians).

The cases of battered children make horrifying reading: there must sometimes be an element of pseudosexual (sadistic) involvement, and the grossly unequal status of the victims is prominent. It is true that the assaults sometimes seem to be made in moments of aberration, which the parent genuinely cannot recall afterwards. Sometimes the battering culminates in murder, as in the American case just mentioned and in an English case where the eight-month-old victim had suffered a fractured thigh-bone some months before the murder, and ten broken ribs the previous month. Many of the actual child-killings, however, are not preceded by deliberate ill-treatment: often the parent or parents had done their very best until their problems became too much for them. Most of the child-killing cases make pathetic and tragic, rather than horrifying, reading; some of them are heart-rending. In sixteen of the forty-one cases we have just specified, the killer attempted suicide. Except in the one category of inability to cope with a crying child (eleven cases), about half the killers were mothers and about half fathers. The total impression is not of parents callously abandoning their parental attitudes, but of real parental concern distorted under stress. Mrs M. D., aged twenty-three, decided to gas herself 'when distraught with worry over financial difficulties and in a severe depression following the birth of her second child' (eleven months old at the time). She 'decided also to gas her son, Robert ($2\frac{1}{2}$), since she was afraid to leave him alone with no one to care properly for him'. The gas killed the boy, but the mother was rescued. Mrs M. M., aged twenty-five, killed her twins and tried to gas herself. She had four children and 'was depressed by another pregnancy'. Judges and juries generally responded humanely to these tragic situations. Mrs L. M., aged twenty-eight, a widow in part-time work, 'became very depressed and worried about her financial prospects and about the prospects for the children'; she turned on the gas and killed all five of them, but survived herself. Mr Justice Salmon observed, 'this is one of the most terribly sad cases which I have ever had to deal with'. The acquittals sometimes indicate other ways in which large families lead to the deaths of children. In the case of Mrs P. H., aged twenty-nine, the court accepted that she gave her three-year-old son a fatal kick when trying to push him away from the fire 'while she was dressing another child, while another was crying out for food' — there were five children altogether.

Like other murders (p. 31), child-murders in England and Wales show a very stable rate. Child-killings by parents numbered 12 in 1957 (last nine months only), 12 in 1958, 13 in 1959, 16 in 1960, 15 in 1961, 14 in 1962. For the whole period, they made up a little over 10 per cent of all murders. In the United States in 1964 the percentage was about twice as high. There is, however, evidence that violence against children increased in the 1950s. This appears from analysis of crimes of violence actually dealt with legally in England and Wales during 1950 and 1957: in the second year, the number of attacks on children had doubled. This was before the discovery of the battered child syndrome, which will certainly lead to more prosecutions. In the interview given by the Home Office pathologist Keith Simpson (p. 166), he is reported to have said: 'I see the problem of battered babies as part of the larger problem of violence which is on the increase in every sphere'. He is almost certainly right, but the battered child discovery has been too recent for conclusive direct evidence yet for a continuing increase in private violence against children.

Whatever is eventually established about rates, the evidence we have just considered suggests very strongly that man, like the higher animals, *does* show a reversal of parental behaviour under stress, in all degrees from neglect to killing. It remains to consider whether human violence does indeed fluctuate with conditions, reaching major outbreak proportions in times of population crisis. Our first question concerned the response of the individual, our second the response of societies as wholes. To answer this, we need to use a longer time-scale, and examine the most formidable symptom of human violence — the relative ferocity of wars, and their destructiveness of men, women and children.

Like every other imaginable situation, war offers opportunities for the display of human intelligence and human feelings. But war in itself is, and has always been, a sickening business. The idea that spears and arrows are less horrible than napalm or nuclear missiles is a romantic fallacy. Anyone who doubts this may go to the Landesmuseum in Zürich, stand in front of the life-size tableau of medieval Swiss pikemen, and imagine himself in the opposing front line. Or he can read the account, in Plutarch's *Life of Crassus*, of the Battle of Carrhae between Romans and Parthians in 53 B.C. (When Crassus's son urged the Romans to charge the heavily-armed Parthian knights, 'they showed him their hands nailed to their shields, and their feet stuck to the ground' by the enemy's arrows.) There was still enough fighting with the bayonet in the Second World War to drive home this lesson. Wounds and violent death, however inflicted, are shocking and nauseating. A woman who had been in the Kentucky forts, in the pioneering days of fierce conflict between Indians and white settlers, described her experiences some years afterwards. She said that, during her first two years in Kentucky, 'the most comely sight she beheld was seeing a young man dying in his bed a natural death'. She and some other people had sat up with the corpse all night, 'gazing upon him as an object of beauty'.

But while war is always horrible, wars do vary in ferocity. A despatch from the British journalist Arthur Cook, dated 19 January 1966, describes one child victim in South Vietnam, and mentions 'the constant floating population of 1500 to 2000 child victims' (of American bombing raids) 'who reach the provincial hospitals in taxis, bullock carts, on shoulders or on stretchers'. Children have not suffered on this scale in every past war. We have seen (p. 9) that in the present century the involvement of civilians in wars has steadily increased, from 5 per cent of the (violent) casualties in the First World War, to at least 50 per cent in the Second World War and 84 per cent in Korea. The proportion of civilians killed is obviously a measure of the slaughter of women and children, and hence of the intensity of the whole violence outbreak, as a means of reducing population. In the Second World War, even this measure is not adequate, for the Russians used women and the Germans used children as front-line fighting troops. But in some quite obvious sense, the First World War was evidently more restrained and less ferocious than the conflict in Korea.

This mounting tide of violence is sometimes ascribed to technological advance in weapons or to increasingly total mass conscription in wartime. Neither of these factors, however, will explain the results of a survey of wars between European powers over the last four centuries. To measure these wars is much more difficult, but attempts have been made to do so, and the results are summarised and surveyed in the text and tables of the American sociologist Quincy Wright's monumental *Study of War*, first published in 1942 and reissued in a revised edition in 1965 (1679 pages). The problem has been approached in various ways, for instance by assessing numbers of casualties in relation to total populations engaged, and by estimates of the relative involvement of civilians. On all the criteria used, one conclusion is clear. The wars of the eighteenth and nineteenth centuries were more restrained and less ferocious than those of the twentieth *and the seventeenth*.* Of the largest-scale wars in this

* The atrocities of the Napoleonic Wars in Spain (nineteenth century), as depicted in the cartoons of Goya, look just as horrible as

series, by far the most cruel, destructive and unrestrained were
the Second World War in the twentieth century and the Thirty
Years War in the seventeenth.

Weapons were far more destructive in the nineteenth century
than they were in the seventeenth, and mass conscription far
more prevalent. Yet the nineteenth-century wars were the most
restrained and least ferocious of the whole series. Why, then,
was the seventeenth century a period of such dreadful violence?
What does it have in common with the twentieth? The answer
lies in the history of European population. Both these centuries
were times of acute population crisis. The population of Europe
was rising through all four centuries, though there was a slowing-
down or halt in this growth in the late seventeenth and early
eighteenth centuries. But in the eighteenth, and still more the
nineteenth centuries, the surplus was funnelled off by massive
emigration of Europeans to temperate regions outside the Continent, especially to North America: more than forty million
had left by the onset of the First World War. At the same time,
during the eighteenth and nineteenth centuries, the Europeans
left in Europe could ease their problems by the massive exploitation of colonial empires outside it. In the nineteenth century,
in particular, the invention of the steel plough made it possible
to plough up the tough sod of the great North American grassland, and of the Eurasian steppe, for the growing of cereals to
feed the hungry mouths of Europe. Hence, during these two
centuries, especially the nineteenth, Europe was cushioned
against a population crisis by the export of people and the import of food and raw materials. In the seventeenth century no
such mitigations were available: the flow of emigration was still
only a trickle, the exploitation of the rest of the world was only
beginning. In the twentieth century, the flood of emigration was
abruptly dammed, especially when the United States, with its
lands rapidly filling up, was obliged to put up immigration

---

those of the Thirty Years War (seventeenth century) pictured by
Callot. But there is, almost by definition, little to choose between individual atrocities. The difference between the centuries was one of
scale.

barriers. The countries of central Europe were short of colonies to exploit. A new population crisis began, first in Germany and Italy, later in the colonial countries as their empires shrank. In short, our own age, like the seventeenth century, is an age of population crisis, and the crisis is growing, just as the ferocity of our wars is on the increase.

It is sometimes argued that war alone is inadequate for significantly reducing the huge populations of modern Europe. But so is the violence in an animal population, considered purely in terms of killing. We have seen that in animals the crisis response works not only through the violence itself, but through the stress it causes, which renders the population vulnerable to disease. And if we survey the history of war, we find that the ages of great violence in the past have indeed been ages when populations rapidly declined, not simply from the wars but from the famine and pestilence for which wars create the ideal conditions, disrupting food production, dislocating trade, weakening public health and transporting crowded bodies of men in unsanitary conditions. We saw that the great advances in modern medicine had reduced this effect by the Second World War, but that nuclear weapons would restore it with a vengeance (p. 12).

With all that we have learned by now about mass redirection (Chapter Three), we need have no difficulty in seeing war as a response to the stresses of a population crisis in each of the contending countries. Indeed it was in this more specific way that Stanislav Andreski formulated his view of civil disturbance and war (p. 109), as 'alternative . . . releases of population pressure, as they are alternative methods of organizing emigration to hereafter'. Alike at the level of the individual and that of the whole society, the case seems clear that mankind has indeed retained the whole system of violence as a means for drastic population reduction in face of population crisis, and that this, and this alone, is the ultimate significance of human violence. The conclusion is full of hope for mankind, and we may well agree with Andreski that 'limitation of the growth of population', and 'a determined attempt to bring the majority of the population of the world out of its present condition of misery, offers the best hope of abolishing war'. Equipped with this general conclusion and this powerful incentive, we are now ready to consider the characteristics of population crises in the huge societies of civilised man. In studying population crises, we can approach an understanding of the age we live in today.

3

While man practised food-gathering and scavenging, hunting, and even shifting cultivation (p. 18), his situation was not fundamentally different from that of monkeys, from the point of view of population control. Gradually improving techniques of food-getting enabled his populations to grow, and the control of fire gave him access to a wide variety of climatic regions. But his communities seem to have remained small; he spread over the world by the ordinary 'monkey' process of band-splitting. Fundamental changes did occur, however, when man began the practise of *settled* agriculture, which enabled him to continue indefinitely growing crops on the *same* plot of land, by means of irrigation and silt, or rotations and animal manure. One result was the appearance of attachment to a fixed territory, evident in the peasant's passionate concern with the bit of land where he makes his livelihood. Another result was the formation of communities enormously large by monkey standards. The vastly greater amounts of food produced by settled agriculture made possible a large population in a small area. Since each peasant could produce more than he and his family could consume, the surplus supported craftsmen, priest-bureaucrats and other full-time specialists. The new, large communities built towns to live in, and these rapidly increased in size; the increase can be seen, for instance, in the succession of settlements on the site of Jericho from about the eighth millennium B.C. By the fourth millennium B.C. sizeable cities had developed in ancient Iraq; at least by the second millennium B.C., they had attained populations of several hundred thousand.

We naturally have no direct evidence about this crucial

transition. But, surprisingly, we have a clue to what may have happened in the observations of the Japanese zoologist Hiroki Mizuhara on the band of Japanese monkeys at Mount Takasaki. In this 'open zoo', where visitors as well as scientists were providing food on the spot, the attractions of a fixed feeding-ground made the monkeys curtail their normal foraging trips in the forest. As their numbers grew, the normal band-splitting process was delayed, creating a kind of population pressure which had dramatic results. When scientists began to feed this band in 1953, the total population was less than 200. There were six leaders and ten sub-leaders, all other males being cadets. By 1956 the population had increased to 440, but there were still only six leaders and ten sub-leaders. It was not until 1959 that the band finally split. Until this occurred, there was considerable tension. The six leaders were Jupiter, Titan, Pan, Monk, Bacchus and Boor, in that rank order. In 1956–7, Monk took a long vacation (180 days) and Pan abdicated: as we saw earlier (pp. 68, 76), both eventually became solitaries. It is possible that, although not initially driven out, they could not stand the increasing tension in the band. In the summer of 1956, Bacchus took a short holiday (80 days); on his return, he was accepted back into the leader class, but demoted below Boor in rank. So by the start of 1957, the effective leaders were, in order, Jupiter, Titan, Boor and Bacchus.

In the period 15–19 January 1957, some of the sub-leaders attempted a *coup d'état*. Jupiter had disappeared for a day, and came back wounded and shaken, perhaps after a fight with a solitary male. Immediately after his return, his lieutenant, Titan, quarrelled with him. There was a free-for-all, which Mizuhara could unfortunately not observe closely, since dusk was falling; but when it was over, Jupiter was closely accompanied by Uzen and Kuro, the fourth-rank and fifth-rank sub-leaders, while Titan was isolated and 'estranged, as if he were a solitary male in the central part'. It appears that the sub-leaders had taken advantage of the unwonted tension between Jupiter and Titan to infiltrate the leadership. On the 16th, they appeared to be dominant over Titan, and Mizuhara suggests that they had combined with Jupiter against Titan in the unobserved battle. After submitting to Uzen and Kuro, Titan redirected his resentment against the first-rank sub-leader, Achilles, chasing and attacking him. The demarcation between leaders and sub-leaders was by now so blurred that Achilles, redirecting in his turn, attacked and dominated Bacchus, currently the lowest-rank leader.

By the 17th, however, normal relations had been restored between Jupiter and Titan, and Uzen and Kuro were decisively driven out of the central circle. With monkey opportunism, Bacchus had helped Titan to punish these presumptuous sub-leaders, and this restored his own position; by the 19th he was definitely dominant over Achilles, and had even recovered his own old rank among the leaders, dominating Boor. Jupiter tolerated all these proceedings. It was one thing for him to use the middle classes to teach Titan a lesson; it would have been quite another to let these upstarts stay indefinitely in the boss circle. In the long run, the solidarity of the leaders made it quite impossible for sub-leaders permanently to rise out of their own class.

A similar barrier was evident between the sub-leaders and cadets. In 1955, the first-rank cadet, Soba, seemed to be ripe for promotion to sub-leader; he was ten years old, very active, and regularly herded females who had strayed into the periphery. But during this year, he gradually lost his influence even there, and by the end of the year he had left to become a solitary. Between 1955 and 1959, two other cadets, Gen and Don, went through the same experience in succession, each reaching first cadet rank, occasionally penetrating the court, gradually losing influence, and finally leaving. Two more cadets become solitaries without even reaching first cadet rank. When the band finally split, the next three cadets, after Soba, Gen and Don, became leaders of the 'daughter' band, but even they had already suffered from a similar discouragement, and in the new band they were subordinate in rank to much younger males. Mizuhara has aptly called this group of cadets a lost generation, and the first rank in such a group the 'jinx' position, where the discouraging effects of totally blocked ambition were most keenly felt. Unable to obtain employment for their obvious gifts as potential sub-leaders, these cadets had no alternative but to emigrate.

The Japanese monkeys have all the ingredients (including family influence, p. 66) for developing a true class system, that is, one in which some individuals remain in a lower class all their lives. But at Mount Takasaki they proved unable to tolerate the tensions of such an arrangement — the band finally did split, resolving the tensions in the traditional monkey way. Man must have been more flexible: he succeeded in settling in towns, and enduring the division into classes which at once appeared in these large communities. Differences in housing in the Indus cities, differences in the richness of early Egyptian graves, attest the appearance of true classes in the earliest civilisations. In ancient Iraq, by the early third millennium B.C., the reforming leader Urukagina of Lagash was indignantly listing the gross inequalities between the priests and the lower classes. He tried in vain to restore the old order 'as it had existed from the beginning'. Class division was here to stay. What we have said of hierarchies can, of course, be applied to classes. With ample mobility between them, with no serious inequality of privilege, classes could be simply a convenient basis for public order and leadership functions. In fact, throughout history they have nearly always been more or less rigid and more or less grossly unequal in rights. Against this persistent background of tension, which only modern technological resources could eliminate for ever, the sharp barriers and glaring inequalities of the population crisis periods stand out luridly. Just as mice can shift from territorial to hierarchical systems, but are then extremely sensitive to food shortage, so human societies have shown a muttering ground level of tension ready to swell into a roar of violence whenever resources ran short.

The individuals in a hierarchy recognise each other as individuals, and respond accordingly. Class status, on the other hand, may be signalled without individual recognition, by insignia of rank, by costly robes, armour, wigs, swords, and, even

today, by the persistent status symbol of speech accent. It was
clear in our comparison of monkey zoo colonies with human
societies (Chapters Three and Four) that all the inequalities produced by crowding between monkey individuals translate, in
terms of human history, into inequalities between classes. Moreover, in the huge communities of man, class division is complicated by labour division and the fact that members of one class
may employ and/or exploit members of another. Traces of this
relationship may indeed be observed even in monkey bands.
Subordinate monkeys may obtain tolerance and even protection
from superiors by grooming their fur, in a client–patron relationship involving personal service (p. 67). On the islet of Kōshima,
Japanese scientists once buried some food in the sight of a monkey band. The president made a perfunctory scratching at the
surface, and withdrew. Immediately, the other monkeys set to
work and cleared the trench. The president now returned, and
the others scattered, leaving him to select the best of the food at
his leisure. This suggests a potentiality for labour exploitation,
but of course it is unlikely to be realised in the natural surroundings of monkeys, where food is obtained without this kind of
labour. In man, relations of employment and exploitation produce a much more complex situation; yet, as we shall see,
the basic principles of the population crisis remain much the
same.

Except in north-western Europe after about 1600, and elsewhere in the twentieth century, the settled civilisations of mankind have generally had high death-rates (3–4 per cent) but
even higher birth-rates (3·5–5 per cent), made possible by the
food production of settled agriculture. Populations therefore
have generally increased by up to 1 per cent each year. They
have not ended up as a sphere of living flesh, etc. (p. 151) because every so often they have been cut down to size by a catastrophic death-rate of 15–50 per cent. History everywhere thus
consists of population cycles, which again and again reach a
crisis. In certain cases, crowding and bad housing have become
important before food shortage, as we shall consider in the next
chapter. But whether a population outran its food supply or

other resources, many of the features of the crisis have been similar, and these we shall consider first. The crisis period begins when population growth begins to outstrip production. Public health is weakened by malnutrition, the stresses of social tension and the effects of increasing violence. The end of every past crisis has been a drastic lowering of the population by epidemics of disease. These are not necessarily especially virulent in themselves, but kill large numbers because they attack a population in poor health, just as among animals. Modern medicine, not without continual struggle and vigilance, is keeping this final killer at bay; but of course a nuclear war would instantly unleash the ultimate horrors of the continent-wide epidemic, or pandemic.

To get a perspective on the modern crisis in the 'affluent' societies, it will be enough at this stage to consider in outline the population cycles of European history. These are unusual in that an exceptional amount of creative advance was made in the *non*-crisis periods, when population was growing but still in step with production, and tensions and violence were at a minimum. The resulting momentum of progress has been able to carry Europe forwards even through the crises, in an advance interrupted only when violence and the other disasters were at their worst.* Hence the extraordinarily confused and ambivalent nature of the age we live in. The momentum of technical progress is carrying us forward at an unprecedented rate, with continual technical advances which can have profoundly valuable social results (for instance, the potential educative effects of television, which can arouse and in part satisfy an increasing thirst for facts on the part of the whole public). Meanwhile we are experiencing all the growing tensions of what could be the worst population crisis in history. This is the predicament we have to understand; for the first time in history, we have scientific re-

* The reasons for the phenomenal success of Europe have nothing to do with any kind of 'racial superiority'; they can ultimately be related to factors of soil and climate. These reasons are too complex to be discussed here; the whole problem has been explored by W. M. S. Russell in a recent book, *Man, Nature and History* (1967).

sources which could release us for ever from the problems of violence and population crisis.

For the ancient Mediterranean world, evidence about population is naturally scanty and inexact. It is enough, however, to give us an outline picture of the cycles. European civilisation began in Greece, which was almost continuously subject to population pressure on its meagre food resources. In the early first millennium B.C., the pressure was relieved (monkey fashion) in a great surge of migration, which planted Greek colonies all over the coasts of the Mediterranean and Black Sea. Meanwhile a few Greek cities (notably Athens and Corinth) began to specialise in industry and commerce, importing their food from Sicily or southern Russia. Athens was assisted by the possession of the most productive silver mines of that age. The result was the flowering of Greek civilisation in the sixth to fifth centuries B.C. But by this time the migration was being blocked by a similar movement based on the coast of the Lebanon, the migration of the Phoenicians. Also, inevitably, industries began to spread to areas outside Greece, which lost its bargaining-position. In the late fifth and the fourth centuries, Greece experienced a major population crisis. Further relief came when Alexander the Great conquered the Near East and planted Greek cities all over it, but by this time the civilisation had been seriously affected, and the crisis continued in mainland Greece. Civilisation and population pressure came somewhat later to Italy. The Italians dealt with it in part by migration but chiefly by the military conquests which created the Roman Empire. The wealth and culture of this empire were not based on adequate food production at home, but on the possession of military power and looted capital in precious metals; most of the food came from colonial exploitation of the Near East and North Africa. Archaeological evidence (for instance, from aerial survey, which shows the extent of cultivated land at various periods) suggests that the population of the Roman Empire was growing, with periodic retreats, right up to the sixth century A.D. But there was a chronic imbalance of payments, and the precious metals inevitably drained East, where the food they symbolised was actually produced. The result was an unusually protracted and dreadful population crisis, which extended from the third to the sixth centuries A.D. The crisis ended with the pandemic of the sixth century (mainly bubonic plague), which lasted sixty years and killed between one-third and one-half the populations of the Empire. The western part of the Empire had already declined and fallen; according to the German historian Fritz Heichelheim, the enormous death-rate of the pandemic so disrupted society that Latin and classical Greek 'ceased to be living languages'.

Before they went under, Greece and Rome had prepared, and bequeathed, two of the ingredients of the final technological breakthrough: fundamental science, a way of organising technical research; and contract law, a way of organising business transactions. The third ingredient was supplied in the early Middle Ages by the peoples of north-western Europe: a new and passionate interest in the technology of power and machines, coupled with a new and boundless confidence in the technical progress of mankind. By the twelfth century A.D. they had begun work on the Gothic cathedrals, an enterprise as daring for its time (and as rich in technical by-products or 'fall-out') as the space programmes of their spiritual successors today. From this century on, Europe was committed to the technological way of life which has transformed the world. Most of the great creative developments occurred in the intervals between crises, when population pressure was relieved. The north Italian Renaissance bloomed in the fifteenth century; the marvels of modern science emerged in that incredibly creative period from the late seventeenth to the early twentieth century, on whose achievement our present technical advances are based. But from the twelfth century onwards the momentum was so great that technical progress continued throughout the frightful population crises that followed; and with technical progress there came, in the long run, progress in the organisation of society.

The population growth of Europe was based on a series of technical improvements in agriculture. These began in the seventh century A.D., with special spurts of advance in the non-

crisis periods — the eleventh century, fifteenth century, eighteenth and, above all, nineteenth century. But population repeatedly grew faster than food production, and every time it
outstripped production a crisis developed. We can dimly dis-
cern a crisis in the ninth century A.D., but know very little about
it. The first major crisis occurred in the thirteenth and fourteenth centuries. Under the pressure of population growth, crop
cultivation spread to areas of poor soil, for which its techniques
were still inadequate; by the end of the thirteenth century,
these marginal areas were beginning to show crop failures, and
the extent of cultivation began to shrink; hundreds of pioneer
settlements in Germany were abandoned. In 1315–17 there was
a catastrophic famine. By this time millions of people were short
of protein, and when the Black Death (bubonic and pneumonic
plague) struck in 1347, the death-rate was colossal. The plague
was not, in itself, terribly virulent. The northern Dutch, who
continued to raise plenty of stock and to eat meat, and who
maintained an independent peasant republic, and had no large
towns to attract invaders, were little affected by the pandemic.
The majority of Europeans, weakened by malnutrition and the
stresses of social tension and war, died in their millions. In five
years the Black Death killed between one-third and one-half of
the population of Europe. The death-roll drawn up by Pope
Clement VI's statisticians came to 42,836,486.* The transitional
languages of medieval times gave way to the national languages
of modern Europe.

The fifteenth century was an age of relief, when nutrition and
living standards improved and violence was less devastating. By

* This medieval estimate is probably not as wildly exaggerated as
it looks. A careful modern study, by the British historian M. K.
Bennett (1954), gives the following estimates for the population of
Europe at different dates (A.D.):

A.D. 1200	61 millions
1300	73 millions
1400	45 millions

It is true that there were serious epidemics in the fourteenth century
besides the Black Death, both before and after it.

G

the sixteenth century, the populations had again begun to grow too big, and another crisis set in, to last until the second half of the seventeenth century. The people's diet worsened again; on the manor of Gripsholm, in Sweden, the number of calories (energy supply from food) dropped by about a third between 1555 and 1653. Violence became appalling; this time it led, not to a pandemic, but to an endless succession of epidemics. Germany suffered worst this time; on the most cautious estimates, her population dropped from 21 to 13·5 millions during the Thirty Years War. The population of Europe as a whole does not seem to have fallen much, but population growth virtually stopped for a long time. By the mid-eighteenth century it started again, but in a changed situation. From the sixteenth century onwards, north-western Europe began to have somewhat lower death-rates and birth-rates in normal years. The natural increase even so, from the mid-eighteenth century onwards, was enormous; it has been estimated that Europeans (at home and abroad) made up about 22 per cent of the world population in 1800, and about 35 per cent in 1930. But north-western Europe was no longer depending on its own food production. From the sixteenth century, it imported grain from eastern Europe. At this stage it was still vulnerable to the unusual event of a bad harvest at both ends of the Continent (p. 27). But in the eighteenth, and above all the nineteenth century, it began to import from the newly exploited temperate regions of the world outside Europe, especially from the great grassland belts opened up by the steel plough. In addition, it was exploiting other world regions on a massive scale, and thus preserving, on the whole, the standards of living of Europeans. Finally, as we have seen, more than 40 million Europeans emigrated. Europe was still pursuing the old colonial methods of Greece and Rome. The result of all this was a temporary relief from population crisis in its worst forms, leading, as we have seen, to a measure of restraint even in warfare (p. 170–2).

The twentieth century has seen the end of both mass migration and colonial empires, and a gradual build-up to the full-scale crisis in which we are now involved. Except in Germany and Italy (which had no adequate empires), the crisis was somewhat delayed by a considerable fall in the European birth-rate. After the Second World War, the birth-rate in north-western Europe and the United States began to rise again. At first this was believed to be the usual temporary consequence of return to peace (soldiers reunited with their wives, marriages of people who had had to wait). But by the early 1950s it became evident that the rise in the birth-rate of the 'affluent' societies was continuing, creating a more and more alarming situation, for by now our normal death-rates are lower than ever before in history. In all the 'affluent' societies, populations have been increasing at a frightening rate, since about the year 1950, that year which we have already seen as such a turning-point in our affairs (Chapter One). The latest European crisis period has begun. What happens in this kind of epoch?

There are some characteristics of excessive population growth that can only appear in the complex societies of human civilisation, though they, too, play a part in bringing about all the responses of an animal population crisis. To begin with, we must notice one simple principle. If anything grows faster than the population, the result is a glut or congestion; if anything grows slower, the result is a shortage. The most outstanding lags occur in the production of food and housing, but the basic principle of relative growth rate applies to many other things. Sometimes a relative rate can change. A case in point is the growth in cities in the early stages of industrialisation. When a critical point is reached, more and more country people flock to the cities. In the United States, country and city people increased in numbers at about equal rates until around 1850; from then onwards, every rise in total population meant a greater proportional rise in city population: hence bigger and bigger cities. The same thing is now happening in the developing countries. Léopoldville (Kinshasa) in the Congo increased by 13,000 people per year in 1950–60; in the same period, the population living in towns in India rose by 42·8 per cent. (One consequence is an alarming spread of certain diseases, such as filariasis, also called elephantiasis, carried by a species of mosquito that breeds in polluted drain-water.) After a certain stage of industrialisation is reached, however, people begin to move out of the larger cities to suburbs and/or the smaller towns. In modern Britain and the United States, it is these units that are swelling most rapidly.

Where most things are concerned, however, relative rates are fixed, at least within certain limits, so that rapid population growth results inevitably in certain gluts or shortages. One thing that inevitably increases faster than population, for simple mathematical reasons, is traffic. Theory and experiment have established that the speed of traffic on a fixed road network goes down extremely steeply with increasing amount of traffic, eventually reaching zero (permanent jam). In Great Britain in 1964, two million man hours were lost by traffic delays. According to a survey issued by the Greater London Council in 1966, the population of London (at the present rate of increase) was expected to rise from 8·8 to 9·1 million in 1981, and the number of cars to double, reaching 2·5 million. Elaborate plans have been made for meeting the resulting traffic problem, but it is obvious that this kind of increase cannot be coped with indefinitely, and everyone in Britain is well aware from daily experience (in vehicles or on foot) — and in many cases nightly experience of noise — that British traffic congestion is getting worse all the time. Even *abandoned* cars are becoming a problem; 6000 a year are dumped in London alone, and it is estimated that in the whole of Britain there may be a million dumped annually by 1970.

Traffic congestion has arisen in earlier population crises. By Julius Caesar's dictatorship (mid-first century B.C.), the foul-up in Rome was so bad that wheeled traffic was banned from the city centre by day — except for the wagons of the building contractors. The noise at night can be imagined (especially by Londoners, for something similar is going on today without any such bans). By the second century A.D., the Emperor Marcus Aurelius had to extend the rule to all the cities of the Empire. The fundamental reason for the jams, as the American architect and 'generalist' Lewis Mumford has put it, 'was precisely the same reason that makes present-day traffic regulations, with the widening and multiplication of traffic arteries, so futile and in-ept: namely, no attempt was made to control the congestion of the land itself, or to reduce the density of population housed in its buildings'. Modern technical advance has presented us with a new traffic problem in addition, on a world scale. The number of transatlantic flights increases by 12 per cent each year, and is already almost saturating the elaborate three-dimensional cor-ridor system of flight paths, designed to avoid the risk of colli-sions in the air. Other forms of transport peculiar to our age show the same relentless population pressures. When the Nor-thern Line of the London Underground was opened in 1906, there were 37,000 passengers on the first day; by 1966, the daily load was approximately 300,000.

Traffic congestion imposes discomforts and anxieties that can amplify other stresses. Another result of population pressure has a more direct and obvious bearing on social tension, inequality and violence. Among the many stresses which can provoke vio-lence in human societies, one of the most important is unemploy-ment: a shortage of unskilled or semi-skilled jobs — or, to put it in another way, a glut of this kind of labour. 'Unskilled' and 'semi-skilled' must of course always be defined in contemporary terms: almost all modern British workers can read and write, a skill often restricted, in past ages, to small élites. The incidence of unemployment, even over large areas, has fluctuated through-out history with a number of short-term factors concerned with methods of production and patterns of trade. Hence the stress of unemployment has arisen at various times and places in both 'crisis' and 'non-crisis' periods, in our present broad sense. This may remind us that even the 'non-crisis' periods have been by no means free from fluctuating stresses, and therefore from fluc-tuating violence, for the response of violence is inexorably locked to the stimulus of stress. We have seen examples of these short-term fluctuations in the incidence and intensity of violence — East Anglia in 1816, Tudor England, the Southern States from 1880 to 1940 (Chapter One). Nevertheless, the pressure of a rising population must amplify any other factors making for un-employment, with its attendant poor working conditions for those employed — for, in the long run, unemployment means a bad bargaining position for the workers. This bargaining position has always been good when drastic fall in population has produced a real labour shortage, as in early fifteenth-century Europe. The great nineteenth-century labour leader Francis Place pointed out that by far the most effective form of strike would be mass birth-control. Hence unemployment has generally reached its most dangerous proportions in crisis periods. The indiscriminate way in which population pressure intensifies other factors can be seen at present in its effects on developing and 'affluent' societies. Both are subject to population pressure, but this interacts with two quite different reasons for a lag in the creation of jobs. In countries such as India, industrialisation has not reached the stage where it provides massive new employment. At the end of India's first Five-Year Plan (1951–6), there were still 5,300,000 unemployed. The second Plan (1956–61) could only produce 6,500,000 new jobs, and meanwhile a further ten million or so people had come on the labour market. The third Plan aimed at creating fourteen million new jobs, while a labour increase of seventeen million people was expected, and the Plan was in any case disrupted by 'defence' expenditure and the war with Pakistan. Thus the problem gets continually worse. Meanwhile the rising populations of the 'affluent' societies are making the difficult transition to full automation, which requires a smaller labour force than at any stage since the Industrial Revolution. The percentage of young people (below the age of 24) in the United States who were unemployed more than doubled between 1953 and 1962. It has been estimated that in the course of the 1960s about twenty-six million young Americans will enter the labour market, 40 per cent more than in the 1950s, and that about 7·5 million of these youngsters will lack the high school diploma which is virtually a requisite for settled employment under modern conditions.

A rapidly rising population can thus mean, under very varied conditions, a glut of semi-skilled labour. On the other hand, training for highly skilled labour takes time, and the production of highly skilled man-power is liable to lag, creating a shortage.

The doctors and nurses who run British hospitals and health services, for instance, are becoming desperately understaffed and overworked, as they strive to care for the mushrooming population of patients. At the Children's Hospital, Sheffield, for instance, between 1940 and 1960, the annual number of admissions nearly trebled, and the annual number of operations increased sixfold. The condition of many general practitioners, rarely able to take even the shortest holidays, is not far removed from a relatively comfortable slavery. One provincial G.P., who was awarded a high medical honour, had to negotiate for weeks to find a stand-in who would free him to go to London for one day and receive his award. In the hospitals, doctors and nurses are grossly overworked. We heard of one very conscientious nursing sister who collapsed in the wards after working thirteen hours a day for months. In the *Evening Standard* issue of 23 August 1966, the journalist Harriet Jillings described a not untypical day in the working life of a twenty-six-year-old houseman in a London hospital: after an emergency call at 6 a.m., the continuous working period began at 8.55 a.m. and continued till 12.45 a.m. the following morning. There had been a total of sixty-seven minutes off for meals. It is scarcely surprising that in 1964, for instance, to quote an article in the *Daily Mail* (8 October 1965), 'legs were amputated in error, wrong blood groups transfused, swabs were sewn into patients and there were cases where the wrong patient went under the knife'.* In May 1965, the matron of a new hospital (which had cost one and a half million pounds) was reported as flying to Malta in a desperate search for nurses: the hospital was 50 per cent understaffed. In September 1965, a survey of five mental hospitals found nursing staff shortages of 106, 200, 74, 169 and 64. At one of these hospitals, four consultants were attending more than

* According to a report in the *Evening Standard* of 25 May 1967, 'the case of a . . . woman who had the wrong leg amputated was the 13th case of a wrong operation in Britain this year' (1967). Over the past six years, the same article notes, 'an average of 17 wrong operations has been reported every year to the Medical Defence Union in London.' The total of wrong operations apparently began to rise in 1964–5.

500 patients each. In the same month, the Treasurer of the
Medical Practitioners Union warned the T.U.C. that the British
Health Service would have collapsed altogether if India and
Pakistan had recalled their medical personnel from Britain for
their war. The French Health Service is facing a similar problem; in July 1966 it was estimated that the number of doctors,
already too low, will actually decrease by 1975, when the 'demand for care will have increased by 100 per cent'. In 1965 the
Federal Republic of Germany was said to be short of 30,000
nurses. Medical staff are only one example, however, of shortage
in highly skilled personnel. Alarm has been expressed in Britain
for several years about the increasing shortage of scientists and
technologists in industry. This shortage may be aggravated by
such factors as the rival attractions of government service and
universities, or the 'brain drain' of emigration to the United
States. In the long run, however, rapid population growth can
only lead to a proportionate shortage of highly trained labour.

Shortage of skilled, glut of unskilled labour: the obvious answer is more education and training. This is, indeed, a necessary
step in the transition to the marvellous civilisation we could
have by means of complete automation. But unfortunately,
teachers themselves need prolonged and intensive education
and training. And just as a medieval farmer, in a bad year,
might have to eat some of the grain he needed for next years'
seed, so, when skilled man-power is short, some potential teachers have to be used in their generation for other skilled purposes. In the present population crisis, the lag between the
production of pupils and the production of teachers is making a
more and more serious shortage. Imaginative use of television
may ease the problem, but it has its limitations: the students at
Berkeley (California) literally revolted against the impersonal
quality of amateurishly produced closed-circuit teaching programmes. In the county of Surrey alone, at the present rate of
population growth, places will have to be found by 1972 for
more than 30,000 additional pupils. In 1965 there were more
than two million British primary school-children in classes of
thirty-six or more; this degree of crowding is itself conducive

more to violence than to education (Chapter Six). In order to reduce classes to thirty or less, Britain will need, within the next ten years, almost double the present teaching force of approximately 300,000. In the Federal Republic of Germany, a leading educationalist, Dr Hildegard Hamm-Bruecher, forecast in 1965 that within five years the country would be short of 300,000 teachers for an estimated eleven million children. Automation needs a smaller *total* labour force than the present one, so even training all the semi-skilled would not eliminate unemployment if the present rate of population growth continues. But, far from achieving this, the continuation of the crisis can only lead to a *decline* in education and cultural levels. A steady decline of this kind was a prominent feature of the protracted population crisis of the Roman Empire.

That Empire also provides a good example of another effect of population pressure. In the course of the dreadful third century A.D., when the crisis was in its worst phase, the price of bread rose to more than 12,000 times the amount it cost in the second century. In effect, the value of money completely collapsed, and society was reorganised on a totalitarian basis, with serfs on the land and everyone compelled to follow the trade of his father. In this particular crisis, precious metals were flowing out of the region. But a rise in prices has been a feature of every population crisis in the history of Europe. Where the society has retained its currency, the effect has been a price revolution, or permanent fall (without complete collapse) in the value of money. The effect is due to two things. First, rising population increases the demand, and therefore the price, of essentials such as cereal grain, flour and bread; other goods gradually rise in price by a chain reaction. Second, the tensions of the crisis lead to increased wastage of real resources on 'defence' expenditure. After the crisis of the thirteeth and fourteenth centuries A.D., when Europe was only beginning to resume a full money economy, the price rise was followed by a rapid recovery. After most other crises, the price revolution was permanent. In the ancient world, real wages were kept down during the crises by expanding slave labour; the price revolution in Greece thus

*

permanently lowered the status of the free working classes, and
eventually destroyed democracy. In modern times wages and
prices have sometimes tended to spiral into inflation, but in the
long run real wages can only decline in a prolonged crisis. In
the price revolutions of ancient Greece and of the sixteenth and
seventeenth centuries A.D., real wages fell to about half their
initial values. Rising population put up the demand for essential goods, and hence raised their price, while increasing the
supply of labour, worsening the workers' bargaining position,
and thus keeping wages down (even without slave competition).
In both cases, another factor accentuated the crisis. While the
outflow of currency during a crisis causes complete economic
collapse (as in the Roman Empire), an increase in circulating
currency promotes and stabilises the rise in prices. In the Greek
crisis, Alexander the Great released the treasure hoard of the
Persian kings into circulation. In the crisis of the sixteenth to
seventeenth centuries, the Spaniards imported large quantities
of bullion from their conquests in Mexico and Peru. In neither
case, however, was this factor the main reason for the price
revolution. In each case the revolution had already begun, as
can be seen, for instance, by comparison of cereal prices and
bullion imports in Spain in 1503 to 1660. In each case the fundamental cause of the price rise was the excessive increase in
population. In the same way, our present price revolution may
be accentuated by the large amounts of consumer credit (hire-
purchase, etc.), which correspond in practice to circulating
money from this point of view; but it is undoubtedly mainly the
result of the rise in populations all over the world since the
Second World War, accompanied by the climbing expenditure
on 'defence'. The present rise in the cost of living, or fall in the
value of money, is world-wide, though it is most obvious in the
'affluent' societies. Nobody needs to be told that the cost of
living has risen since the Second World War, but a few figures
may be worth quoting. According to President Johnson, the
cost of living rose between 1961 and 1966 by 8 per cent in the
United States, 17 per cent in the Federal Republic of Germany,
21 per cent in Britain and 29 per cent in Italy. The rise in the

United States became much steeper in the year 1966 itself, because of increased expenditure on 'defence', especially the Vietnam war. The corresponding fall in the value of money can be seen in the depreciation of government bonds, surveyed in 1966 by the American currency expert Franz Pick. He studied the values of government bonds in seventy-seven countries (containing about 90 per cent of the world population) between 1940 and 1966. The bonds in all these countries have lost at least 25 per cent of their purchasing power during this interval. In thirty-eight countries, including China, the Soviet Union, Japan, France, Italy and the Federal Republic of Germany, the depreciation has been more than 90 per cent. It will be clear that political systems have nothing to do with this problem of population growth. Pick has aptly called government bonds, of whatever country, 'certificates of guaranteed confiscation'. There is, however, one important difference between the present price revolution in the 'affluent' societies and those of earlier crises. In former times, when population outran food production, the first and steepest rises were in the prices of cereals. In the modern 'affluent' societies, food price increases have become serious only in 1966. The main 'essentials' of which we are short have so far been land, housing and (in Britain) transport. The price of agricultural land in southern England doubled between 1962 and 1964. In 1951 the London County Council bought building land on the average for £8,800 per acre; by 1963, the average was £61,800. Within ten years, two cottages in Hampstead increased their price more than a hundredfold. British cost-of-living increases in 1965 were highest (apart from the heavily taxed alcohol and tobacco) in housing and transport.

Unemployment, shrinking education and price revolutions are all obviously liable to increase real inequality between classes, and we have seen that inequality is increasing in modern Britain and (steeply) in the modern United States (pp. 34, 141). With this effect, we are back in the world of animal population crises, and all the complexities in human societies add up to the same fundamental consequences. The non-crisis periods in European history have regularly seen relatively free movement between classes and the birth or rebirth of democratic institutions; the crisis periods have seen the hardening of class barriers, the growth of serious inequality between classes, and the suppression of older liberties. The supreme expression of inequality is sadistic pseudosex (p. 130), and legal torture has been abolished and reimposed several times in the history of Europe: it was restored in sixteenth-century Germany, for instance, by the Holy Roman Emperor Charles V. In the long crisis of the Roman Empire, cruel methods of execution, originally restricted to slaves, were gradually extended to the whole population.

The Greek crisis expanded and stabilised slavery as a basis of ancient Mediterranean society. The crisis in the Roman Empire introduced serfdom to Europe. It was already present in the densely peopled imperial province of Egypt, but even there the Imperial Government deprived the peasants, in the early first century A.D., of their age-old right to strike, in order to guarantee food production for the swelling populations of the Empire. In the early Middle Ages, it was not too difficult to become a feudal lord; as the crisis of the thirteenth and fourteenth centuries developed, the lords became as exclusive as the leaders of Mount Takasaki. The military order of the Templars was founded in 1119; it consisted of two categories in different uniforms, knights and serjeants. The earliest Rule of the Order (1130) does not specify which recruits were to enter which category: evidently there was room for considerations of merit or personal influence. The second Rule (1250) specified that a recruit could only become a Knight Templar if he was the son or descendant in the male line of a noble. Not only could he become a Knight, he must do so; if he concealed his origin, enlisted as a serjeant out of Christian humility (or to preserve an incognito), and was eventually found out, he was put in irons. This is typical of the hardening of class barriers all over Europe during the period. During the same (thirteenth and fourteenth) centuries, at the bottom of the feudal ladder, equally rigid distinctions formed between big farmers, small farmers and labourers. Conditions relaxed in the fifteenth century, to be followed by new rigidities in the crisis of the sixteenth and seventeenth centuries, though the lines were in different places in different countries: in England, the barrier rose between the landed gentry, together with the city merchants, and the rest, in France, between the smaller class of nobles and the commoners. At the same time, the Europeans opened up the slave-trade, creating slavery outside Europe but under their control, on a scale unknown since the early Roman Empire. In our present crisis, the trend seems rather to be towards wage-slavery. Business corporations grow ever more comprehensive in controlling the lives of their employees; hire-purchase (which mortgages the incomes of the poorer American workers for two years in advance) keeps the labour force docile and dependent, though obviously with an undercurrent of resentment, ready to break through into violence.

Along with social inequality, the crisis periods have brought a suppression of individual freedom and privacy, the fundamental territorial rights. In Leyhausen's terms, in man as in cats, relative hierarchy is converted to absolute hierarchy (pp. 56, 147). Leyhausen himself has expressed this well: 'overcrowded conditions are thus a danger to true democracy. . . . Tyranny is the almost inevitable result, whether it be exercised by personal tyrants or by an abstract principle like the Common Good, which is no longer any good at all to the mass of individuals. *For this is an unalterable law*: as long as density is tolerable, sacrifices made for a common cause will, one way or another, pay dividends to the individual and contribute to his own fulfilment. Beyond this point, however, the demands of the Common Good rise steeply, and what is taken away from the individual is gone for good; he cannot even see that it goes in any sizeable amount to others, for they are likewise robbed without reward' (his italics). A striking example of the mechanics of this process is provided by the history of the three-field farming system in medieval Europe. In the early Middle Ages, the land in many areas was farmed in a three-year rotation, wheat or rye being sown in the first year, oats or beans in the second, while the land was left fallow in the third year. Three huge open fields were generally used, one being in each state in any given year. Such a farm was worked by a group of peasants living near by; each had a set of small unfenced strips in each of the three fields. The animals for draught and manure, meat and wool, were grazed on common pasture-land between or around the crop-fields. Some co-operation was necessary, especially in the provision and operation of draught animals for ploughing, but otherwise each peasant could suit himself about sowing and harvesting dates and the choice of crops to sow in each phase of the rotation, and even about which strips he left fallow in a given year. In the late twelfth and thirteenth centuries, the swelling population demanded more staple food, and therefore more cereal production. The result was a spread of crop land at the expense of pasture and hay meadows, while at the same time more horses and oxen were needed for draught. Hence the animals were now allowed to graze the fallow field and the stubble on the cropped fields after harvest. Since the individual peasants each owned many small unfenced strips of land, their operations now had to be synchronised, and their freedom to choose their own crops and timings disappeared, a uniform plan being dictated by a manorial or village council, which naturally controlled the peasants' work ever more closely. The loss of individual freedom did not do much for the Common Good, for even the grazing of stubble and fallow did not solve the problem of the lost pastures and meadows. Hay for winter feeding became particularly scarce. Shortage of manure brought down cereal yields. People ate less meat and dairy products, hence less protein. Since oats were vital for feeding the draught animals, and choice of crops became standardised by the village councils, it is probable that fewer beans were sown, hence reducing an alternative source of protein. Eventually, as we have seen (p. 181), malnutrition through shortage of protein exposed the regimented peasants to all the horrors of the Black Death. In modern Britain, individual freedom is being curtailed in a different way by the imperious demands of high-density housing. The point was vividly brought out in a documentary produced by Jill Craigie, shown on BBC television on 2 February 1967. As the film demonstrated, people in London are being compulsorily turned out of sound and comfortable homes of their own, in which they have lived happily for years, to be rehoused on skyscraper estates where the children have nowhere to play, and amuse themselves (in the only way left to them) by putting the lifts out of order, so that mothers must drag their prams and toddlers up many flights of stairs: a Common Good which is, to say the least, of exceedingly dubious value.

Growing social inequality and loss of individual rights are, as we have abundantly seen, features of animal population crises. Whether monkeys, under crowding, become less tolerant of departures from the cultural traditions of a given band, is an interesting research problem yet to be studied. In the human societies of Europe, the population crises have always brought increased intolerance and increased censorship of minority thought, practices and communications. The crisis in ancient Athens brought with it a fierce intolerance of criticism, real or imagined, of the state religion, typified by a savage witch-hunt in 415, and by the conviction of Socrates in 399 B.C. Similar trends can be observed in the Roman Empire, sixteenth-century Europe (in both Catholic and Protestant states), and the modern United States, where Senator Joseph McCarthy was able to ruin a great many people by accusing them of Communist sympathies and 'un-American' activities. In the United States, indeed, the trend is opposed by new factors, such as television, as well as by robust traditions of free speech, which sometimes take delightfully piquant forms. Harvey Matusow, one of the Senator's paid informers, eventually repented of his work, and wrote a book about it, called *False Witness*, which was accepted by a publisher. A court order was made for the confiscation of the manuscript. The publisher defied the order at a television and press conference, and the order was withdrawn. A succession of New York printers were browbeaten into refusing the book by agents of the Federal Bureau of Investigation: in one case the work was actually taken off the press. Finally, however, one sturdy printer, a staunch conservative Republican, 'having forced an admission from the F.B.I. agents that nothing in the book was illegal, turned them out of his office, saying ... that their governmental interference with private business was socialistic and un-American'. Conservatives (in the general sense of the word), who always take some earlier period as their reference-point, may of course favour or oppose movements of freedom and equality: it depends whether their reference-point lies in a non-crisis or crisis epoch.

The European Middle Ages offer a striking example of the gradual destruction, as the crisis developed, of a really remarkable level of freedom of thought and speech. In the twelfth century virtually anything could be freely discussed and written about. Public debates between Catholics and the more organised heretics continued until 1204, the proceedings being controlled by a jury of twenty-six, on which each side was equally represented. The University of Paris retained its freedom rather a long time; there, as late as the mid-thirteenth century, Siger of Brabant was openly teaching a frankly atheist view of the universe; he denied the creation of the world and the immortality of the soul, and argued that religion was needed only to control the masses, and superfluous for educated people. There are universities today (for instance, in the Southern States of America) where Siger could hardly teach as he did. This wide tolerance naturally gave opportunities to those who were trying to reabsorb, via the scholars of Islam, ancient Greek principles of fundamental science. Christians, Moslems and Jews worked freely together in scientific information bureaux under royal patronage, in Spain and Sicily and Provence.

In the course of the thirteenth century, as population pressure rose, all this was drastically changed. Siger's own views were condemned by the Church in 1270, and he himself was murdered, while in the custody of papal officers, in 1282. The century witnessed a whole series of such condemnations of leading thinkers and writers, together with the founding of the Inquisition by Pope Innocent III, and the ferocious crusade against Provence, where organised heresy was especially prevalent, though there were Catholic nobles on the Provençal side, including some from Spain who had been fighting the Moslems.

This war raged from 1208 to 1229, and destroyed the magnificent Provençal civilisation. In 1231 and 1232 Pope and Emperor, respectively, introduced into their dominions the penalty of burning at the stake for heretics. By the fourteenth century, almost any kind of saying or writing outside the very narrow (and constantly changing) orthodoxy approved at the papal court became heresy, or, as we might call it today, revisionism.

Growing intolerance of this kind formed the background for mass redirection of resentment to minority groups who were more vulnerable than the upper classes. Once again we are on familiar monkey ground; but of course, in these human societies, the scale of cruelty and killing was enormously greater. In the thirteenth century, the victims were chiefly heretics, accused of beliefs and practices contrary to Catholic orthodoxy. The massacre began in Provence, and continued over the rest of Europe. Mass redirection in human societies is liable to get out of hand, and lynchings often went further than the authorities desired. In 1233 Conrad of Marburg was made Chief Inquisitor of Germany. Assisted by his sinister colleagues, Conrad Dorso and John the One-handed and One-eyed, he stirred up the masses into an orgy of lynchings, in which men and women of all social classes were often accused and burned on the same day. This medieval Hitler reduced all Germany to terror for two years. The local bishops were completely intimidated, but the local nobles declined to put up with this indiscriminate campaign; some of their knights assassinated Conrad in 1233. Only then did the Archbishop of Mainz dare to report to Pope Gregory IX, who was deeply shocked. The persecution of heretics nevertheless continued fiercely throughout the century. In the following (fourteenth) century, the chief victims were the Jews, assailed by the most terrible *pogrom* before Nazi times, and the 'witches', people accused of the enigmatic crime of witchcraft. A second appalling wave of witch-hunting developed from the late fifteenth to the early seventeenth centuries, during the next crisis. In the course of the mass redirections again heretics, Jews and witches, many thousands of people perished.

The Jews were, of course, completely innocent of the various

charges brought against them (usually poisoning wells and
spreading plague). The more intelligent fourteenth-century
chroniclers were perfectly aware of this: the money of the Jews,
wrote one of these chroniclers, was 'the poison which brought
their death'. 'If the Jews had been poor, and rulers of the
countries had not been in their debt', wrote another, 'they
would never have been burnt.' Growing financial activity by
Christian bankers, who saw the Jews as rivals, was another obvious factor in steering the redirection this way. Thousands of
victims accused of heresy were probably 'innocent' of even this
'crime', succumbing to personal enmities or the ravings of other
victims under torture, or, of course, like the Jews, to debtors or
those who coveted their wealth. The actual heretics themselves
seem to have been rather decent, if somewhat priggish people,
to judge from the desperate plea of one poor wretch to the Inquisitors of Toulouse in 1230. 'Lords: hear me', he implored, 'I
am no heretic; for I . . . lie and swear, and am a faithful Christian.'

In the conditions of the witch-hunts, where torture was unsparingly used and no ordinary legal rights were conceded to
the accused, thousands of totally innocent people undoubtedly
also perished. At Bamberg, on 24 July 1628, the Burgomaster
smuggled a heart-rending letter to his daughter from his prison
cell. The executioner, himself appalled by the tortures he was
inflicting on the Burgomaster, had begged him to confess 'something, whether it be true or not', and he had finally admitted to
being a witch. 'For whoever comes into the witch prison must
become a witch or be tortured until he invents something out of
his head.' The writer begged his daughter to conceal the letter,
which asserted his innocence, 'else I shall be tortured most
piteously. . . . Good night, for your father Johannes Junius will
never see you more.' On the margin, he added a note, stating
that six other victims had accused him, 'all false, through com-
pulsion, as they have told me, and begged my forgiveness in
God's name before they were executed'.

When every allowance has been made for this sort of thing,
and for the leading questions of interrogators with their heads

full of rubbish from past trials, there remains considerable evidence that witchcraft was a real movement, strongly prevalent in the fourteenth and in the sixteenth and seventeenth centuries. In 1451 (in the calmer mood of a non-crisis period), Alphonso de Torado, Bishop of Avila suggested, with remarkable insight, that the stories of witches' sabbats were delusions caused by taking drugs. Half a millennium later, a modified form of this hypothesis was presented, in 1965, by the British psychiatrist Bernard Barnett. He adduces a great deal of evidence from the witch-trial records, of a kind which the interrogators had no special reason to concoct and impose on their victims. The candles at the sabbats (witches' meetings), for instance, always burned blue — as they would if certain kinds of plants were burned in them, plants containing hallucinogenic substances. Some of these substances induce delusions of being changed into an animal form, with hallucinations of growing fur or feathers. The accused witches often complained of symptoms in the intervals between sabbats, which are strongly reminiscent of the withdrawal symptoms of modern addicts. Some of them claimed to have gone through the whole experience of a sabbat at times when they must have been at home in bed: like the modern taker of lysergic acid diethylamide (LSD), they were 'taking a trip'.

If we accept the idea that the actual witches were taking drugs, and proceed to take some of the witch-trial 'evidence' at its face value, a picture begins to emerge which in modern times is all too familiar. The personnel of the movement were divided into witches and devils — or, as we might today call them, junkies and pushers. There were local devils, presiding over the small local sabbats, and grander devils, appearing at great conventions (for instance on the Brocken or Blocksberg in the Harz Mountains of Germany, the Blocula in Sweden, the top of the Puy-de-Dôme in Auvergne). In the course of the hunts, thousands of witches went to the stake or gallows, some of them persons of high social status. But remarkably few devils were caught, and none of the boss devils. At all sabbats, the devil himself was masked. Often he wore an additional mask on his rump, which the witches would kiss in a pseudosexual ceremony which parodied the kiss on the mouth between a vassal and his lord in the legal ritual of feudal homage. While the devils were unknown to the witches, they knew all their subjects, and in the seventeenth century the witches were even required to sign a pact with the devil. Such a document, if handed to an Inquisitor, was a sentence of death, so the witches were completely in the power of their devil bosses, who could not only cut off their drug supply but denounce them to the authorities at any time. It was widely understood that the devil usually betrayed his followers in the end.

There is always money in drugs, and some of the drug preparations were probably in the form of seeds, portable and even storable. Some of the witches reported paying dues at the sabbats. Modern experience, particularly in the United States, has shown the very close connection between drug addiction and crime, for addicts will do anything to obtain the money for supplies. In 1961 and 1965, waves of violence hit New York when heroin ran short after the discovery and seizure of large shipments by the authorities. In 1955 a United States Senate subcommittee questioned some 2000 police and law officials, and concluded that narcotics addiction was connected with one-quarter of all crimes committed in the United States, and about one-half of the crimes committed in many of the larger cities. In New York, half of all the criminals are addicts; it has been estimated that by 1959 $150,000 a day was being stolen to pay for drugs. In the United States and much of western Europe, both the narcotics trade and virtually the whole of organised crime is controlled by the Sicilian organisation called the Mafia. (In France they give way to a similar organisation of Corsicans, and until recently they have not sought to operate on a large scale in Britain — p. 145.) It is true that the leading Mafiosi are not obliged, like the medieval devils, to wear masks. Their names have been known to the police for a long time, and even to the general public since the partly televised hearings of the Senate Committee to Investigate Crime, led by Senator Kefauver, in 1950–1. Some of them actually appeared as witnesses before the Committee. They have close relations with large industrial concerns: the committee uncovered contracts between the Ford Motor Company and leading Mafiosi, dating back to the 1930s when the Mafia supplied strike-breakers to the Company. ('In fairness to Ford Motor Company', states the Committee's Report, 'it should be noted that it is taking vigorous steps to dissociate itself from these racketeer-held contracts.') They also have large holdings themselves in legitimate industries. Frederic Sondern's book, *The Mafia*, lists the chief business interests of thirty-one leading Mafiosi, as well as the family relationships of seventeen leading Mafia married couples. The Mafia can tolerate all this publicity because they can afford the best legal advice and colossal graft expenditure, and the terror they inspire in their petty criminal (often addicted) followers makes the task of getting direct evidence against them extremely difficult for the numerous honest and devoted law officers who have been on their track for many years. They got their grip on the United States in the Prohibition Era, but the core of their activities ever since has been the narcotics trade.

By analogy with the modern situation, we may conceive it possible that some of the medieval inquisitors were honest men trying to grapple with what they dimly perceived to be a cruel and dangerous racket; for after all, if some officials of United States Federal Agencies spend their time harrying printers of outspoken books (p. 195), others (including F.B.I. men) work unsparingly, with intelligence and often with great courage, to undermine the power of the Mafia. The witches were absolutely in the power of their masters, and were in a position to engage in plenty of petty crime and protection rackets; they needed no magic to poison cattle or even (as some of them certainly did) people. The take in a little fourteenth- or seventeenth-century village might seem trivial, but the vast profits of modern organised crime are accumulated precisely by the organised collection of dues from thousands of petty operations: the revenues of the Mafia in the United States alone have been estimated as 30,000 million dollars a year. Needless to say, no hint of the finances of witchcraft emerges from the trials. Besides their well-preserved anonymity, the devils could obviously have afforded considerable influence; for all we know (again by modern analogy) some of the Inquisitors were on their pay-roll, if not devils themselves: some of them knew an awful lot about the procedure of the sabbats. If even a fraction of this conjecture is true, the two ghastly episodes of witch-hunting appear in a new light.

Drug addiction is obviously likely to increase in periods of severe stress. The mounting population crisis in modern Britain is finally leading to the spread of drug addiction in this country, especially among teenagers. The increase began in the 1960s. In 1959 there were 454 registered addicts, of whom 50 were under thirty-five years of age. By 1964 there were 753, of whom 297 were under thirty-five and 40 under twenty. By 1965 there were 927 registered addicts, of whom 145 were under twenty (including one fourteen-year-old boy). Pushing in schools is reported to be on the increase. The Brain Committee, set up to investigate addiction in Britain, reported in 1961 that there was no serious problem; by 1965 they had grounds for changing their verdict. Valuable observations by British journalists, such as Anne Sharpley, in 1963–4 caused considerable anxiety at the Home Office. A. Linken, after personal observations in London coffee-bars, estimated in 1963 that out of 'say 150 young people in an all-night coffee-bar', thirty would have taken drugs that evening. In the United States, where poverty and housing problems have been more serious for some time (p. 35), the number of known addicts has been put as high as 50,000: the actual numbers, of course, in both countries, must be considerably greater than that of 'known' cases. From all this, it appears likely that increased drug addiction and organised crime are regular symptoms of population crises, and that both the witches and the witch-hunts were reactions to the same fundamental stresses in European societies of the fourteenth and seventeenth centuries.

The mass redirections of the population crises failed to prevent class conflict. The Greek crisis led to vicious class wars within each city-state. The crisis in the Roman Empire (especially in the third century A.D.) produced terrible conflict between the peasants in the armies and their exploiters in the cities. The thirteenth and fourteenth centuries saw bloody peasant risings, and fierce conflicts between businessmen and skilled workers in the urbanised regions of Italy and Flanders (Belgium): in Flanders, actual civil war raged from 1297 to 1328. Class warfare, more or less disguised, was a feature of the sixteenth and seventeenth centuries, and class conflict has been an obvious feature of the twentieth century itself.

We have already seen that increased ferocity in war, with fewer restraints and greater civilian involvement, was characteristic of the seventeenth- and twentieth-century crisis periods (p. 170). In earlier ages, accurate figures are, of course, much harder to come by, but the general impression bears out the main principle. The wars between Greeks in the late fifth and fourth centuries were certainly much less restrained than those before and after this period: in the third century, there were all sorts of 'rules of war', providing a certain protection for both soldiers and civilians. In thirteenth-century Europe, the Swiss introduced not only horrible new weapons but the principle of killing all prisoners; this kind of atrocity at first shocked all the other states, but naturally spread. Historians of military technology have noticed an alternation between the predominance of weapons of defence and attack. This cycle roughly but imperfectly coincides with non-crisis and crisis periods. A survey of all the crises leaves little doubt that warfare in these periods pulled no punches and knew few rules or restraints. An interesting and quite regular feature of the crisis periods was that their earlier wars were ideological; their later wars, perhaps through a greater efficiency in organising mass redirection, were between geographical units.* The Peloponnesian War of the late fifth century B.C. was a fierce ideological conflict between Democrats and Oligarchs: the fourth-century wars were between shifting combinations of states with no ideological dividing lines. The wars of the thirteenth century were ideological:

* Differences in ideology are connected with differences in levels of economic development; patterns of development may change considerably in the course of decades, within and between regions.

the crusade against Provence, and the ferocious conflict between Guelphs and Ghibellines (supporters of the Popes and the Hohenstaufen Emperors, respectively); the wars of the fourteenth century were national wars, like that between England and France. The same transition was evident in the sixteenth and seventeenth centuries, where Protestant–Catholic conflict gave way to wars between national combinations irrespective of religion. We seem to be at a turning-point in a similar transition, after the Communist–Capitalist conflict of the Cold War: France is withdrawing from the American alliance, China and the Soviet Union are becoming increasingly hostile to each other. It is sometimes suggested that ideological wars are particularly cruel, but this is doubtful. By the middle of the particularly appalling Thirty Years War in the seventeenth century, there were plenty of Catholics in the armies of the Protestant states, and vice versa.

Every time the population of Europe rose, the event was marked by a great extension of cultivated land, driving into the great forest that once covered all Europe. Every time a crisis developed, cultivated land retreated and the forest returned: there are places in Europe which were probably more densely populated in the thirteenth century than they are today. During these retreats floods and erosion damaged the land in some places. But these disasters were minor and easily reversible, and each time, as the population rose again, the clearing of the forest was resumed. The special climatic conditions of Europe permitted a rapid recovery of areas lost for a time to cultivation. Hence the violence of the crisis periods did no permanent damage to the natural resources of Europe. If we ignore the frightful load of suffering and the interruption of technical and social progress, then we can say that the violence of the population crises fulfilled its old animal function. It dealt with excessive population growth in such a way that no resources were permanently damaged, and there was always food available for the recovering populations. But this has not been so in all regions of the world. We have seen how in one vast belt, stretching from Morocco to Turkestan, the violence of crisis periods eventually destroyed the resources of the land, making the whole belt a region of poverty today (p. 10). Nuclear war could have the same disastrous effect over the whole earth, even in the most favoured and temperate regions (pp. 11–13). Hence violence in man can no longer serve the fundamental function for which it was evolved in animals — the conservation of the natural resources of a species. On the contrary, it threatens to do the exact opposite, destroying irretrievably the food resources on which our species must depend in the future. Even if we could tolerate the cruelty and waste of violence, we can no longer afford its terrible destructiveness. Instead, we must find a way to control our population growth by other means, to bring the present crisis peacefully to an end, and to ensure that it is the last in human history.

Six/Numbers and Needs

1

The word 'population' was introduced into the languages of modern Europe by Francis Bacon, in the essay we have already mentioned (p. 28) on the causes of violence. In considering the remedies for violence, he related the two things in a definite way. 'Generally', he wrote, 'it is to be foreseene [ensured] that the Population of a Kingdome (especially if it be not mowen downe by warrs), doe not exceed the Stock of the Kingdome, which should maintain them.' By the word 'Stock', he seems to have meant productive resources. The whole accumulation of fact in modern times, which we examined in the last chapter, has abundantly borne out this magnificent 'educated guess'.

We started our enquiry with the problem of the modern 'affluent' societies, where serious *food* shortage has not yet set in, but where symptoms of violence are yearly increasing. This situation became intelligible when we observed how animals regulate their populations; how the whole complex of violence is a device to reduce the population drastically and for some time, to allow natural resources to recover; how the stimulus for this whole complex is provided by the stresses of *crowding*; and how abundantly evident is the presence in human societies of the whole terrible machinery of the population crisis. In some earlier European crises, shortage of food was so prominent as to mask the effects of sheer crowding; in the modern affluent societies, these effects stand out in bold relief.

If we conclude, simply, that crowding produces violence, we are faced with some apparent difficulties. On the one hand, some societies have lived (and are living) at extremely high densities without *continuous* anarchy and slaughter; on the other hand, violence occurs among and between tribal groups spread thinly over wide areas of land. But the animal evidence showed us that there is a complex interaction between 'want of room' and 'want of nourishment' (to use the expressions of Malthus). The territories of birds are larger when food is in short supply (p. 156); conversely, when food is abundant, some species (mice and moles) can tolerate even the complete loss of individual territories, and their replacement by absolute hierarchy, but they are then acutely sensitive either to food shortage or to still further crowding (p. 159). At the lower levels of food-production technology in human societies, population density is limited by food resources.

It is only recently that a uniform high level of food-producing technology has begun to spread over the whole of mankind. Throughout earlier ages, brute factors of geography and climate blocked the progress of smaller or greater fractions of our species, leaving societies specialised or 'frozen' at a whole succession of technical levels, so that today there are still many different kinds of food production, and correspondingly many levels of tolerable density. It is these less-favoured peoples who today make up the 'developing', or in plain terms the poorest societies of man.*

In most of the places where they are found in modern times, the population density of hunting and food-gathering peoples is exceedingly low. When Europeans first settled permanently in Australia, for instance, they found only an estimated 300,000 aborigines in the entire continent, divided into between 500 and 700 bands, of a size comparable with those of monkeys. The population density of aborigines ranges from one person per 35–40 square miles to three people per square mile in coastal districts, where they can supplement their diet by fishing. Modern tribes of this kind probably never achieve a higher density. At one period of human prehistory, however, towards the end of the fourth Ice Age, some 15,000 years ago, game and fish

* The failure of all these peoples to make the final breakthrough achieved in Europe has nothing to do with any kind of 'racial inferiority'. This failure, ultimately related to factors of soil and climate, is the other half of the problem examined in W. M. S. Russell's book, *Man, Nature and History* (see footnote, p. 178).

were so plentiful in parts of France and Spain that a kind of civilisation appeared which produced the magnificent paintings of
Lascaux, Altamira and other caverns in these areas. As the Ice
Age ended, floods and changing climate reduced the game supply. We can only conjecture whether there was a population
crisis of the pattern we have seen in later history; certainly the
'civilisation' disappeared. The modern tribes, 'frozen' at this
technical level, seem to have evolved sustained, systematic forms
of violence which keep their numbers down. The anthropologist
J. B. Birdsell reported in 1953 some illuminating facts about the
aborigines of inland Australia. He found that within areas of
less than eight-inch rainfall (hence very poor natural food resources) all the tribes deliberately mutilated their children; the
boundary of this practice exactly followed the rainfall line on
climatic maps. Within the five-inch rainfall line, the children
were further mutilated. On the border region around the eight-
inch line, tribes mutilating their children were smaller in numbers than those not doing so. Yet the practice was clearly
spreading. In particularly bad times, when food was very scarce,
some of the mutilated children, weakened by malnutrition,
would certainly succumb to infections and die. Hence the tribal
population would go down, and the tribe would have an advantage over other tribes in times of scarcity. In this way systematically violent practices arise, spread and are preserved.

The most primitive form of agriculture was the 'shifting cultivation' practised by the Danubians (p. 18). All over the world,
throughout the vegetational region of tropical rain forest (and in
Africa for many miles around this region), agriculture became
fixed at this level. The crude practice of clearing a plot, cultivat-
ing it for a while, and moving on, became converted into a
sophisticated kind of land rotation, called swidden farming
(after the Anglo-Saxon word for a burned clearing). A plot is
cleared, burned, cultivated for a few years, left for a considerably longer period to revert to forest, and then cleared again. In
1957 it was estimated that 200 million people were still practising this form of agriculture. Since any given plot is only used
for 10–20 per cent of the time (being unproductive forest for

80–90 per cent of the time), the technique demands a consider-able amount of land for each farming family. On an estimate made in 1957, the average density of swidden farmers was fifteen people per square mile. In 1940 J. A. Van Beukering, of the Java Department of Economic Affairs, estimated that swidden farming could support, at the very most, 125 people per square mile, and this figure is generally accepted. If density rises higher the cultivation period lengthens, the forest 'fallow' period shor-tens, soil fertility declines and the land is subject either to heavy soil erosion or to invasion by tall grass weeds, hard to eradicate. Only one civilisation has been based exclusively upon swidden farming, that of the Mayan Early Empire on the uplands of Central America. It managed to survive from the third to the eighth centuries A.D., to succumb at the end of that period to a population crisis of a drastic nature. Archaeological evidence strongly suggests there was a revolution. The upper classes fled to the unhealthy jungles of Yucatan, where their civilisation declined and became riddled with human sacrifice. Most of the other peoples practising swidden farming have evolved syste-matic forms of violence, involving mutilations even more severe than those of the aborigines, human sacrifice, and recurrent, al-most regular intertribal wars. These practices, together with the many diseases of the tropical rain forest region, kept their popu-lations small until modern times, when European or Japanese colonial administrations put down tribal warfare and introduced enough modern medicine to reduce the natural death-rates. The result is a population crisis all over these regions today, which has already brought serious erosion or grass invasion in many places, and forms the background to the intertribal conflicts evi-dent in many tropical regions; the most massive and frightful of these outbreaks, of course, has been the tribal Civil War in the Congo.

Apart from the Early Mayan Empire, all civilisations outside Europe have been based partly or wholly on 'hydraulic agricul-ture' — irrigation, the use of fertilising silt, and the control of floods. Such civilisations appeared in Mexico, Peru and parts of Africa (where industry and trade was a further necessary basis).

The chief region of hydraulic civilisations, however, was a vast belt extending over the Old World, where rainfall is irregular and irrigation an absolute necessity. This region includes the dry stretch from Morocco to Turkestan (p. 10), embracing North Africa, the Near and Middle East, and some of Central Asia; in addition, it includes the whole of northern China. It was in the heart of this belt, in the great river systems of the Euphrates, Nile and Indus, that civilisation based on settled agriculture began. It later extended to the great river systems of the wet tropics, in southern China, India and south-east Asia, where it permitted the growth of more than one rice crop a year, and also to the islands of Japan.*

The enormous productivity of this kind of agriculture, far greater than that of Europe before the late nineteenth century, made possible extremely high densities of population. In the first century B.C., for instance, Egypt probably maintained about 700 people per square mile; by contrast, in the sixteenth century A.D., the province of Holland in the Netherlands was unusually densely populated for Europe — at less than 100 people per square mile. The demands of hydraulic engineering for mass labour, together with the inevitable effects of crowding of this order, produced extreme class distinctions and rigidly hierarchical states, in which subservience was ensured by torture and appalling methods of execution. Between the middle of the third millennium B.C. (when the great reformer Urukagina of Lagash was destroyed by a neighbouring ruler) and the twentieth century A.D., not the faintest whisper of democracy disturbed the bureaucrats from China to Peru. The whole area of hydraulic civilisation was thus in a state of permanent latent crisis.

The copious food supply when the irrigation and flood-con-

---

* Though showing many of the 'hydraulic' features, Japan had some peculiarities of her own, mainly due to the absence of great unifying river systems: large-scale bureaucracy, which in the other hydraulic societies strangled progress, developed only very late in Japan, which was able to introduce modern technology in the closing decades of the nineteenth century. This special problem is also dealt with in *Man, Nature and History*.

trol works operated well, together with the insatiable greed of
the bureaucrats for mass labour, produced high birth-rates and
constantly rising populations. Full-scale population crises, even
worse than those of Europe, naturally recurred at intervals. The
first population crisis to be the subject of a written account is
described, in legendary terms, in the world's first book — the
ancient Iraqui epic of Gilgamesh, parts of which existed in
written form early in the second millennium B.C., and may have
been written much earlier still. The crisis occurred in the city of
Shurrupak, on the Euphrates. 'In those days the world teemed,
the people multiplied, the world bellowed like a wild bull.' The
gods (that is, the priest-bureaucrats) decided that 'the uproar
of mankind is intolerable'. If we are to believe the legend, they
dealt with the problem with hair-raisingly callous logic. They
fomented a war, in the course of which they 'pulled out the
dams' and 'threw down the dykes', so that the Euphrates
(which runs above the level of the plain) flooded the whole region. The destruction, however, went too far, and threatened to
leave the priests with no labour force at all. Even the priests
were 'terrified at the flood, they fled to the highest heaven' (the
highest storeys of their pyramid-like ziggurat-temple); 'they
crouched against the walls, cowering like curs', and regretted
their sweeping measures. Fortunately one priest, more far-
sighted than the rest, had warned one group of people to withdraw to the coast, where they survived to produce food and
luxuries for the priests, who 'gathered like flies over the sacrifice'.

The earlier population crises readily turned into wars between neighbouring states. The desperate need of each state
for the river-waters led to fierce disputes over water-rights. This
factor continues to operate today; it underlies much of the tension between Israel and the Arab States (some of whom seriously contemplate throwing good fresh water into the Mediterranean without using it, sooner than let it flow into Israel), and
the conflict between Pakistan and India over Kashmir, the
source of waters they both need for irrigation. In modern times,
rivers in these regions are often also the main source of power

for electrification. It is probable that China entered the Korean war at the end of 1950 (converting it from a brief episode to a terrible three-year conflict) out of fear for her hydroelectrical works on the Yalu River, which supplied power to Manchuria, then the only industrialised part of China.

The early wars of the hydraulic societies resulted in the unification of large regions by the most heavily militarised states — societies of unusual cruelty and destructiveness, like the state of Ch'in (p. 8) which unified China, the Assyrians who unified most of the Near East, the Incas who extended their cruel Empire over the north-western quarter of the South American continent. The first two powers were finally destroyed in universal outbursts of resentment by their victims; the Incas were repeatedly obliged to kill tens of thousands of rebels, and would doubtless have succumbed to revolution if they had not first been overthrown by the Spaniards. The Incas alone, in their terribly efficient ant-hill, seem to have attempted deliberate, if brutal, birth-control, by regulating the entry of recruits into the corps of sacred virgins. In the Old World, the increasing efficiency of large-scale engineering works made possible a gradual increase in the food supply, and hence in the populations it could support. But the populations again and again outran the food resources, breaking into frightful crises of civil war in which (as in ancient Shurrupak in the Gilgamesh story) hydraulic engineering works were destroyed, drastically reducing the food supply and ushering in appalling famines and consequent killing epidemics. Food shortage was even more prominent in these crises than in those of medieval Europe, as indeed was observed by Hung Mai (p. 18). Indeed the story of the whole region is vividly summed up in a ritual still practised today in the Shinto Shrine of the Three Mountains in Japan. One night each year, 2000 young men, wearing only loin-cloths, are jammed literally solid into the courtyard of this temple, where they fight for scraps of a single cake of rice tossed to them by a priest. Although they fight only with their bare hands, broken limbs are common, and a few years ago seven men were killed.

The hydraulic civilisations reached their peak when large

regions were completely organised in terms of water engineering works and canals; this happened all over the Old World in the first millennium A.D. From then on, civilisation declined in China, and over the rest of the belt even the resources of the land were steadily eroded and destroyed. Each cycle brought further decay. The reasons for this story of decline and fall are partly connected with the permanent latent crisis and the rigid kind of society it perpetuated, and partly with the enormous destructiveness of the crises themselves. The early censuses of China are unreliable in detail, but they give rise to relative population estimates which can be trusted in broad outline, and which give us a fantastic picture of rising population with catastrophic periodic population crashes. The population of China, thus estimated, shows the following fluctuations:

A.D.	
754	52 millions
839	30 millions
1125	100 millions
1290	59 millions
1661	105 millions

The extreme, unimaginable sufferings of the crises, and their dreadful destructiveness of land resources in all the regions west of China, were in part due to another factor. Settled agriculture began as mixed farming, with crops and stock. But the extremely specialised nature of hydraulic agriculture, especially its demand for labour on engineering works, led to the virtual exclusion of stock-raising, except for draught animals. Beans were used to supply food proteins, and even as 'green' (plant) manures. In the steppes and deserts outside the great river valleys, the excluded stock-raisers were forced to develop a no less specialised but quite different kind of society, which we call nomadism. The nomads (Bedouin Arabs, Berbers, Kurds, Turks and Mongols) wandered over the arid, riverless wastes with their stock (mainly sheep), searching for water and grass; so powerful did their wandering urge become, that they finally failed to stop even in favoured spots long enough to grow crops or hay or even to dig wells. This way of life did not permit a density greater on average than two people per square mile — a

H

figure comparable with that for the more favoured of the food-gathering tribes (p. 207).

The nomads were subject to crises not only of their own populations but also those of their animals. Since sheep or cattle were their only form of wealth, and easily multiplied, it was tempting to breed too many. The result was overgrazing, which caused more and more of the arid land to be destroyed by soil erosion. A vicious cycle of this kind is evident in the small region of Karamoja in Uganda, where a mission from the Food and Agricultural Organisation of UNO reported their observations in 1963. Improved control of cattle diseases, together with continued overbreeding, had caused a drastic increase in the cattle population, leading to serious overgrazing. 'As pasture deteriorates from overgrazing,' runs the report, 'tribes begin to jostle', as 'groups, deprived of their traditional grazings, move elsewhere to survive.' The result was inter-tribal violence. Among the much more mobile nomads on the wide steppes and deserts of the great dry belt, this tribal 'jostling' produced a kind of chain reaction, which could be studied in detail, on a relatively small scale, in the Sudan in the nineteenth century. After each battle, the losing group would join the winners. In this way, at certain critical periods in world history, great hordes of nomads have rapidly coalesced under conquering steppe emperors: the most famous of all these hordes made up the Mongol armies of Genghis Khan at the beginning of the thirteenth century A.D.

Though the nomads normally lived at the density of food-gathering peoples, they were a very different proposition for their neighbours. Phenomenally mobile, on their fast ponies or camels, united in hordes, equipped by their way of life for flexible military operations, they became, under population pressure, a terrible menace. Though their absolute total numbers were not large, they could rapidly assemble from areas of thousands of square miles, to concentrate their forces and appear before the gates of a city in overwhelming strength. To the terrified peoples of the hydraulic civilisations, they appeared innumerable, like the Midianites who descended upon Israel at the end of the second millennium B.C.: they 'came up with their cattle and their tents, and they came as grasshoppers for multitude; for both they and their camels were without number: and they entered into the land to destroy it'.

The combination of military efficiency with an insatiable demand for vast areas of pasture made the nomads the most destructive of all societies before Nazi Germany. They descended on the hydraulic societies, especially when these societies were themselves collapsing in crisis and civil war, and turned great tracts into permanent wilderness. It is a measure of the unusual personal ability of Genghis Khan that he resisted the temptation to turn the whole of northern China into grassland. Elsewhere, the nomads were less restrained, and it is they who above all created the spreading deserts of the dry belt. The resulting population imbalance was corrected by the simple method of taking numerous cities by treacherous promises of quarter, and then depopulating them to the last child. The nomads killed hundreds of thousands of people at a time; they were chiefly responsible for the colossal crash of the Chinese population between 1125 and 1290 — a reduction of more than forty millions (pp. 8, 213). Because of their mode of food production, and their inability to alter it, they evidently felt crowded at more than two per square mile; and they constitute the extreme example in history of violence under population pressure where the limiting factor was food-production technique.

In the Far East, the vast resources of the continuous land mass of China made possible the final conquest and taming of the nomads, and the ending of their way of life, though not before Chinese civilisation had suffered serious damage. In North Africa, the Near and Middle East, and western Asia, the civilised regions were split by tongues of intervening desert, and were also assailed from both the south (Arabia and the Sahara) and the east (central Asia): over this whole region, the nomads won, converting vast tracts into man-made desert, and utterly impoverishing the remainder (with the help of malarial mosquitoes, breeding in the ruined canals). By the twentieth century, all civilised regions outside Europe were poor, 'developing' nations. The single exception was the island people of Japan;

apart from other advantages, they had succeeded, with the help of wind and waves, in utterly destroying the Mongol Armada sent against them.

Even the nomad population crises, though apparently explosive, must have been building up for some time in advance. All the other kinds of population crisis we have considered were relatively gradual in their onset. The world today is faced with two new kinds of population crisis, which may fairly be called population explosions. In the developing nations, the crisis has come from a sudden drop in the normal death-rate, occurring in a situation where the birth-rate is very high. In the developed, 'affluent' nations the crisis is coming from a sudden rise in the birth-rate, occurring in a situation where the normal death-rate is very low. Both kinds of change are extremely explosive, causing very rapid increases in population. Previous crises involved no such sudden changes: they resulted simply from the cumulative effect of the birth-rate being higher than the normal death-rate, both being very high.

The basis for the present situation was laid in the eighteenth century in north-western Europe, when improvements in medicine, public health and related factors caused the normal death-rate to begin to fall lower than ever before in history. As we have seen (p. 182), the European populations increased enormously as a result; but the effect was mitigated not only by emigration and food imports, but also by the fact that the birth-rate in north-western Europe was already lower than anywhere else: why this was so, we shall consider later. In the late nineteenth and the first half of the twentieth centuries, the birth-rate in north-western Europe and the United States fell still lower, somewhat easing the drastic effects of the damming of emigration.

The developing nations, however, retained in the twentieth century the very high birth-rates which had been balanced by high normal death-rates and periodic catastrophic crises. The coming of modern methods of controlling famine and disease (and tribal wars), brought by colonial powers, caused a sudden drop in the normal death-rates of these countries. In Ceylon, where the effect was particularly dramatic, the DDT campaign against malarial mosquitoes lowered the normal death-rate from 2 to 1·4 per cent (per year) in the single year 1946–7; the birth-rate remained over 4 per cent. Evidence in some places (such as British Guiana) suggests that the campaigns against malaria, in particular, even increased the birth-rate as well, by rendering people less weak and inert. The result has been a spectacular increase in the *rate* of increase of all these populations. Thus between 1891 and 1921, the population of India rose by only 5 per cent. Between 1921 and 1951, when major famines and epidemics were under a considerable measure of control, it rose by more than 1 per cent *per year*. The annual population increase of Ceylon, which was 0·46 per cent in 1871–80 and 1·71 per cent in 1941–5, rose to 2·74 per cent in 1948, after the DDT campaign. The situation of the developing countries may be represented by that of the little island of Mauritius. If its present rate of increase continued, this island of 720 square miles would have quadrupled its present population and have nearly three million inhabitants by the end of this century: a density of more than 4000 people per square mile.

These changes became most intense and widespread after the Second World War. A little later, in the 1950s, the birth-rate began to rise again in the 'affluent' developed societies. The result is that these societies are beginning to develop a population explosion of their own, for of course their death-rates are already extremely low. A study, published in 1966 by the Food and Agricultural Organisation of UNO, shows that between 1952 and 1965 populations were rising in every country of the world except Ireland (which showed a very small decline). The average annual percentage increases ranged from 0·3 per cent in Austria to the terrifying figure of 3·5 per cent in Venezuela. (Israel had an even higher rate, 3·9 per cent, but this was partly due to immigration.) The average rate in the United Kingdom was already 0·6 per cent during this period — serious enough in our overcrowded country; in the United States, where (as we have seen) poverty, inequality and violent crime are all already much worse, the rate was 1·6 per cent. These increases, of course, are all at compound interest (p. 151).

At the Brussels International Exhibition of 1958, we saw what was perhaps the most frightening exhibit ever put on show. It was a little gadget like the mileometer on a car dashboard, clocking away quietly, the end digit constantly changing, the next one every few seconds. But it was not recording miles travelled; it was registering the growing population of the Commonwealth. One needs such aids to the imagination (two new babies every second, considerably more than a new United Kingdom every year) to get even a faint grasp of the present population explosions. They have surpassed all expectations. In January 1964, the Minister of Health announced that 'the birth-rate in Britain had risen more sharply than any expert could possibly have foreseen', and that births in 1965 would probably equal what the experts, a few years earlier, had predicted for 1975. The Minister's experts were not the only people to be taken by surprise; the *rate* of increase is rising so rapidly everywhere (2 per cent in 1960, 2·8 per cent by 1964 in India, for instance). In 1950 Sir Julian Huxley was considered an alarmist when he suggested the world population might reach 3000 millions by the year 2000. United Nations estimates prepared in 1951 predicted more than 3000 millions by 1980. In fact, according to the estimates of the Food and Agricultural Organisation, the world had *already* passed that figure in 1962. By the end of 1967, the total will probably be more than 3500 millions. Current estimates suggest that, if the present trend continued unchecked, world population would reach nearly 6700 millions by the end of the century, and perhaps 22,000 millions by the year 2040. All the evidence we have considered suggests, however, that, if the trend *did* continue unchecked, war, famine and disease would produce a record population crash long before the middle of the twenty-first century.

At the level of world population, we have already entered upon a grave food crisis. It is generally considered that about half the people in the world eat a diet inadequate for complete health, and that some hundreds of millions are seriously undernourished. By prodigies of technological effort, world production of food increased by well over 10 per cent between 1958 and 1964, a staggering and unprecedented advance. Every year, the Food and Agricultural Organisation publishes a report on *The State of Food and Agriculture*. Normally the cover is a staid affair, containing only the title. In 1965 the Organisation was sufficiently startled to provide, on the report's cover, a three-colour diagram with three graphs. The first showed the huge increase in food production we have just mentioned. The second showed the rise in world population over the same period, which easily kept pace with the food increase. The third showed food production *per head* — which had remained constant from 1958 to 1964. ' "Now *here*, you see," ' said the Red Queen to Alice in *Through the Looking-Glass*, " 'it takes all the running you can do, to keep in the same place." ' The following year, after the 1965-6 drought, world food production per head had *fallen* by 2 per cent. The increase of food production on land is approaching (though it has not yet reached) the region of diminishing returns; the full harvests of the seas, at present barely touched, could add only as much food again. And of course, no conceivable increase in food production could keep pace indefinitely with a population rising continuously by compound interest (p. 151). Food crisis had to come, and we seem to have reached it already, on the world scale. In the developing countries, food production per head is very much *lower* than it was before the Second World War.

The food crisis in the developing nations is clearly already causing trouble; these regions have been full of wars and other violence since the Second World War. The 'affluent' societies, however, are only just beginning to feel the pinch. In the long run (as Malthus predicted), unless the crisis is solved, they must go the way of Athens and Rome: no countries can permanently thrive at the expense of others. Their huge expenditure on defence has already begun to produce the usual result; food prices rose seriously (10–20 per cent) in the United States for the first time in 1966, and about the same time anxiety about bread prices began to be felt in Britain. By 1961 the British and Dutch peoples already had less than half an acre of farmland apiece. The new British Government plan for the London overspill encroaches seriously on farmland. Strange new problems are arising in the attempt to feed our swelling population. The new 'animal factories' for meat and poultry involve the drastic crowding of our domesticated animals. Hens have been crowded so densely that they had to have their beaks cut off to avert continuous lethal fighting (a fact which need not surprise us after the accumulated evidence we have already considered on the effects of crowding). A recent report to the British Government has made a number of recommendations about minimum densities for poultry, pigs and cattle: as often, the British people are ready to tackle any problem first in terms of animal welfare. The concern is practical as well as humane. The British pathologist Joan Taylor has suggested that present conditions of meat production and distribution are liable to lead to an increase in salmonellosis (food poisoning). Nor, with all this food production effort, are we quite as well-fed as we supposed until recently. In January 1967 the British physician Geoffrey Taylor reported signs of malnutrition in as many as 40 per cent of the seventeen-year-old army recruits examined by him in the previous two years. Other sources indicate that children in the poorest British families have a diet seriously deficient, on average, in calories, protein and calcium.

When all this has been taken into account, the fact remains that food shortage in the 'affluent' societies is not yet the major problem it has been in many past population crises, or in the present crisis in the developing nations. In considering population density and violence in the 'affluent' societies, we must turn our attention from food to another kind of problem, more obviously related to our study of affluent monkey crowds: the problem of *housing*.

2

The densities we have been discussing so far are averages for large areas. Enormously higher densities are, of course, attained

in cities, as is shown, for instance, in the following list of densities
(number of people per square mile):

United Kingdom	550	London	25,000
United States	49	New York	32,000
Japan	650	Tokyo	40,000

The most densely populated city in the 'affluent' world is the
city of Paris, with 80,000 people per square mile. This degree of
density appears sufficient to produce appreciable effects on
parental behaviour. According to a recent estimate, more than
half the children admitted to Paris hospitals are not ill; their
parents simply do not look after them.

The cities of the hydraulic civilisations (the developing
countries of today) attained even higher densities; it has been
estimated that the Iraqui city of Ur, in the second millennium
B.C., was twice as densely populated as modern Paris. They have
no doubt always had housing problems, and some of them have
spectacular housing problems today. In modern Calcutta, 17
per cent of the population have no homes at all, another 15 per
cent live in shops and a further 30 per cent are housed at three
families per room. But in these societies problems of housing
have always been combined with recurrent problems of food
supply.

The first example of a major population crisis in which food
shortage played no part occurred in the city of Rome, in the
first half of the first century B.C. Rome had taken over the food
policy of the later Greek city-states; the government paid heavy
subsidies to the shipping corporations who imported food, and
supplied the citizens with flour or bread at fixed cheap prices,
or even for nothing: by the middle of the century, 320,000 Romans were getting their staple food free. The population in that
century was enormously swollen by freed slaves (whose parents
had come from all over the known world); for any slave freed on
certain territories became a Roman citizen. Unlike classical
Athens, the city of Rome provided very little industrial employment (it made all its money by exploiting its empire); but the
immigrant masses could make a modest income by selling their

votes at the frequent elections to offices of state, and by forming
paid mobs for purposes of political intimidation. The attractions of cheap or free food and small graft payments caused
Roman citizens to swarm into the city; by the mid-century, the
total population was nearing the million mark. The people
were housed in wooden skyscrapers, in indescribable conditions,
at the mercy of ruthless building contractors, and of slum land-
lords even less restrained than the worst ones in London before
the 1965 Rent Act. Here was a situation of ample food supply
combined with intense crowding, comparable with that of the
modern affluent societies or the monkey colonies in zoos. We
have no information on crime rates in the first century B.C., but
there is no doubt about the extent and intensity of violence.
Much of this was expressed in the dreadful systematic redirection of the Roman live spectaculars — super-colossal shows
where gladiators killed each other and slaves and criminals were
torn to pieces by live wild beasts. But neither bread nor circuses
prevented more straightforward violence, in this city of high-
density slum housing. Half a century of almost continuous revolution and counter-revolution, in which the two main political
parties alternately massacred each other, ended in the fall of the
Roman Republic and its free institutions, giving place to a one-
party dictatorship controlled by the business leaders of Rome
and the other towns of Italy. Freedom of speech disappeared,
and opinion was efficiently controlled by a propaganda machine
which busily rewrote Roman history.

The new one-party government dealt ruthlessly with the
Roman population problem. Now that it had won, it had no
further use for mob violence. The dictator Julius Caesar, with a
stroke of the pen, reduced the free bread list from 320,000 to
150,000, and settled 80,000 of the disqualified citizens in colonies abroad. His successor Augustus removed the Roman monopoly of elections by establishing polling stations all over Italy:
there was in any case less opening for graft now that everybody
voted a one-party ticket. The live spectaculars were expanded
and made ever more colossal. Finally, in A.D. 64, Rome was de-
cimated by an appalling fire. It was widely believed that the

Emperor Nero had started the blaze, using fire in much the same way the priests of Shurrupak had used flood. After the fire he employed intelligent town-planners, who rebuilt the city in brick with maximum density regulations. During the century that followed, Rome was noticeably less violent and government became noticeably more liberal, until Rome became involved in the wider population crisis of the Roman Empire.

In modern times, the connection between high-density slum housing and violent crime rates has been evident again and again. When 800,000 Irish emigrants fled from Ireland in the 1840s, to escape the appalling famine there, they were able to find food in the United States and Canada. But most of them went to the cities, where they immediately formed terribly congested slums; many if not most were forced to live in cellars. At Boston, one cellar 18 feet square and 5 feet high was occupied by eighteen persons; the normal number of occupants of a cellar ranged from five to fifteen. A return from the Clerk of the Boston Police Court for 1848 illustrates the result. The document is summarised in a recent account of the Irish famine by the British historian Cecil Woodham-Smith. 'During the previous 5 years, complaints for capital offences had increased 266%, attempts to kill 1,700%, assaults on police officers 400%, aggravated assaults committed with knives, dirks, pistols, sling-shot, razors, pokers, hot irons, clubs, iron weights, flat irons, bricks and stones, 465%.'

When different areas are compared in the same period, those with worse housing conditions regularly show higher rates of violent crime. The number of persons per room varies considerably between geographic districts of the United States, and rates of violent crime vary accordingly. In 1951 the murder rate was eight times higher, and the aggravated assault rate nearly eighteen times higher, in the poor, badly housed South Atlantic region than in relatively affluent and well-housed New England. McClintock and his colleagues (p. 30) made a detailed study of the incidence of crimes of violence in the various police subdivisions of London in 1950, 1957 and 1960. The high rates in

1950 were sharply localised to 'black-spot' districts of dense bad
housing, such as the Kilburn and Harrow Road area and parts
of Stepney. It was established that the criminals generally lived
in the areas where the crimes occurred. As the population of
London increased, these areas became still more densely populated, and showed a continuous increase in their violent crime
rates. Meanwhile other areas, such as Notting Hill, where density was increasing rapidly, also became black spots. Even in
Harrow and Uxbridge, where housing conditions were less slum-
like, increasing density brought increasing violent crime rates.
However, a number of suburban areas near the green belt retained a fairly low density throughout the three years examined,
and there was no sign that violent crime was spreading into
these districts. The greatest increases took place in the original
black spots, where the housing situation was getting worse and
worse. Over Britain as a whole in the fifties, violent crime was
increasing chiefly in the large and medium-sized towns. Between 1950 and 1958, juvenile delinquency increased by 124
per cent in towns of more than 100,000 inhabitants each, while
in smaller towns the rise was only 28 per cent. In the United
States, suburbia has become the main scene of increasing population density; people are moving out of the largest city centres.
Accordingly, in 1964, American crime rates increased by 8 per
cent in the countryside, 9 per cent in the big cities and 17 per
cent in the suburbs.*

Only two detailed studies appear to have been made on the
effects of rehousing on juvenile crime rates. The British sociologist J. H. Bagot studied the Liverpool housing estate of Norris
Green in the 1930s. The occupants had come (in the late 1920s)

---

* On 5 September 1967, Gordon Cherry, working in the city
planning department at Newcastle, reported at a British Association
meeting the result of a comparison of the most and least crowded
thirds of that city. The most crowded third produced more than 5
times as many offences against the person, more than 4 times as
many larcenies, 7 times as many people on probation, 3 times as
much juvenile delinquency, and more than 5 times as many cases of
neglect of children, as well as 5 times as much venereal disease and
43 per cent more prenatal deaths.

from some of the worst slum districts of Inner Liverpool. The
young people who had lived more than about seven years of
their life in the slums had the usual slum rate of delinquency
even in their new surroundings. But those whose families had
moved when they were very young, or who had been born on
the estate, had delinquency rates far below the average for the
whole of Liverpool by 1936. By the 1960s, according to another
British sociologist, J. B. Mays, Norris Green 'is now widely accepted as a normal lower-working-class neighbourhood with no
unusual social problems'. Even more rapid improvement was
obtained on a housing development at New Haven, Connecticut,
where delinquency among 649 youngsters was studied by the
sociologist N. Barer and the statistician F. S. Chapin. Within
four years of the families moving in, their juvenile delinquency
rate had halved, though the rate for the region as a whole was
rising. Both these housing estates, naturally, had both lower
densities and better living conditions than the slums from which
their occupants had moved.

Against this background, the crime explosion in the 'affluent'
societies becomes completely intelligible. The great climb in
British crime rates began in 1955 — the very year in which the
birth-rate began its upward surge. Babies do not, of course,
swell the ranks of violent criminals as soon as they are born.
What they do effect at once is an increased pressure on housing.
In the United States, where the average population increase has
been nearly twice as high, the crime explosion has been correspondingly more spectacular (p. 31). The United States, unlike
Britain, faces no serious shortage of land for food production. It
does, however, already face a very serious shortage of water
(along with forty-three other countries, according to a recent
United Nations survey). The urban areas on the East and West
coasts are already feeling the pinch: in the drought summer of
1965, the water-supply system for New York was nearly half-
emptied, and restaurants in the city were forbidden to serve
water unless it was specially requested. Water is necessary not
only as a food and for irrigating crops, but also as a component
of housing: the serious American housing riots in the summer of

1966 were partly connected with the shortage of water for washing. But this is only one aspect of the American problem. Alike in Britain and the United States (and in north-western Europe), the central problem of the 1950s and 1960s has been the supply of adequate housing for the rising populations. It is above all through the density and quality of housing that *crowding* expresses itself in civilised human societies; and the 'affluent' societies of the modern world are in precisely the situation of the well-fed, crowded monkey colonies of the zoos.

Unless we can halt (and preferably reverse) our population increase, the race to house the growing millions is as unpromising as is, on the world scale, the race to feed them (p. 219). To grasp the pressure of population increase on housing, more aids to the imagination are required. At the present rate of population increase, in the course of the rest of this century, Britain would have to build a new Sevenoaks every fortnight, a new Wolverhampton every four months, a new Leeds every year, a new Manchester every eighteen months. And it has been estimated that, at the present level of population, a quarter of a million new houses every year are required *for replacement purposes alone*. We have seen how the American building programme actually fell off in 1966, as a result of the Vietnam war (p. 115). There are indications that private building in Britain is likely to decline by the end of 1967. At the same time, there is a steady decline in the quality of housing from the point of view of crowding and social space. According to a survey by the Co-operative Building Society, published in November 1966, Britain's new homes in that year had less floor space and fewer bedrooms than in 1962, though they cost much more (only 28 per cent cost less than £3000, compared with 65 per cent in 1962). Since 1952 British governments (of either party) have tended to accept, in town-planning schemes, densities of over 50,000 persons per square mile, more than twice those previously considered desirable by governments and still considered desirable (according to a recent review by the geographer R. H. Best) by the people who have to live in these estates.

Density in human housing is, admittedly, a more complicated

affair than the density of monkeys in zoo enclosures. The number of people per room may be more important than the number of people per square mile. In 1951, the murder rate was four times as high, and the aggravated assault rate more than six times as high, in the South Atlantic than in the Middle Atlantic region of the United States. The latter region had more people per square mile, but it had considerably fewer per room. In McClintock's study of violent crime in London (p. 223), some suburban areas with relatively high densities per square mile had few crimes of violence. It is obvious that certain qualities of housing can mitigate stresses of crowding that would otherwise develop at a given moderate density. Clearly, for instance, sound-proofing enables people to live closer together than would otherwise be tolerable. Noise is one of the major stresses of crowding in modern human societies. Its relation to violence has not been investigated, but some of its other effects have been known since the beginning of the 1930s; the level of noise in a busy London street at *that* period was already enough to increase the energy expenditure of a typist working at a given rate by about 75 per cent, and to increase the errors in a telephone exchange by about the same proportion. It was agreeable to hear that in February 1966, more than thirty years after these experiments, the Greater London Council was considering a report that noise might be affecting the Londoner's health, though the report was optimistic, in our experience, in claiming that traffic noises in inner London faded out as early as one o'clock in the morning.

Sound-proof walls can blank out the noise of the crowd; suitably designed houses can give a sense of privacy; suitable town-planning can give opportunities for the satisfaction of other human needs. Obviously, if the population pressure continues, sheer density on the ground (persons per square mile) must rise so high that nothing can be done to make it tolerable. But while we are solving the main problem of reducing our populations, it is important to determine how best to dispose people at any given density. Planners and architects in some London districts (such as Lambeth), for instance, are finding that equivalent

densities can be attained without the use of the skyscrapers that
mar other new estates. There are certainly plenty of objections
to 'high-rise' (skyscraper) housing, notably the difficulties of
mothers with young children and the lack of play opportunities
for older children (p. 195). One London magistrate is reported
to have observed succinctly that, in his experience, juvenile delinquency 'varies directly with the distance of the family's flat
from the ground'. If we are to keep to an absolute minimum the
stresses that lead to violence, we have to find out a great deal
more about the manifold needs of human beings, and the ways in
which they can be satisfied.

After food, the most obvious need of human beings is the need
for bodily comfort. In hopeless conditions, people can lose much
of their awareness of this need,* but the underlying stress must
remain. When the technical facilities are available for providing
the various comforts of life, it is natural enough for people to
want them, and feel frustrated if they cannot have them. A
BBC television programme in 1966 followed the route and the
conversations of a party of modern pilgrims to Canterbury.
These pilgrims talked much along the way of the evils of the
affluent society, of people's increasing materialism and greed
for money. The leader of the party, Malcolm Muggeridge, asked
one silent young man whether he, too, shared the deplorable
urge to be wealthy. He admitted he would like to be rich. Muggeridge asked him why. The young man explained that he
would like to have hot running water in his dwelling, a luxury
he had never enjoyed in his life. Natural human wishes of this
kind account for much of the 'materialism' which rouses indig-
nation in so many people who have had access to hot running
water all their lives.

Unfortunately, the pressure of population increase makes it
more and more difficult to provide enough housing of ordinary

---

* For instance, in tropical districts infested with poverty and
disease, children permit flies to crawl over their faces, without attempting to brush them off; this can be watched in many a television
documentary. Children never behave in this way, if they are still
aware of the difference between comfort and discomfort.

comfort, apart from the increasing density which comfortable housing might do something to relieve. The trouble with slum clearance is that the slum-dwellers have to be housed somewhere else, while the increasing population continually increases the demand for new housing (1·6 million new households were formed in Britain in the 1950s). It is rather like the problem of finding jobs for existing unemployed while more and more people are entering the labour market (p. 186). While slums are being pulled down, their occupants are increasing the demand, and sheer shortage begins to produce slums elsewhere: for slum conditions are themselves closely connected with crowding. All the work of the Victorian charitable trusts, clearing slums in London from 1845 to 1875, was sufficient to house only six months of London's population increase; the demand today is, of course, much greater. In the affluent, materialistic, gadget-ridden Britain of 1966, more than half the homes were without refrigerators. According to the American sociologist A. L. Schorr (publishing in 1964), over a third of the council houses in Liverpool lacked 'a reasonable number of power points', and could not therefore enjoy 'heating and other modern utilities'. But this is at the luxury end of the scale. In 1951, 850,00 British houses were reported 'unfit' by local authorities, but their standards were very modest: of those houses counted as 'fit', well over 1·5 million had no fixed bath, no wash-basin and no water closet attached to the building. In 1958, 29 per cent of British households had no fixed bath, and 28 per cent had no hot-water supply. In affluent London, in 1965, more than half a million families had no access to a bath. When the Katherine Buildings, Stepney, were opened in 1885, the British reformer Beatrice Webb observed that 'within these uniform cell-like apartments' there were no sinks or water-taps, and that the 'miscellaneous crowd of men, women and children' were obliged to use communal lavatories. In 1962 Katherine Buildings still had communal lavatories, and half the flats still had no water-taps.

In the United States, according to Gabriel Kolko (p. 34), 'from 1937 to 1953, when it lost momentum, the public housing programme razed only 200,000 "slum" dwellings.... in many

instances ... they have been pushed into other slums to make
room for the middle and upper income groups that will occupy
the new, high-rental apartments built on the old site'. In 1960
an American Census Report described 3 million housing units
as 'dilapidated', and another 8·3 million as 'deteriorating'. Of
the remainder, 3·8 million lacked a lavatory, bath or running
water. In Kentucky, Tennessee, Alabama and Mississippi, 40
per cent of all housing was 'dilapidated'. In 1965 New York
had at least 100,000 families on the waiting-list for new homes;
they were *officially* described as 'living in hovels'. Words like
'dilapidated' and 'deteriorating' do not perhaps adequately
evoke the conditions they describe. In 1963 the American journalist Edgar May was acting as a caseworker in the course of his
valuable investigation of welfare conditions in the United States.
He describes his visit to one particular dwelling on Chicago's
South Side. The first thing he saw when he entered the kitchen
was a large wire basket filled with loaves of bread, hanging from
the ceiling by a string. The occupant explained it was 'on account of the rats. I can't leave nuthin' on the table. At night
they gets right on that table'. The occupant had tried traps, but
'that one rat, he was so big he drug that trap right under that
tank. I killed it with a stick. ... Them things will run right over
your foot. ... I am so nervous from those things I ain't sleepin'.'
   Slum conditions are generally accompanied by crowding in a
fairly obvious sense. In London in 1965, 7 per cent of all households were living at more (often much more) than three people
per two rooms. The need for bodily comfort is straightforward
in principle; and the frustration of this need, in the conditions
of British and American housing, goes far by itself to account
for the crime explosions. The need for territory or social space requires more discussion. It can be quite a complex matter, even in
lower animals, as appears from some experiments published in
1958 by the Dutch zoologist Jan van Iersel. The male three-spined
stickleback, a little fish, sets up a territory during the breeding-
season, within which he builds a nest. He admits a female long
enough to obtain eggs, which he fertilises, and he then rears the
eggs by himself in the nest. If another male enters his territory,

he will attack; if he encounters another male outside it, he will flee. In natural conditions, sticklebacks build their nests in streams abounding in water-plants. Van Iersel found that if he put a row of plants in a stickleback's territory, provided it was more than thirty centimetres from the nest, the owner promptly treated it as the boundary, cheerfully resigning the area beyond it. (This happened only if the stickleback had a neighbour; otherwise he was only mildly reluctant to cross the new border.) The same effect could be achieved by inserting two small bundles of bicycle-spokes, placed far enough apart to leave a passage between them. The important thing, therefore, was to have a boundary *marked*. The fish's aggressiveness towards intruders fell gradually with increasing distance from the nest, but dropped quite suddenly at the boundary. If the boundary was present before the nest was built, the fish chose a nest-site as far from it as possible. The effect of the marked boundary reminds one of the chalk circles drawn round their bodies by ex-prisoners (p. 58). It suggests that, in the fixed territories of human civilised societies, higher density might be tolerated if boundaries of ownership are clearly marked. This accounts for the importance, in relation to crime rates, of number of persons *per room*. But it might have many other useful applications in house and town planning, and would be a fruitful subject for research. Even in the stickleback experiments, however, there was clearly a minimum size of acceptable territory (a radius of thirty centimetres around the nest).

There is an abundance of evidence, of various kinds, for the human need for territory, social space, privacy, freedom from continuous social stimulation. In the late 1940s Swiss psychologists discovered that the mental health of children in institutions showed a substantial improvement, if each child had a clearly marked area of personal ownership. In the open prison at Ford, in Sussex, some of the prisoners have single rooms. According to the British journalist Charles Lyte, who visited the prison in February 1967, 'probably because this is the first time many of the men have had a decent room of their own, they go to great pains to make them cosy and intimate with curtains, pot-plants and extra pieces of home-made furniture'. In the grounds, they have little private patches of garden, and on these some of them build miniature green-houses from pieces of scrap. To have a territory of one's own seems, indeed, a necessary condition for appreciating that other people have similar needs. When people have little or no privacy or personal territory, small groups of them behave astonishingly like monkey zoo colonies. In 1964 the British zoologist and behavioural scientist Ewan Grant studied small groups of patients in a mental hospital, having their lunch-break together in a room with a one-way glass partition. Some of the groups had an unstable dominance hierarchy (as in the extreme zoo conditions), but some had a hierarchy very clearly marked. The ranks could be measured, exactly as in animals, by the number of times each patient showed aggressive or timid postures (previously worked out) in encounters with each other patient. In the group studied most closely, the three members of the establishment moved around together, separated from the rest by a regular social space, exactly like the three leading rhesus monkeys at Regent's Park (p. 90). The nurse occupied a special position as a super-leader, and any patient near her acquired a high dependent rank, like a consort (p. 91). Patients would attempt to use her against each other, in gambits of diversion and protected threat, without overt pseudosexual elements, but otherwise exactly like those seen among monkeys (pp. 131 ff.). Among the low-ranking patients, cut-off postures (p. 122) were common, including that of curling up in a chair as if to sleep. (We have seen this posture in ordinary social situations, when a person feels under threat but unable to leave the gathering.) A low-ranking patient would show great reluctance to approach one of higher rank, and might walk back and forwards several times before circling the superior to get to some objective.

In every society where it has been possible to be both rich and independent of social pressures, the wealthy have always chosen to live in uncrowded conditions, with plenty of space indoors and out. R. H. Best has described a recent survey of the homes of *architects*. 'It revealed that the great majority reside in anything but the high-density dwellings they are frequently so keen on designing for other members of the community; indeed, as many as 20 per cent of the total actually lived out in the country with a surfeit of private open space around them'. Even at work, all who can achieve it like to have their own offices, with their names clearly marked on the doors. Some enlightened architects and officials (for instance in the Lambeth district) are beginning to take the revolutionary step of asking people what they want *before* planning the estates where these people are to be rehoused; and social surveys of this kind are being conducted by an increasing number of bodies. The latest Rowntree Trust Housing Study indicates that more than 80 per cent of households wishing to move expressed a preference for a house as against a flat. A Greater London Council housing committee report in 1966 stated that 75 per cent of applicants preferred a house with a garden. A house, of course, provides much more clearly marked *boundaries* of ownership than can be obtained in a flat, particularly a skyscraper flat, and people, like sticklebacks, prefer this sort of demarcation. A social survey carried out by the Ministry of Housing and Local Government, reported by Joan Ash, discussed the problems of housewives interviewed on high-density estates in recently redeveloped areas of Liverpool, Leeds and London. An overwhelming majority expressed a preference for living in a house; in their present dwellings, they complained of insufficient space, inadequate play facilities for children, too much noise and lack of privacy. Paul Leyhausen is almost certainly right in claiming that 'what every normal man wants for himself and his family is a detached house in an adequate garden, with neighbours close enough to be found if needed or one feels like a social call, yet far enough away to be avoided at other times'.*

* In a recent broadcast interview, Leyhausen enlarged on the importance of timing in this connection. Commenting on the fact that cats will stay close together at times, and at other times keep well apart in their territories (p. 57), he remarked that 'we invite guests to our home, at some times, but we certainly would be very astonished to find one of our guests about two o'clock in the morning at the hall of our home uninvited, lounging around there — any one

Both aspects of this relationship with neighbours are important. Sociologists in the past have been much puzzled by the reluctance of people in crowded slums to accept rehousing, or the
related phenomenon of crowded citizens spending their holidays in packed sea-side resorts, when quiet beaches are available
near by. Resistance to being moved is often a resistance to being
pushed around by planners who do not consult anybody's
wishes; it may also involve a fear of unfamiliar surroundings,
and this can also apply to holiday habits. People's awareness of
the need for privacy (as of the need for comfort) can become
blunted, though the need is there and its frustration must cause
stress. What little shreds of familiar territory have been acquired
then become indispensable, not to be given up by moving to
strange new quarters. But a more general reason for these puz-
zling reactions is the need for company, or neighbours, and the
fear of finding these necessities lacking on lonely beaches or,
more seriously, on unfriendly new housing estates.

The need for neighbours is evident even in highly territorial
animals, and makes sense in terms of mutual protection against
fresh intruders, or against predatory enemies. Cat neighbours
like to go hunting together: on the Welsh farms where he studied
them (p. 55), Paul Leyhausen found it 'usual to see two or
three cats hunting within 30 to 70 yards of each other ... although rabbits seemed to abound everywhere'. In man, the

---

of us would probably feel very differently than he would have done
a few hours ago when this same man or woman was invited.' He drew
attention to the temporary nature of human fairs, markets and similar festivities when people are free to disperse again when they
choose.

In the same interview, he gave several examples of the human
need for territorial privacy, 'all the more obvious in over-crowded
communities of prisoners-of-war. When, for instance, such prisoners
were suddenly released into a new camp, you could observe a rush
of the men to the single huts or tents, and within the huts a rush for
certain cots, and immediately after that each one started to fence off
a certain part of the floor space left, with string or pieces of card-
board or whatever was at hand, and thus defined their individual
territories.' Compare Andreski's observation on prisoners in transit
camps (p. 58).

need for company can be very powerful, and can even override the need for privacy, especially if some degree of crowding has been present for generations. The Irish emigrants to North America are a case in point. Back in Ireland, one of the more humane landlords, Lord George Hill, found his Donegal tenants unwilling to accept new and better houses if this meant separation from neighbours. In North America, where farmland was incredibly cheap, the great majority of the Irish immigrants preferred to stifle in the indescribable city slums (p. 223). One of the few who made it as a farmer, in Missouri, provided the explanation. He had worked in Ireland for sixpence a day; in Missouri he had land, stock, no rent, light taxes and social equality; yet he regretted his Irish life, where, after work, 'I could then go to a fair, a wake or a dance, or I would spend the winter nights in a neighbour's house, cracking the jokes by the turf fire. . . . But here everyone can get so much land, that they calls them neighbours that lives two or three miles off — och the sorra take such neighbours I would say'.

The need for company and the need for privacy have not always been easy to harmonise in human societies, even among the privileged. In the huge country houses of the eighteenth-century British aristocracy, each member of the family sat in his or her room, separated by long corridors from the others. The privacy was ample, but the need for company was so frustrated that 'silent companions' were necessary: two-dimensional pasteboard figures, covered with paper likenesses of servants, and cut out to shape; they are still to be seen in some of the stately homes today. On the other hand, eighteenth-century German princelings, caught up in curious aberrations of social pressures of custom and upbringing, might show behaviour fully as absurdly gregarious as that of the crowds at modern sea-side resorts, or more so. A case in point was the week-end cottage of the Duke of Pfalz-Zweibrücken. In 1777 a relative of his mistress wanted to sell one of her farms. The Duke was taken to see the place. The peasants paraded in their Sunday best, and served up delicious butter and cream. The weather was fine, the courtiers admired the view, the court physician praised the climate. What a delightful place for a quiet retreat! The next day, the Duke (who had bought the farm) summoned his architect. The farm stables must be enlarged, the rooms altered, decorated and furnished, a cottage built for the farmer and his people, the grounds properly landscaped. In a few weeks, a village of workmen had gathered on the site, in specially built huts. At first the Duke drove over for afternoons, but later he wanted to dine in his country home. This required a new kitchen wing and a huge dining-room. One thing led to another, and gradually the farm grew, until the Duke was living there permanently. By 1786 it had become a town, with stables for 1000 horses, kennels for 1000 dogs, quarters for equerries, grooms, keepers, cooks and servants; a subsidiary palace for courtiers, officers, doctors, chaplains and gardeners; a picture gallery and library, a theatre, a zoological garden and barracks for 1400 men. Without gaining him anything in the way of personal privacy, the Duke's country retreat had cost him seventeen times the annual income of the Duchy.

For well-to-do people in modern societies (like successful architects) it is not too difficult to obtain both privacy and company. But unfortunately high-density housing can combine all the disadvantages of loneliness and crowding, producing what the American sociologist David Riesmann has called a 'lonely crowd'. In the cramped flats of the most densely populated city of the Western world, modern Paris widows sit with silent companions more macabre than those of the eighteenth-century British nobility — scale models in wax of their late husbands. In the skyscrapers of high-rise housing estates, while privacy is daily invaded by disturbance and din, sociable relations between neighbours are difficult to develop, wives work alone in their flats all day, small children above the fourth floor cannot be allowed out for fear of accident, and mope by themselves indoors. Company is thus another need more and more liable to be frustrated in the conditions of modern population pressure.

Finally, besides the needs for food, comfort, privacy and company, there remain even less tangible needs, by no means fully explored yet, but certainly impeded and thwarted in many ways by crowded conditions. Even animals need interests and activities, things to see and do. Canyon mice, offered alternative treadmill wheels for exercise, choose the ones that require the greatest agility and skill. Rats flourish and put on more weight when given a loose ring of wire as a toy. Monkeys will solve difficult problems when the only reward is the opportunity to look out of a window or play with apparatus. Chimpanzees, given the chance, will spend hours painting for pleasure. The needs of human beings for interests and activities are much more powerful. Well-meaning parents, rightly anxious not to frustrate their children, are sometimes led to believe that children only need to have things, not to do things. An observant mother of our acquaintance had been giving her baby a bunch of grapes, and letting him cut himself small twigs. Once, when she absent-mindedly cut a twig herself and gave it to him, he burst out crying. He had wanted the activity of cutting himself a grape, not so much the grape itself. Hence, when children are immediately given every material *thing* they appear to ask for, they may still be frustrated in their need for activity: they will then show resentment, which is liable to be misinterpreted as some form of innate aggressiveness.

Crowded zoo monkeys suffer from a lack of their usual interests and occupations, so abundantly provided in the long daily excursions of wild monkeys in search of food (p. 89). Human beings in the affluent societies are continually deprived by population pressure of opportunities for play and constructive activity. The process begins early, and continues throughout life. The population crisis causes a shortage not only of teachers (p. 188) but of those qualified to look after younger children. In Britain, there were 1500 day nurseries in 1945, and only 472 in 1961. This led to such scandals as the child-minder in north London who kept babies entrusted to her in garden sheds, and left slightly older children in front of an open coal fire with no guard. Absence of day nurseries and the conditions of high-rise housing can obviously combine to deprive a small child of any play in the company of other children. Shortage of teachers in

Britain meanwhile is beginning to push up the age for starting school. At school, population pressures have still other unfortunate effects. A New York educationalist, asked how to reduce delinquency in an overcrowded slum, suggested more parking space for the school-teachers' cars; it was accordingly decided to reduce the school's playground by more than a quarter of its area, to make room for the cars. It is the intrusion of traffic and parked cars that has deprived children of play areas in some London high-rise estates. In 1965 a Greater London councillor suggested that schools in the London area should give up their playing-fields, so that the land could be turned over to housing. School-work itself is rendered difficult for the children by their crowded classes, due in turn to the shortage of teachers; by 1965 West German industrialists were complaining that most young Germans leaving school were only half-literate. In Britain in the same year, more than two million primary school-children were working in classes of thirty-six or more. Violet Frieslich, who has been specifically studying aggression among young London school-children, confirms the impression (widespread among teachers) that children quarrel far less in classes of twenty than they do in classes of forty. Class-room and playground crowding can evidently combine to increase the tensions. In January 1967 British journalist Vanessa Lederer visited a London school where, in their breaks, the 275 children occupied a concrete playground 'no larger than half a netball court', with fast trains racing past one end. 'Please, Miss,' asked one little girl, 'can we have two playgrounds?' Differences between schools have been shown to produce big differences in delinquency rates, even in the same area (ranging from three to twenty court appearances per hundred boys aged 12–14 during two years, in one east London borough).

Finally, for those who reach university, crowding and population pressure continue to frustrate needs for interest and activity; they can have a brutalising effect, so that awareness of the needs may be reduced, while the stress of frustration remains. With the help of sociology students at the University of Reading, British sociologist Martin Albrow made a study of the activities of students in halls of residence (where they can get both privacy and company) and in lodgings (where privacy is restricted and opportunities for company are less varied). Thirty-two students in each situation were studied, carefully matched for sex, age, study subject, type of school, achievement at school, grant income, social class, parents' education, religious and political views, career plans and number of brothers and sisters. The two groups showed striking differences. Hall students had more conversations about academic subjects, attended more society meetings, read more non-fiction books, spent more time in private study, entertained visitors of the opposite sex more often, talked more with other students on general subjects, had more dates, attended slightly more lectures and made more detailed plans for activities during the vacation. Lodgings students, appreciably deprived of all these activities, resorted much more to cinema visits and team games. Some of them were still keenly aware of their frustrations. Eleven of them said university life had fallen below their expectations (compared with three of the hall students); sixteen of them wanted to live in halls (compared with two hall students who wanted to live in lodgings). But they were obviously being forced into a kind of 'mass culture' (as it has been called), both lonely and indiscriminately gregarious. Housing deprivation on a greater scale can evidently lead to the kind of mass culture developed in Rome in the first century B.C., where the first commercial use found for the new invention of blown glass was the mass-production of mugs stamped with the name of your favourite gladiator. Mass culture of this kind greatly facilitates mass redirection of all the resentments generated by the other stresses of crowding — whether the redirection takes the form of Roman circuses, persecution of minorities or mass support for aggressive war. With this and all the other consequences of population pressure, the wonder is not that the affluent societies have rising violent crime rates, or that the one with the most desperate problems (of water, housing and employment) has supported the cruel war in Vietnam. The wonder is that human beings in these societies still have so much capacity for tolerance and human feeling. Man is, after all, the most

sociable of all beings, and the first who can hope to solve for ever
the terrible problem of violence.

3

When Stanislav Andreski was working out his theory of revolution and war as alternative responses to population pressure (p.
172), he was interested to come across the observations of Han
Fei-Tzu, a Chinese writer of around the fifth century B.C. In
former times, before the coming of agriculture (wrote Han Fei-
Tzu), 'without working there was enough to live, there were
few people and plenty of supplies, and therefore the people did
not quarrel. . . . But nowadays people do not consider a family
of five children as large, and, each child having again five children, before the death of the grandfather, there may be twenty-
five grandchildren. The result is that there are many people and
few supplies, . . . so the people fall to quarrelling, and though
rewards may be doubled and punishments heaped up, one does
not get away from disorder.' As we have now abundantly seen,
this admirable conjecture came very close to the truth. Crises
and violence must indeed have arisen before agriculture, but
with the coming of settlement and large towns and civilisation,
there came periodic crises of enormous scale, in response to repeated pressure of population. Sometimes the populations outran food resources, sometimes, like the affluent Western baboons
observed by Hans Kummer (p. 149), they outran the production of housing while food was still abundant. In either event,
the pressures of crowding produced that complex sequence of
inequality, tyranny and violence which we explored in the history of Europe. We have seen, too, that the present crisis is
world-wide, and more serious than ever before; and that, because of nuclear and other modern weapons, a full-scale outbreak of violence today, far from preserving our natural resources, could irretrievably destroy them. Violence, then, can
no longer be tolerated on any account. At the same time, man
alone has the power, by intelligent planning and research, to

regulate his population growth by birth-control, and thus to make violence for ever redundant.

To solve this problem, the most momentous that man has ever faced, much research will be required. To begin with, we have to determine, in terms of human needs, what population figures to aim at. Automation requires a small total amount of man-power, and it is probable that we should aim at reducing the world population, not merely stabilising it at its present level. The British population was over fifty-four millions by 1966, and would, at the present rate of increase, at least exceed sixty millions by 1981. In September 1966 the President of the British Association for the Advancement of Science, Sir Joseph Hutchinson, recommended for Britain, as an ultimate target, the figure of forty millions. This target was based on considerations of land use for recreation as well as food production; it took into account water-supply and industrial pollution; and it appears reasonable at present from every point of view. Similar targets need to be worked out for other countries, and given wide publicity; they may, of course, need continuous revision in the light of ecological research and technological change. Above all, we need much more information about the effect of different densities on the supply of all kinds of human needs, and about the exact thresholds at which stresses become sufficiently severe to provoke violence. Meanwhile, we can only aim at halting population growth and reducing populations as much as we can.

Technical research and large-scale government action to facilitate birth-control are obviously a first requisite, including in particular the diffusion of information. Sir Theodore Fox, head of the Family Planning Association, has suggested that the prevention of *unwanted* pregnancies alone could give Britain a stable population. But the number of British families with more than five children increased by nearly 50 per cent between 1953 and 1960. It is doubtful if this increase was entirely the result of *consciously* unwanted pregnancies. If we are to reduce the population of Britain, it seems likely that the present trend towards large families will have to be reversed. Our problem is to change

patterns of breeding without infringing further on personal freedom, already threatened by the pressures of crowding (p. 193).
We therefore need much more information about the social and
economic factors which govern the breeding rates of civilised
peoples.

One approach to this large problem is to consider when and
where in history breeding patterns have occurred which led to
low birth-rates. In this connection, an interesting discovery has
been made by the British demographer J. Hajnal. He considered
a variety of kinds of evidence about the marriage patterns of
civilised peoples: recent census returns, parish records, medieval tax returns, grave inscriptions in the Roman Empire, and
particularly the marriage records of British royal and ducal
families, which cover a span of some six centuries. Hajnal was
able to show that there have been two quite different marriage
patterns. The 'early-marriage' pattern is found in north-
western Europe up to about the late sixteenth century A.D., and
in all other civilised regions throughout history. The 'late-
marriage' pattern appeared in north-western Europe around the
time of the late sixteenth century, and persisted there until about
1940; since then, the region has been tending to revert to the
old world-wide early-marriage pattern. In the early-marriage
pattern, both men and women marry young and very few people
remain single throughout life; in the late-marriage pattern, both
men and women marry late and a substantial number of people
remain single throughout life. The average age of women in
particular, at their first marriage, tends to be over 23, usually
over 24, in the late-marriage pattern, and below 21 in the early-
marriage pattern. Between the sixteenth and the mid-twentieth
centuries, north-western Europe tended as a result to have substantially lower birth-rates than the rest of the world has always
experienced.

The north-western marriage pattern in this period was not
only 'later' than usual, but remarkably flexible. Within the
whole period, there were two epochs when women married even
later and birth-rates were substantially lowered, at least in
Britain. The later epoch has long been well known: it is the

epoch of modern birth-control, stimulated by the writings of nineteenth-century pioneers like Francis Place, Charles Bradlaugh and Annie Besant. The early epoch has been revealed by an extremely recent discovery, using the method of 'family reconstitution' to make sense of early parish records — individual people, named in the marriage entries, are traced back to their own birth entries, so that average ages at marriage can be reconstructed. The discovery was made, by this method, in the parish records of Colyton, in Devon; search in other places has already indicated that Colyton was probably typical of much of England during the epoch. The news was first broadcast to the world in a talk on BBC radio (Third Programme) in January 1966, by the British demographer and historian E. A. Wrigley. The discovery was this. From 1560 to the mid-seventeenth century the average age at first marriage for both men and women was 27 (already in the late-marriage pattern). From the mid-seventeenth century to about 1720, the average age at first marriage for *women* rose from 27 to well over 29, so that brides were generally older than bridegrooms. More surprisingly, the demographic evidence makes it certain that married couples during this period were practising birth-control by some contraceptive technique (of unknown nature). This practise gradually ceased during the eighteenth century, and had died out precisely by the time Malthus wrote his first essay, which may account in some way for his silence on the subject (p. 153). Meanwhile the average age of women at first marriage fell again, reaching about 26 by the end of the eighteenth century, and 23 by the 1820s: this is at the low extreme of the late-marriage pattern. Between 1647 and 1719 only 4 per cent of first-time brides were in their teens; between 1825 and 1837, 25 per cent of such brides were teenagers.

Now we have seen that the mid-seventeenth century was the peak of a population crisis, while the later epochs saw an increasing relief by emigration and exploitation of the rest of the world (pp. 181 ff.). For four centuries, therefore, north-western Europe not only had a pattern of late marriage, but one which could be adjusted to population crisis by making marriage for

women even later and adding the further regulation of contraceptive birth-control. It is possible that this regulation helped to
make the seventeenth-century crisis, at least in England, less
devastating than that of the thirteenth and fourteenth centuries.
It is almost certain that the whole system was connected, in
many ways, with the great technological success of north-western
Europe in the modern period.

The reasons for the appearance in sixteenth-century north-
western Europe of a fundamentally new pattern of breeding are
still far from certain. But there is one factor which must have
been important, namely the nature of the family grouping. Anthropologists have devised very elaborate ways of classifying
family structures, but for our purposes we can make a simple distinction between mass-families and individual-families. The
mass-family system has been prevalent all over the world
throughout history, including north-western Europe up to the
Middle Ages. It may be illustrated by one of its more extreme
forms, the mass-family system of traditional China. In this system, close social and economic relations are found between all
people sharing a common great-grandfather, or even great-
great-grandfather, in the male line. This large aggregate of
cousins works as a social and economic unit. It provides social
insurance for the poorer members — so effectively that in the
United States, even during the worst of the Great Depression of
the 1930s, no Chinese immigrants had to apply for government
relief. It provides mutual protection in periods of lawlessness. It
provides employment for all members: in Canton, in 1950, out
of all the 20,000 industrial and commercial enterprises large or
small, about 94 per cent were mass-family businesses. On the
other hand, the system clearly provides little or no economic
freedom for individuals, except in some ways for the male who
happens at any moment to be the head of the mass-family.

This system promotes early marriage and high birth-rates in
two ways. On the one hand, a youth or girl can get married
with little or no income or capital of their own, for the mass-
family can support them and their children until their own contributions to the family wealth become considerable. On the

other hand, the older generations are insatiably eager for large numbers of children and grandchildren and great-grandchildren, to ensure their own support in old age, and make the whole insurance and employment system work. In China, this was symbolised by the urge to acquire children (particularly males) who could ritually support their ancestors in the afterworld. All marriages were arranged by the elders through go-betweens. To ensure a bride for their son as early as possible, many families bought infant girls and reared them till they could be married. The anxiety to marry sons as soon as possible was indeed extreme; a folk story records the pride of a man who, at the age of thirty-six, could show off a grandchild.*

In the larger civilised societies, the mass-family system has nearly always been arranged around the male line of descent; this is true for the whole of China and most of India, for instance. In China, the bride immediately counted as a member of her bridegroom's family: her own parents were not even invited to the wedding. The division of labour between the sexes was strict (it was one of the main principles of Confucius) and the status of women, particularly after a series of population crises rotted civilisation, could become extremely low. This was in itself another factor making for a high birth-rate. Among monkey societies where the status of females is low (for instance, among cynocephalus baboons), a female can only gain privileges by having young offspring: this will, for instance, permit her to move in the centre of a band (p. 60), and gain easier access to food. In a community under moderate stress, it may also protect her from threat and attack. Among the hamadryas baboons at Zürich, subordinate animals, under threat from superiors,

* In southern China, people even took 'daughters-in-law-in-anticipation', before their son was born, to make sure he could marry when he appeared. When the Chinese Government introduced divorce in 1950, a twenty-eight-year-old woman in Hupeh Province brought her eight-year-old husband in her arms to the divorce court. This particular practice might, of course, tend to reduce the birth-rate, but it certainly failed to counterbalance the general tendency to high birth-rates under the Chinese mass-family system.

I

would engage in 'pseudomaternal' behaviour, picking up a
younger animal and embracing it or giving it a piggy-back ride.
This no doubt began as a conflict activity, like pseudosex, but
it probably caught on because, to some extent, it worked: subordinates playing at being mothers were attacked only half as
often as subordinates by themselves. In a human society like
traditional India, where women are enormously lower in status
than their menfolk, their only protection from continual humiliation and ill treatment is the possession of children, particularly sons. It is no wonder that, to this day, when the population
pressures in India are so appalling, the trees are still hung with
the ritual offerings of women praying for children: in parts of
southern India, barren women lie in the street to be trampled by
a male priest, in a ceremony (all too symbolic of their social situation) which is believed to improve their chances of conception.

It is easy to see how the mass-family system tends to produce
early marriage for men and women, with few people single for
life, and hence a high birth-rate. Now the mass-family system
was clearly present in north-western Europe in the early Middle
Ages. The mass-family was treated as a unit for purposes of the
vendetta. At Sepulveda in Castile in the thirteenth century, a
man could literally get away with murder if he could prove that
the victim had previously killed somebody with the same great-
great-grandfather as himself (the present killer). In the early
Middle Ages, also, no contract of sale was valid if even the re-
motest member of the vendor's mass-family turned up afterwards to say he had not been consulted at the time: property
still belonged to the mass-family. One factor in the breakdown
of the mass-family in this region was certainly the attitude of the
medieval Church, which naturally did not want gifts and sales
to the Church by individuals to be repudiated later by their remote relatives. Property law was adjusted throughout the
Middle Ages, by a series of compromises (such as permitting
other members of the family to repurchase the property after the
sale at the same price), until by the sixteenth century the individual owned his own property for most purposes, and could to
a large extent dispose of it as he liked.

The attitude of the Church, though important, was not the only factor which in this one region tended to disintegrate the mass-family. The great French historian, Marc Bloch (murdered by the Gestapo in 1944), brought out a more fundamental factor. Among the Germanic peoples who set the tone of medieval north-western Europe, the status of women seems to have been unusually high. In this period and region it seemed perfectly natural for women to vote in plebiscites: at Provins in Champagne in the mid-fourteenth century, in a plebiscite to decide whose jurisdiction the town would accept, 350 of the 2700 voters were women. One result was that people could never quite decide which was more important, their father's line or their mother's. Naming practices reflected this indecision. In the village of Palaiseau in the ninth century, the peasant Teud-ricus and his wife Ermen-berta baptised one of their sons Teut-hardus (after father), another Erment-arius (after mother) and the third Teut-bertus (after both). At her trial in the fifteenth century, Joan of Arc said she was sometimes called Jeanne d'Arc (after her father) and sometimes Jeanne Romée (after her mother). The result of trying to work a mass-family system based on both male and female lines soon became chaotic, because the whole affiliation altered in each generation. In Beauvais in the thirteenth century, two sons of the same father by different marriages went to war with each other (with social approval) because of a quarrel between their respective mothers' families: a situation considered shocking by other civilisations. By the end of the thirteenth century, the system was being discarded as unworkable. Beaumanoir, who wrote at this time a kind of practical handbook on what you should do in a vendetta, admitted that in his day only second cousins, or sometimes only first cousins, felt obliged to avenge each other. As the mass-family system broke down under the strain of working out exactly what family each individual belonged to, its place was gradually taken by the individual-family of modern north-western Europe, in which the social and economic unit is essentially the individual, or at most the married couple with their children. Now this revolutionary new social arrangement had

obvious economic consequences, besides its enormous importance in developing the individualism that made possible the
modern age. If supporting a family was up to the individual, a
couple must wait to get married until the man had a high
enough income and the woman had saved up a sufficient capital
(in the form of a dowry). This situation would lead not only to
late marriage, but also to a flexible regulation of the birth-rate;
in times when money was hard to come by, like the late seventeenth century (after a price revolution), women would take
even longer to accumulate capital, and the married couple
would use birth-control to keep their family small. The decline
of the mass-family can thus account for the late-marriage pattern and all that it entailed.

The population problem of the developing countries of today
may therefore be solved when their mass-family organisation
breaks down. The Chinese Government have tried to achieve
this rapidly by a systematic onslaught. One can sympathise with
their attempt to destroy a system of cruel tyranny (especially for
women and the young), but such abrupt changes from above
are liable themselves to lead to violence. In a society under tension, sudden disruption of the existing hierarchy is all too likely
to lead to violent disturbance, as in the baboons at Regent's
Park (p. 41). In 1950, the year after it assumed control of China,
the Chinese Government introduced a set of Marriage Laws,
which simply provided for the ordinary rights of women taken
for granted in most societies of north-western Europe and the
United States: monogamy, married women's property rights,
facilities for divorce. The reaction of the long-established hierarchy was ferocious. It has been estimated that some tens of
thousands of Chinese women, who claimed their rights under
the new laws, were tortured to death by their husbands and
mothers-in-law, or forced (by threats of torture) to commit suicide. The government redoubled its efforts to destroy the mass-
family. Now that the first generation has grown up under this
struggle, the result has been the serious civil disturbances of
1966–7 between the Red Guards — teenagers, potentially very
destructive, torn out of the mass-family structure and uncertain

where to go next — and the more traditional older (especially male) communists, who approve of political action against land-lords but wish to retain the right to knock their wives about, or, more reasonably, fear that social changes are getting out of control.

In Japan, on the other hand, the disruption of the mass-family seems to be coming about more peacefully, through the provision of other kinds of social insurance. Six times between 1950 and 1961, the Mainichi newspaper chain asked a representative cross-section of Japanese: 'do you expect to depend on your children in your old age?' In 1950 more than 55 per cent answered 'yes'. The proportion giving this answer declined steadily during the period, reaching 27 per cent by 1961. The mass-family in Japan must evidently decline under these conditions, and in fact during this decade the Japanese birth-rate fell from 2·8 to 1·7 per cent. But even the peaceful disruption of the rigid family hierarchies, in this already desperately over-crowded country, has produced the potentially dangerous mass movement of Soka-Gakkai, which claims a following of millions. The American sociologist W. J. Goode has made a world survey of modern family patterns. Publishing in 1963, he concluded that the mass-family was already everywhere declining and giving place to the individual-family of north-western European type, under the impact of modern technical and social change. Mass movements, filling the vacuum, certainly constitute a danger, as will appear later (Appendix Four). But on the long term, it seems likely that the disappearance of the mass-family will go far to solve the population problem in the developing nations. The people of these countries have often turned out to be much readier to accept birth-control than anyone expected. The organisers of a birth-control campaign in Taichung (Formosa) in 1963 were pleasantly surprised to find that 20 per cent of the positive response came from outside the city, where no direct approaches had been made: the attractions of the new methods had spread by word of mouth.

There remains, of course, the serious problem of the renewed trend to early marriage, large families and high birth-rates in the 'affluent' societies. Now it is true that vestiges of the mass-family system remain in these societies, even performing a function. After disasters, such as floods, remote relatives from distant towns are apt to turn up and shelter victims who cannot immediately be cared for by the authorities. In the survey of elderly people in Britain in 1962 (p. 36), it was found that they depended very largely on family support: of those whose sole income was a retirement pension, for instance, 73 per cent were keeping house with others. 'Of course *I* live with my daughter — and she's a good girl', said one of them; 'I don't know how those on their own manage it.' Even those living alone, especially the poorest old women, received considerable support in money or food from their relatives. In spite of this, there seems little doubt that the 'affluent' societies are still firmly based on the individual-family system. The problem is, therefore, why do people now marry early and have large families even under this system?

The new trend seems to have developed first in the United States, where half of all women marrying for the first time were under twenty years four months by 1950. In Britain it developed chiefly during the 1950s. New pressures towards large families must therefore have set in at about these times. This is a problem for future research, for which no simple answer has yet been found. Clearly we have to look for pressures to produce mass labour, like those which operated in the hydraulic civilisations (p. 211), but in a new form; and this just at the time when automation promises to make mass labour, and all the inequality it entails, permanently redundant. These new forces may be connected with the huge expansion, at precisely the same times, of consumer credit based, not on capital (like a dowry), but on future income, which tends to produce a form of wage-slavery. It is possible that something like the mass-family is appearing in the new form of certain kinds of organisations employing large numbers of people.

Our analysis of population crises in animals and man has suggested that, if the population problem is not solved, nothing can avert nuclear war. But in spite of all the difficulties, there is no

reason to believe that, given sufficient effort, we cannot solve the
problem. Already beginnings have been made and local suc-
cesses achieved. Throughout world history, Japan has been re-
nowned for efficiency in adopting and adapting the innovations
of other societies. In this matter, however, the Land of the Rising
Sun has given mankind a welcome lead. Public education has
been so effective that by 1959 only 8·8 per cent of Japanese dis-
approved of birth-control, and nearly half the married women
under fifty years old (46·8 per cent in the cities, 40·8 per cent in
rural areas) were using contraceptive methods. Between 1948
and 1961 the birth-rate in Japan fell from 3·4 per cent to 1·7 per
cent. More limited success has been achieved even by some of
the developing regions: the birth-rate in Puerto Rico dropped
from 4·2 per cent to 3·4 per cent between 1947 and 1956. In
Britain the Royal Family has performed its now usual function
of leadership in social progress: in November 1964 the Duke of
Edinburgh made a public speech on the importance of birth-
control. The British birth-rate actually went down slightly in
1965. Ever since the loss of so many men in the First World War,
French governments have been concerned with maintaining the
population of France; but in 1966 all political parties became
aware of public demand (especially among women) for birth-
control, and government policy began to change accordingly.
In Australia, the birth-rate was reduced from 2·2 per cent in
1962 to 2·05 per cent in 1964. Similar achievements have been
made in some Communist countries, notably Czechoslovakia,
and the Chinese Government, after twice changing its mind,
appears to be seriously promoting birth-control. In 1965 India
prepared a £70 million plan for reducing her population. In the
United States in 1965, the Supreme Court overrode as unconstitutional a State law of Connecticut against birth-control. The
United States Federal Government has so far been less active
than most others in promoting birth-control; but when it does
make a serious effort, its great capacity for large-scale planning
may be expected to produce rapid results. Altogether, there are
signs everywhere of an awakening of public and official interest
in the population problem. In India, true, the position is so

desperate that only very large-scale help by the rest of the world
is likely to avert very high death-rates from famine and/or violence. But, for the world as a whole, the problem seems far from
insoluble, given a great effort of research and action; mankind
has solved many other serious problems in a long and difficult
career.

Even the complete regulation of populations, even the discovery and satisfaction of all the complex needs of human beings,
may not immediately eliminate all trace of violence. Past stresses
continue to operate for several generations, and this lag must
leave, for a time, many residual tensions. The sudden disruption
of long-established inflexible hierarchies may facilitate the
growth of mass-movements which are a particularly dangerous
response to population crisis. There is need for serious considera-
tion of the means of controlling violence during this transitional
period. These three problems could each be the subject of a
large book: they are glanced at in our last three appendices.

But, from all the evidence we have considered, the problem
of violence is fundamentally the problem of population, and if
we can solve the one we can solve the other. Birth-control can
make violence redundant as a means of regulating our populations. All the complex needs of man should not be hard to discover and satisfy in a world equipped with modern technology.
The possibilities for social progress and creative living, in a
world freed from unskilled monotonous toil by automation, and
freed from stress by regulated population growth, are scarcely to
be imagined. The renaissances of the past non-crisis periods
could be eclipsed by the abiding splendour of such a civilisation.
The choice before mankind is a choice between paradise and
hell on earth, between a holocaust worse than any in history and
a prospect of continually increasing happiness for all, such as no
past age had the resources to offer. It lies in our hands to make
the third millennium A.D. the Millennium; to enter at last into
that peaceful paradise earned by so many centuries of hard-won
technical and social progress; to write a happy ending to the
troubled story of violence, monkeys and man.

I sail to an appointed tide,
Where time does never wait,
A crested wave, an awesome ride,
Emprisoned freedom's fate.

I fly above the clouds of snow
To meet the morning sun —
I meet the blood-stained evening glow . . .
The ride's not yet begun.

Among the spring and autumn leaves
I read of love and woe,
Of hour hands that creep like thieves;
Rare flashes come and go.

Summer's temptation's rich and green,
Cold-shouldering winter's bare . . .
At fever pitch — what have I seen?
Asleep — am I aware?

I drift to an appointed tide,
Where time does ever flow;
A nightmare abyss opens wide
As down and down I go.

Enough! Today I am awake,
I'm sailing with the tide —
Astride a crested wave I'll break
Free from that fateful ride.

*

Appendices

One/Violence, Hunting and Man

I T is widely repeated, and quite untrue, that human beings are more cruel and destructive to each other than are other animal species. The massacres on Monkey Hill (p. 41) or the merciless treatment of Bruce (p. 104) are sufficient to illustrate the violence and cruelty of which monkeys, no less than man, are capable under the stresses of crowding. Konrad Lorenz has told of two doves caged together in too close confinement: one of them plucked and flayed the other alive, feather by feather, wound by wound, until Lorenz returned to the cage and parted them. If animals under stress do not use the rack and the stake and the bomb, it is only for lack of technical equipment.

Those who accuse man of greater violence than monkeys often argue that man is inherently more aggressive because he is a hunter, whereas the monkeys are peaceful vegetarians. Specialisation for hunting is supposed to have left man with an innate or inherent aggressiveness, so that he can never have societies as peaceful as those of monkeys in the wild. There are two further fallacies underlying this argument.

Man's teeth, like those of monkeys, are the teeth of an omnivorous animal; they lack the shearing blades of the carnivore. The contrast of man as hunter with monkeys as vegetarians is, to say the least, very unsatisfactory in itself. Jane Goodall has reported that chimpanzees, so peaceful in the wild, are capable of catching, killing and eating small monkeys. All monkeys are food-gathering opportunists, ready to vary their diet in any way they can. For something like 90 per cent of his time on earth, throughout most of the Old Stone Age, for over a million years, man was a food-gatherer little better equipped than the monkeys. It has been shown that his crude stone 'hand-axes', though useful for butchery, were useless as missile weapons for big game: they will not even kill a calf. He was a snapper-up of unconsidered trifles, fruits, seeds, the odd small animal: if he did diverge from the monkeys, it was in a tendency to extend his foraging range, following the tracks of the real carnivores, mobbing them off, and grabbing what he could of the carrion. Thus do the Hadja people, in Tanzania, to this day, watching vultures to find and scavenge lion's kills. But the bulk of his diet was certainly vegetable matter, 75 per cent of it according to one estimate, like that of many 'hunting' tribes today (70–80 per cent among the Australian aborigines, 80 per cent among the Kung Bushmen of southern Africa). As the British anthropologist M. J. Megitt has put it, 'this "vegetarian" stress seems to be one of the prime distinguishing features of hunting, fishing and gathering economies'. It was only for what is, by comparison, a very short period (some 50,000 years) that man, in the late Old Stone Age and Middle Stone Age, lived to a large extent by hunting, with much more efficient weapons than his ancestors had possessed. Even then, fishing was often as important as hunting or more so, women probably concentrated entirely on collecting vegetable food, and it was precisely those societies which placed most emphasis on fishing (which leads to settlement) and plant food-collecting (which leads to agriculture) that gave rise to the huge populations of settled, farming, civilised man. For the last 10,000 years or so, mankind has been overwhelmingly vegetarian, subsisting largely on plant crops; millions of people to this day never eat meat at all. It is therefore far from clear in what sense 'man is a hunter'.

At certain stages of human military history, hunting had enough techniques in common with warfare to serve as a training or exercise for it; hence military aristocracies have generally practised, and often tried to monopolise, the activities of the chase. But there is certainly no evidence that social violence has been more prevalent or intense in carnivorous hunting than in vegetarian agricultural societies. Nor is there any evidence of the contrary relationship, to suggest that agricultural communities, frustrated in their drive to hunt animals, have hunted each other instead. There is simply no relationship at all. Hunting peoples have sometimes been extremely warlike; but no human group has produced more peaceful communities than some of the

Eskimos, who have been carnivorous hunters, presumably, since the later Old Stone Age. Agriculturalists show a similar range between peaceful and warlike extremes. Cannibalism (with or without murder) has also been practised by societies of all kinds of diet and economy, either under food shortage (as frequently in the population crises of civilisations) or, afterwards, as a ritual maintained by other forms of stress. Whatever their diet or mode of procuring it, the amount of violence in human societies is always related to the amount of stress, as we have tried to show by abundant examples in this book.

Animals inflict injury or death upon each other in three situations. A predatory animal will naturally attack its prey. A prey animal, in defence of itself or its young, may attack a predator. Finally, an animal may attack another (of the same or a related species) *which exploits the same natural resources* of food, shelter or the like. It is this third, competitive, kind of attack which we commonly call aggression, and we have used the words 'aggression' and 'violence' throughout the book in this restricted but quite usual sense. Now, from all that we know of animal behaviour, the two drives of hunting and social attack seem to have been kept strictly separate by natural selection: there are obviously good reasons for this. Even when animals, under stress, cannibalise their young, there is no evidence that they are using the behaviour patterns of hunting; behaviour of this kind is related to something quite different (pp. 163 ff.). There is no evidence whatever from the behaviour of mammals that social violence is more prevalent or intense among carnivores than among herbivores: in both alike, it is a function of stress and especially crowding (Chapter Five). Everything suggests that social violence was evolved in relation to population control, a problem faced by carnivores and herbivores alike. The evidence from human and animal societies alike makes it clear that, whether or not 'man is a hunter', there is no reason for this to influence his social behaviour. We can confidently expect that those conditions in which space abounds and all needs are satisfied, which produce peaceful societies of monkeys, can also produce peaceful societies of man.

Two/Violence, Ants and Man

THE higher mammalian societies are based on low fertility, and fundamentally individualistic in character, with a high valuation on the life of each individual (p. 54). The starting-point of their whole social organisation is the crucial pair of needs which each individual shows — the need for privacy or social space, and the need for company. Territory, relative and absolute hierarchy (pp. 55 ff.) are all responses to the problem of balancing the needs of individuals, and the whole complex of violence, as a means of reducing excess population (Chapter Five), is operated by the stresses affecting each individual. Given ample space and resources, the whole system is designed for the safety of the individual and the peace of the community.

The social insects represent a system diametrically opposite to this in every way. They are adapted to a phenomenally high fertility, and behave as if they were frozen in a never-ending population crisis. They are a kind of orderly pests. A highly evolved ant or termite society is exceedingly populous, although only a very few of its members breed. The rest are divided strictly for life into labour castes, each with its specialist role. Insect caste differences extend even to bodily form. There are termite societies in Africa and Australia containing millions of members each, with as many as eight distinct castes. The queen of such a society may be 20,000 times the body volume of a proletarian termite, and may lay as many as sixty million eggs in a life of ten years.

A community of this kind is more like one giant organism than it is like a collection of individuals. Non-breeding workers or soldiers (the overwhelming majority of the community) are replaceable and expendable, and the evolution of such communities has placed no value at all on individual life. Because it is so populous, an ant society requires a foraging area enormous relative to the size of the nest. If another community (of the same or a related species) appears within the area, the outcome is liable to be total war, with compactly drilled task forces despatched on definite missions, regardless of casualties. Relatively few elaborately social ant species have survived, for a grim reason. In the early stages of their evolution, such societies are vulnerable to determined attack by more advanced ones. When an advanced ant species (*Pheidole megacephala*) arrived (in a man-made ship) on the island of Bermuda, it found a bigger but socially less organised ant in occupation (*Odontomachus haematoda*). The invaders built up a ring of posts round the beaches of the island. Then, gradually but systematically, they narrowed the circle, entering the nests of the native ants and patiently exterminating them.

Other ants have found a different use for organised war. With equal thoroughness and system, they enslave their closely related neighbours. By comparing a series of distinct living slaver species, we can reconstruct the evolution of such a society. The story begins with a species that raids its neighbours to steal their offspring. The raiders return with the grubs as food for their own young, storing some for future consumption. Some of these happen to grow up, and settle down as labourers in the raider community. Another species raids its neighbours in a similar way, killing any that resist; but when the captive grubs are brought home to the raiders' nest, most of them are reared as slaves (an easy transition from the first situation). Their duties include construction work, caring for their masters' young and especially taking over and rearing the next lot of grubs of their own species to be captured and brought in. When the masters move to a new nest, they literally carry all the slaves along with them. The logical next stage is found in yet another slaver species. This ant is specialised wholly for war, with jaws which are useless for foraging and only good for crushing the heads of their victims, adult neighbours who are trying to protect their young. These slavers live in idleness. They are fed by their slaves, and will starve in the presence of food if no slaves are around. In this society the slaves have taken over the job of nest-moving. They select a new site, excavate a new nest and carry the slave-holders into it. These warrior slave-holders require and obtain far more slaves than the first two species we considered. The next stage is represented by a species with similar weapon-shaped jaws, but such feeble muscles that they can only use their jaws for threat. To capture fresh supplies of slaves, they train earlier slave batches (obtained by bluff) as janissaries (slave soldiers); the slaves now do most of the fighting as well as all the work. Finally, a species is found which must have gone through all these stages to the final stage of decadent effeteness which is the nemesis of slave-owning. They can neither work, fight nor even threaten, but continue to be reared and fed in thriving communities of their ex-slaves, as mere parasites. Since slavers at this stage are extremely rare, it may be conjectured that they are finally liquidated as superfluous rubbish by the ex-slaves, leaving a perfectly normal community of ants — though indeed, from the point of view of an ant, there can be no significant difference between being a slave in another nest and being a worker in one's own. Such is the logical evolutionary outcome of exploitive war.

Not surprisingly, aggressive behaviour in an individual ant is quite unrelated to its own needs and situation, and instead governed by simple rules related to the intolerance of the community as a whole. Since no ant individual is concerned to preserve its own social space, no ant individual holds territory or acquires rank in any kind of hierarchy. There are no individual territories and no individual ranks; and no quarrels between individuals over social space. The British zoologist D. I. Wallis has studied the behaviour of guard ants of the species *Formica fusca* at the entrance of a nest. Towards ants coming from the interior of the nest, they show virtually no aggression at all in any circumstances. Any ant approaching the nest, even if it is a resident that has only been outside for less than a minute, is likely to be examined and threatened. It is treated as guilty (of being an alien) until proved innocent. If it is in fact an alien, it is savagely attacked and dragged away from the nest. The pass-port seems to be a particular odour, to which the community is accustomed, and which aliens will not carry. The passport de-vice is obviously liable to abuse. Slave grubs, reared in their masters' nest, become conditioned to their masters' smell and show them complete allegiance. On the other hand, the Ameri-can zoologists C. P. and E. F. Haskins isolated sections of one ant community from each other long enough for their smell to change, and found they became permanently hostile to each other. However, in principle, the whole system of ant aggression is clearly designed to ensure complete peace within the nest and merciless hostility to all potential rivals of the community as a whole. There could not be a more complete contrast with mon-key bands, more prone to internal dissension than war (p. 161), or human communities, oscillating between civil and foreign conflict, and requiring every encouragement of mass redirection to make them engage in warfare (pp. 110 ff.).

Since the *Book of Proverbs* was written ('go to the ant, thou sluggard'), many people of an orderly turn of mind have lavished admiration on the ant society. But in fact this warlike totalitarian system is rigidly specialised, and highly resistant to innovation. Bodily caste differences are found in ant fossils some fifty million years old, so the ant form of social organisation must be even older. A few ant societies have achieved rudimen-tary forms of agriculture and stock-raising. Human societies of comparable complexity are less than fifty thousand years old, and if you seek *their* monuments, look around you. Man has ad-vanced so much further and faster because his social behaviour is fundamentally of the individualistic mammalian kind (pp. 54 ff.), with great potential for individual variability and flexible behaviour. It is true that population pressures, especially in the hydraulic civilisations (p. 209), have repeatedly produced super-ficially ant-like traits in large human societies, suggesting many parallels;* but these have always been transient, and always

* The high valuation on the individual in mammal societies is based on the protracted parental care of individuals (p. 54): both trends reach their culmination in man. Under population crisis, as

disrupted by the fundamentally mammalian needs of the individual human beings within them. Given room and resources, freedom and peace are the natural heritage of man.

---

we have abundantly seen, parental care and regard for the individual break down together. The prolonged latent crisis conditions, in the densely populated hydraulic societies (p. 210), could thus somewhat suppress (though they could never eradicate) human individualism.

Three/Violence through the Generations

WE have seen that the whole complex of violence, in response to stress, is designed to produce effects over several generations, thus reducing the population long enough to permit complete recovery of natural resources (p. 157). In animals as socially simple as voles or musk-rats, this many-generations effect is probably limited largely to physiological disturbances (p. 158). In animals with appreciable amounts of parental care (including even mice), a further many-generations effect can be produced, by means of disturbances in the upbringing of the young. The stress, which causes some parents even to kill their offspring, causes others to bring them up with some degree of neglect or hostility, and the effects of such early experience lead to violence in the next generation, who in turn bring up their own young with inadequate or distorted parental behaviour. It is to be expected that this stress effect would gradually diminish after removal of the original stress, and finally fade out altogether. The Biblical estimate, that the stresses and violence of parents are visited on their children 'unto the third and fourth generation', may not be far out. If this were not so, the non-crisis periods in human history would be just as violent as the crisis periods, whereas we have seen that they are appreciably less violent (Chapter Five). This may give us reason to hope that, if we do solve the population problem for good, the residual violence will gradually diminish and fade out, provided we can adequately satisfy all the needs of a reduced world population. The results of the rehousing experiments (p. 224) strongly support this conjecture, for in each case, after a lag, delinquency did decline in the rehoused families. But in the history of human civilisation up to the present, many stresses have been almost continuous, and the major stresses of the population crises have recurred again and again, often at relatively short intervals (for instance, the non-crisis period of fifteenth-century Europe was only two or three generations long). There has therefore, up till now, been no opportunity for complete recovery, and no age has been completely free from violence.

The stresses to which civilised societies have been exposed in history are of many kinds. They include all the stresses of the crisis periods, including famines, epidemics and wars: for, by a vicious cycle, the disasters of war can often produce further violence. They also include natural disasters, which in any case hit a crowded population hardest. Each such stress can produce all the characteristic effects of the violence complex, including mass redirection and the breakdown of leadership selection. According to Dr Hachiya, Director of the Communications Hospital at Hiroshima, within a couple of weeks from the fall of the atom bomb, 'the ruthless and greedy were ruling the city'. The Hundred Years War in France and the Thirty Years War in Germany produced appalling outbursts of private crime. Thucydides, who observed the pestilence in fifth-century Athens, and medieval observers of the Black Death, agreed in noticing the terrible effects of epidemics on social behaviour and family life. The Black Death was the immediate occasion for the great *pogrom* of the fourteenth century (p. 197). The Great Fire of London in 1666 led to delayed mass redirection against Catholics (accused, certainly falsely, of having started it), and prepared the ground for the witch-hunt against Catholics which developed a few years later. After the ghastly earthquake and fire of Tokyo in 1923, there was a massacre of Korean immigrants (500 according to the Japanese government of the time, 6000 according to Korean sources). The devastating effects of this fire were partly due to crowded housing, and form part of the story of population crisis in Japan which put militarists in power and led to the Far Eastern part of the Second World War.

A dispassionate review of the famines, epidemics, wars and other disasters, suffered by civilised man within a few hundred generations, will remove much of our astonishment and incomprehension at the spectacle of human violence. It will make us,

rather, marvel at the persistence and even progress of human
social institutions and human personal feelings, which can still
make their presence felt even during the most acute stresses, as
observers of all these disasters have also recorded. If man does
differ from all other animals, it is certainly not in being more
aggressive (p. 257); it is rather in his exceptional capacity for
positive social relationships. And this, of course, is obvious on reflection; for man is unique in the length and amount of parental
care he must lavish on his children, and in the development of
true language, the greatest of all innovations in social behaviour.
Nevertheless, every one of the stresses, to which civilised man
has been exposed, must have had its effects on succeeding generations.

Whenever a society is exposed to any kind of stress, the children (as in animals) are particularly vulnerable. Psychological
tests, given to children, are extremely revealing of the condition
of any society. One such test, commonly used, is to show pictures and ask the children to make up stories about them. The
American social scientists T. Alexander and R. Anderson did
this with children of a community of Cheyenne Indians in
Montana. The community was badly housed, undernourished,
heavily afflicted with tuberculosis, and could generally be described as living in a rural slum. One of the pictures showed 'a
small boy . . . seated in the doorway of a log cabin. His elbows
rest on his knees and his chin on his hands'. A typical story,
produced by a fourteen-year-old boy in this community, was as
follows: 'Once there was a log house. A little girl live in it. Her
father die when she was a little baby, then her mother starts
another man, then her stepfather make a log house, then her
stepfather die, then she got no father, then about in two years
then her mother die. Now she is sitting outside, worrying about
her mother and two fathers. That's all.'

Stresses experienced in early life, either directly from the surrounding conditions, or indirectly from parents themselves
under stress, can produce permanent effects. In the Liverpool
rehousing study (p. 225), we saw that those youngsters, who had
lived for more than seven years in the slums, continued to show

slum delinquency rates. In 1960 the British statistician L. T. Wilkins made an extremely ingenious study of crime-rates among young people of different age-groups. He found that there was a special tendency to crime among those who had passed their fifth year of life *either* during the Second World War *or* during the early 1930s when the Great Depression was at its worst. In the case of disasters earlier in history, we can trace effects over several generations. In 1909, more than sixty years after the Irish famine of the 1840s, there was still enough bitterness among some of the Irish in Canada to induce them to set up a monument on Grosse Isle, in the St Lawrence River, to the immigrants who had died of disease on this quarantine island 'while fleeing from foreign tyrannical laws and an artificial famine'. Indeed, vivid memories of the famine are preserved in many Irish families to this day.

While many stresses may be experienced directly by children, the more fundamental effect is produced indirectly. The parents are under stress, and their treatment of the children is correspondingly affected, as in animals, all the way from neglect to competition, domination, attack and killing. These processes are fundamental aspects of the whole violence complex (p. 163). Since the children, when they grow up, may have *their own parental behaviour* permanently affected, they can pass on the original stress to a third generation. In this way, violence may still be present in a family generations after the original stress. In some of the cases of battered children studied in America (p. 165), the parents who attacked their children were socially and economically reasonably well off. In such cases, it was generally possible to find that the parents had been beaten up by *their* parents in early childhood.

The permanent effects of early experience, and the transmission of stress through the generations, have been demonstrated even in animals. The Belgian psychologist Eliane Beniest studied mice reared in various ways, making a complete biography of each animal. She found remarkable differences in personality between them, which could be related to their experiences in early upbringing. Mice reared by an aggressive parent were highly aggressive themselves; isolation at particular stages led to sustained aggressiveness later on; and the most aggressive mouse of all, Othello, had had a traumatic shock at fourteen days of age, just when his eyes opened for the first time: alarmed by a radio suddenly switched on, he leaped from the observer's hand to the floor, where he was chased all round the room by a cat. Aggressiveness was measured by readiness to attack intruding adults. The seven mice which were most aggressive in this sense also regularly tended to kill infant mice placed in their cages. Those who would sniff at an intruding adult, before deciding to attack him, behaved similarly to the infants; those who, so to speak, shot first and asked questions afterwards, also instantly killed infants as soon as they were placed in the cage. Othello was 'extremely cruel' to the infants he killed, biting them savagely. Three mouse mothers also killed their own young. Two of them had been disturbed by the camera and lights used for filming. The third, highly aggressive and regularly killing strange infants, killed her own young in a fit of straightforward redirection: placed in another mouse's territory, she was bitten by the owner, whereupon she 'fled and arrived near her nest, where she roughly fell upon the infants and killed two before we could remove her from the cage'.

Further insight comes from the studies of the American psychologist Harry Harlow and his colleagues, on rhesus monkeys. A number of these monkeys were reared from birth in isolation in separate cages, each deprived of all social contact with his mother or any other monkeys. Some of them were supplied with imitation mothers in the form of crude robots. These isolated monkeys behaved rather like human extreme schizophrenics. They sat in their cages, staring fixedly into space, circled the cages in a stereotyped routine, or clasped their heads in their hands and rocked back and forth for long periods of time. Sometimes they developed compulsive habits, like pinching themselves in the same place hundreds of times a day; occasionally, they even bit or tore at themselves. When placed with other monkeys they either ignored them completely or fought;

aggression seemed to be the only kind of social behaviour they developed.

This very severe condition could be completely prevented, or cured if isolation lasted not more than eighty days, by giving the young monkeys some time every day in a well-equipped play-room where they could play *with each other*. For the development of social behaviour in monkeys, it seems that the presence of mothers or other adults is not vitally necessary. The vital requirement is the play-group (p. 71), in which peaceful hierarchical arrangements and friendly relationships can be developed. Evidently this cannot be true for human children, who need very much more care and education by adults — they need, for instance, to be taught to talk. Nevertheless, the monkey experiments do suggest that nursery-schools may play a very positive part in human social education, and that children deprived of adequate play with others of their own age may suffer severely. We have seen that this kind of isolation may arise for small children in high-density, high-rise housing (p. 236).

Equally striking were the results of rearing by mothers in various conditions. A mother monkey and her son were caged together for seven months, and so were another mother and her daughter. Then the cages were put near together, and small doors were opened in them, so that the two young monkeys could come out and meet each other, while the mothers could not. In three months of observation, the boy monkey never left his mother's cage. The girl monkey sometimes did come out and approach him, but the boy's mother always drove her away by threats, and would not let her within arm's length of her son. When later placed together in a play-room, the two youngsters showed no social behaviour except mutual threat; they were almost as lacking in social response as the isolated monkeys. Normal monkey mothers defend their offspring from strangers only when they are very small babies, when it serves a function of protection. But evidently a very unhealthy relationship had developed between the mother and son in this experiment, because of the mother's isolation from adult neighbours. The son was several times seen to mount his mother, always in a pseudo-sexual manner. This experiment may also have considerable bearing on human social behaviour. Human mothers and sons may be caged together in isolation to a rather considerable degree in certain social conditions, associated with certain kinds of housing development — for instance, again, the upper floors of high-rise estates, as well as certain kinds of suburb.

A few of the motherless females, reared in isolation by robots, were finally impregnated by very experienced and persistent normally reared males. Each of them was observed with her offspring in an isolated cage, but the young were allowed some facilities for play with each other: it probably saved them from the worst consequences of their mothers' behaviour. For these motherless mothers treated them with anything from indifference to violent aggression, so much so that they would certainly not have survived outside the laboratory. They ignored them completely whenever they could. The young monkeys showed an ineradicable urge to approach their mothers for feeding and comfort, but every time they did so they were brutally beaten. Two of the mothers finally passively permitted their young to suck, but hit them or crushed them to the ground even more savagely than the other mothers, whose babies had to be bottle-fed. Doubtless because of their opportunities for play with other youngsters (like human children in street gangs), these young monkeys proved capable of some social behaviour later. But they played less, tended to be exceptionally aggressive, and showed precocious pseudosexual activity. They could fairly be described as juvenile delinquent monkeys. Experiments of this kind show clearly how violence in one generation may be a consequence of stresses experienced in childhood by the *previous* generation. The situation on shipboard of the monkeys transported from India to Cayo Santiago (p. 105) combined many of the stresses in these experiments. Each mother was confined separately with her young, and the mothers were under such stress that some of them killed their babies. It is no wonder that the next generation, on the island, showed a great deal of violence and permitted the rise of an aggressive dictator (p. 106).

In a wild animal community that is not under serious stress, the very young are not treated as competitors, and therefore have no need for rank in the adult hierarchy. They are treated with tolerance and permitted to share social space. At adolescence, they enter into the hierarchical system, like the young Japanese monkey males who are sent out of the court and become cadets on the periphery (p. 64). If there is no serious stress, this need not cause them serious hardship. But in the crowded colony at Whipsnade, the transition could be a painful one. The four-year-old male Tom was just becoming adult during the study by Reynolds (p. 102). At first, Henry tolerated Tom's youthful exuberance, but there came a time when he began to regard the young monkey as an adult. He then turned on him, supported by Dick, and severely attacked him several times. Tom was so upset that he 'wailed loudly' for several days. This strange call is apparently uttered by rhesus monkeys when some painful change in their social relationships has occurred — for instance, by a mother whose infant has died. For Tom, the passage from being a young monkey to being an adult of low rank was clearly a time of stress. In a human society under stress, the time when a young man becomes a member of the adult hierarchies may be a similarly disturbing period. He is passing at once from a tolerated and protected position to the lowest of ranks in a harsh world of social tensions. This change normally hits the teenager who starts to earn his living. In Britain, the number of married women at work increased by 39 per cent between 1952 and 1962, to a total of one wife in three. Nowadays, girls, no less than boys, must expect to enter tense adult hierarchies at adolescence. This may account for the findings of a Home Office report, published in 1966, on young women in prisons. Many of these teenagers, according to the report, 'do not wish themselves to become adult' and have a wish to be supported. Like Tom at Whipsnade, these girls must be mourning their lost childhood, unable to tolerate the tensions of the adult hierarchies into which they are plunged.

When an animal community is under very severe stress, even the very young are no longer accorded special tolerance: they are treated as competitors of the lowest possible rank, as we saw particularly clearly in the white-tailed deer (p. 163). Instead of being permitted to share social space, they are treated as intruders, and, as we have seen, this can go all the way to killing them. In a human society under stress, there are similar tendencies for parents to treat their children as intruders and rivals, inevitably of the lowest possible rank (often emphasised by the legal rights of parents) and therefore fitting objects for redirection of all the resentment aroused by stresses outside the family. People are sometimes puzzled by the violent aggressiveness of individuals who, as adults, appear to enjoy ample food and room, every kind of comfort and high social status. One explanation, of course, is the fact that even the high-ranking members of a community under stress are never free of tension: they feel their privileges threatened, whether they are Henry of Whipsnade or Henry VIII of England. Another explanation comes from the lasting effects of early experience, and the inevitably low status of children in any family under any kind of stress. A prince or the son of a millionaire may have a high dependent rank outside the family, like the son of a Japanese monkey matriarch (p. 66); within the family, his rank must be low. When he was nominally King of England, young Edward VI was kept short of pocket-money by one of his uncles and had to beg for tips from the other. In monkeys or man, age-classes are the oldest and most fundamental kind of class. The Roman slave-owner and the twentieth-century colonialist both called their servants 'boys'. The Celtic word from which 'vassal' and 'valet' are derived originally meant 'young boy'; the Scandinavian word 'dreng' had a similar history. Whether they enter the hierarchy at adolescence, or are driven into it at birth, the young are always the lowest in rank, with all the tensions this entails: and the effects of these tensions must persist during the life of the individual.

The greater the stresses acting upon the parents, either in the present or back in *their* childhood, the more their true parental relationship with their children, tolerant and protective, will be distorted by relations of dominance. The simplest expression of

this is for parents to redirect against their children the resentment aroused by pressures outside the family (as in the case of
the mouse mother who killed her young). To the extent that
dominance relations prevail in it, the family may be analysed in
much the same way as a colony of zoo monkeys under stress,
with all the resulting complications. Brothers and sisters, for
instance, may redirect against each other the resentment
aroused in each by threat on the part of the parent, who may
encourage this process by some form of diversion. Or, just as a
people may redirect resentment against foreigners, so children
may be caused to redirect resentment against those outside the
family. We have tried to explore the ramifications of dominance
relations in the family, in our book *Human Behaviour: a New
Approach.*

In a monkey society under stress, adults are liable to impose
pseudosexual activities on the very young, who are treated as of
very low rank. At Whipsnade, Henry sometimes held down a
one-year-old infant with one hand, on its side or back, and
played with its genitals with his other hand. In the human
family, the presence of dominance tensions must result, sooner
or later, in personal conflicts and hence pseudosexual involvements for the children, including involvements in sadism and
masochism (p. 131). Family backgrounds vary widely, and some
human individuals are much more prone to violence than others.

Research into the relations between family background,
pseudosex and violence is barely beginning. But something, at
least, can be said about the most extreme case of all, the case
of the mass-murderer, and his place in society, thanks to an
extremely illuminating book, *Murder for Profit,* published in 1926
by the imaginative but unfortunately short-lived writer William
Bolitho, South African by birth, British by nationality, French
by domicile. Bolitho made a detailed study and comparison of
five famous mass-murderers: William Burke, an Irishman executed in Edinburgh in 1829 for the murder of a number of
people whose bodies were sold for medical research; Jean-Bap-
tiste Troppmann, an Alsatian executed in Paris in 1870 for the
murder of a family of eight persons; George Joseph Smith, exe-

cuted in 1915, who had drowned at least three brides in baths; Desiré Landru, executed in 1921 in Paris for the murder of an unknown number of women; Fritz Haarmann, executed at Hanover in 1924, after the murder of probably at least twenty-two teenage boys, whose flesh he not improbably sold as meat. From Bolitho's work a kind of pattern emerged; there were common features in the lives of these men. The discoveries of Bolitho are fully borne out by the stories of more recent mass-murderers, such as Marcel Petiot, executed in 1946, who killed a large number of Jewish refugees in German-occupied Paris, taking all their property, after promising to help them escape from France.

The mass-murderer seems to begin with a terrible kind of parental neglect early in life, which leaves him with some of the characteristics of an isolated rhesus monkey: he has no responses at all to fellow human beings except aggression. The point is vividly illustrated by Smith, who constantly aroused suspicion by his mean and callous behaviour after each murder; as Bolitho points out, he could only have done his dreadful work by thinking of his brides, not as human beings, but as business operations. The mass-murderer's father tends to be a petty, unsuccessful businessman or official, his mother intensely resentful. In adolescence, the mass-murderer tends to drift about from job to job; often, he has a spell in the army. He is almost never a skilled specialist worker of any kind. Inevitably, he tends to become a petty swindler: this is the feature most commonly found. He enters, in Bolitho's words, 'that large class of unspecialised, sharp individuals to which, along with a tremendous majority of persons inoffensive to the life of their fellow-creatures, our mass-murderers clearly belong'. This career encourages his callous sense of human beings as business projects, his conceit in his own cleverness, his fantasy that his survival is always in danger and the only thing that matters. From second-hand clothes he can move on, like Burke, to second-hand bodies. At some stage, feeling by this time he can get away with anything, he gets away with murder. The act always has the qualities of a pseudosexual orgy. At first it is intensely secret, but as the exercise is repeated the mass-murderer increasingly loses all touch with reality, and retreats into his fantasy world. The last murders of Burke and Haarmann, for instance, were committed with only the most perfunctory regard for the risk of discovery. Once on trial, the mass-murderer shows the extreme poverty of his imagination, born of some terrible poverty of colour and interest in his childhood; his lies are repetitive and based entirely on the fantasy which has driven him. In court, in fact, he appears again as the petty swindler.

His activities, and the very possibility of his career, are closely connected with the state of society. Burke and his colleagues were backed by a leading medical man; their work was the result of senseless restrictions on the supply of corpses for medical research. The police of the Weimar Republic, coping desperately with a chaotic society and violence of all kinds, were driven to use characters like Haarmann as spies; his official position made his murders possible (he collected stray teenagers from the railway station in his role as police official). The greater horror of Nazi proceedings in German-occupied Paris supplied Petiot with a stream of victims. More subtly, the background of tension and violence in a society provokes and stimulates the mass-murderer to his work, as its most extreme expression. The violent summer of 1966 in the United States, marked by riots in several cities, also produced a terrible mass-murder, the stabbing and strangling of eight young nurses in a Chicago hostel, on 14 July. The murderer must have been stimulated by the mounting tension in the city, for the very next day the most serious Chicago riot broke out, in which three people were killed and at least fifty injured.

The most terrible outbreak of violence in history, the rise of Nazi Germany, had two famous mass-murder trials to usher it in. The murders of Landru had occupied almost exactly the period of the greater killings of the First World War. In 1919 Clemenceau's French government seized on his trial as a heaven-sent distraction from the deals they were engineering at Versailles, which did so much to ruin Germany. Clemenceau instructed the police and the magistrates to 'cherish the Landru case': the result was a court packed with press and spectators, and astonishing scenes like the moment of his sentence, when 'at precisely the right moment the photographers fired their illumination. There was a great glare of light over him. From every part of the massed hall arms protruded upward with black boxes, cameras which aimed at him . . . One man . . . actually succeeded in leaping to one of the advocate's benches, and stood there, hilarious, with opera-glasses to his eyes, greedily scanning the lost criminal's expression.' This was in November 1921. Three years later, the trial at Hanover of Haarmann, who had practically run a private extermination camp in one room (and who probably worked on the side for one of the right-wing terror movements), provided a fitting introduction to the age of the Nazis, when a mass-murderer, who obligingly fits all the specifications we have drawn up, became the absolute ruler of a modern industrial nation.

Four/Violence, Rats and Man

ANY approach to the problem of human violence must deal with the greatest of all violent outbreaks — the career of Nazi Germany. From this episode, two major facts stand out. First, even with the Nazis already in power and in control of the police, in 1933, the German electorate gave the Nazi Party only 43·9 per cent of their votes.* This will dispose immediately of any muddled ideas about the inherent aggressiveness of the German people. It helps us to understand much that is admirable in modern German civilisation, for instance the outstandingly high quality of the best German journalism, and its exceptional vigilance in observing Nazi-like or militarist movements not only within the Federal Republic but outside it, for instance in the United States. Second, even before the Nazis were in power, they were able to obtain as many as 36·8 per cent of the votes.* This is enough to indicate that there was a terrible sickness in German society in the late 1920s.

In the attempt to understand this sickness, we have to turn our attention to an animal we have not so far considered in detail — the brown rat. We have seen how mice and moles, faced with a shortage of space while food is abundant, can shift from a territorial to a hierarchical way of life (p. 159). Under certain conditions, rats will do the same. But rats have a third form of social organisation, not yet observed in any other mammal. It was discovered in the 1940s by the German zoologist Fritz Steiniger, and it appears to be a response to *sudden* crowding.

Steiniger installed up to fifteen rats in an open-air enclosure of approximately 689 square feet. This is a ratio of one rat per 46 square feet. Now we have seen (p. 150) that Calhoun had put

* Both the percentages mentioned are proportions of the total of votes actually cast.

a very few rats in an area of 10,000 square feet, and let them breed: they became violent before they reached 200 by gradual natural increase, a ratio of one rat per 50 square feet. Hence Steiniger's rats were faced suddenly with a degree of crowding which Calhoun's rats had found intolerable even when they reached the limit gradually. The result was dramatic.

Each rat, male or female, set up a territory by digging a burrow in the ground. At the feeding-place, an absolute hierarchy prevailed, but each territory-owner was secure in his own burrow. The males began to court the females, each trying to enter the burrow of a female. For a time, all the females resisted entry. Finally one female accepted her suitor, and a pair formed. This pair now embarked on a system of patient, systematic massacre. One by one, over a period of two or three weeks, they cornered and killed every one of the other rats, biting them to death. The couple now had the enclosure to themselves, and they proceeded to breed without restraint. Whereas all the other responses to crowding we have considered produce the effect of reducing the population, this response can give rise to a collection of rats more numerous than the original inhabitants of the enclosure. They will apparently go on breeding as long as the food supply remains adequate; if it fails, they break out of the enclosure.

The rat-gang thus formed had properties quite unlike those of other mammalian societies. The crucial property of individual distance had simply disappeared; social space had imploded. The individuals of the gang simply did not show the need for space around themselves, fixed or moving. As a result, there was no question of priorities, no territories, no social hierarchy, relative or absolute. At the feeding-place, it was first come first served; young rats could with impunity snatch food from their elders' mouths. Since there were no pair territories, the young were communally reared; as soon as they could walk, they would return from an excursion to the first 'mother' they found. In all their behaviour, the rats showed a kind of 'mass culture': moods were transmitted and actions imitated with great speed and regularity, so that if any rat did anything others were likely

to join in. What was done about a strange object was determined by the reactions of the first rat to approach it.

The collapse of social space was made possible only by unusually frequent and pervasive pseudosexual activity. The rats
repeatedly crept over or under each other, their tails quivering
in a kind of pseudosexual convulsion. This mutual creeping is
seen only in the course of mating in rats who are in the territorial or hierarchical phase. In the gang, it became a continual
promiscuous activity between all rats, a permanent reaction to
the tensions of this community without vestige of individual privacy. Mating itself in the gang was not selective, as in the territorial phase, but completely promiscuous: when a female came
on heat she ran round the enclosure, pursued by all the males,
copulating within one or two seconds with each in turn as he
caught up with her. When she retired to her burrow for a brief
rest, males would squeeze in after her indiscriminately, sometimes jamming in the entrance. On the day of her heat, she
might copulate between 200 and 400 times.

With one exception, fighting between members of the gang
was completely absent; on the other hand, any strange rat
placed in the enclosure was attacked and killed by the gang.
The stranger was probably recognised as of a different smell.
Steiniger noticed the fate of crates of wild rats collected in the
field and sent on rail journeys. If the rats had come from the
same district, being presumably members of the same gang, they
all survived the journey in these very close quarters. If they had
come from different areas, hence from different gangs, there
would be corpses in the crate on arrival. Under the pressure of
the special stress which produces gang formation, rats seem to
develop an almost ant-like community. But they are still mammals. When an intruding stranger is being killed, the members
of the gang show a certain irritability with each other. It seems
that violence within the gang is averted not only by ceaseless
extreme pseudosexual activity, but also by a kind of permanent
redirection against outsiders. This idea is confirmed by the one
exceptional case of two rat brothers in the gang who quarrelled
over the possession of a burrow and fought each other viciously:

the tail of one was so badly bitten that it decayed and dropped off. The hatred of the brothers was brought to an end when three strangers were placed in the enclosure. The brothers joined the rest of the gang to kill the strangers, and never quarrelled with each other again. In the wild, when conditions prompt the formation of gangs, mass redirection seems to work regularly. Rat-gangs are known to make merciless war on competitors of the same or closely related species: in this way, for instance, the brown rat nearly exterminated the black rat in Europe within the last few centuries.

In human societies, sudden stress can arise in various ways, and it can produce social behaviour strongly reminiscent of the rats. A mob always forms in response to some sudden event, and it may behave very like a rat-gang for hours. In certain human societies of a relatively simple kind, some of the rat-gang patterns can persist for some time, after they have been evoked by sudden stress. The population crises of the nomads may have been fairly sudden in onset, and the nomad hordes had something of the seething mass culture, and all the pitiless hostility to outsiders, shown by the rat-gang. It is doubtful if a whole human civilised society could behave exactly like a rat-gang for long periods; the economic and social complexities are too great to be run by a simple mass social system of this kind. However there are several ways in which a *clique* system (the human equivalent of a persistent rat-gang, characterised by absence of hierarchical organisation within, and implacable hostility to outsiders) can exert considerable influence over a civilised society.

One possibility is the growth and development of a clique system outside official society: this is exemplified by the Sicilian Mafia. The island of Sicily has had a long history of spoliation and misgovernment by foreigners — Romans, Ostrogoths, Byzantines; then (after a respite of competent government by the Norman kings) Germans, French and Spaniards. In the sixteenth century, the population of Sicily rose from 600,000 in 1501 to over one million in 1570. Up to that time, the island had always exported cereals; by the end of the sixteenth century, it had to import them from the Baltic. It is possible that this supreme blow, which was followed by three centuries of misgovernment by local dynasties (briefly relieved by one competent king), brought about the conditions for the formation of the Mafia. This association, which now controls organised crime in the United States and much of Europe (p. 200), is curiously lacking in hierarchical structure, and appears to consist of cliques of roughly equal bosses at different levels. It has all the extreme exclusiveness of a rat-gang. The Mafia obtained its grip on American crime through its most famous agent, Scarface Al Capone, whom it supported until he became careless and provoked federal intervention. Although Capone was the Mafia's recognised chief executive for years, he was never admitted to membership: he was a Neapolitan. He obtained his scar as a young man from a Sicilian barber, whom he had beaten up when the man refused to give him the characteristic Mafia hair-cut.

The Mafia operates completely outside society. A clique system may impinge on official society if it is promoted by factions within the society's hierarchies. The formation of a mass culture of teenagers within modern China may be a reaction to the sudden forcible breakdown of the rigid hierarchies of the mass-family (p. 248), and also to recent sudden misfortunes of the Chinese people, such as the food crisis at the beginning of the 1960s and the very rapid withdrawal of Soviet technical assistance. This mass emerged into official life as the Red Guard movement, which appears to have been raised by one faction of the Chinese Government against another faction, as Jupiter raised Uzen and Kuro against Titan (p. 174). Just as Uzen and Kuro were finally driven out of the central court, so the Red Guards were discouraged from entering government headquarters to drag out party leaders. But they appear to have got out of hand: they caught one government minister and 'interrogated' him to death. The outcome in China seems to have been some degree of civil war, in which hundreds of lives have probably already been lost. The hierarchy here is at grips with the clique (p. 248).

To rule a large civilised society, a clique system must command the society's main hierarchical systems. This seems to have happened when the sheep-rearing corporation called the Mesta obtained control of late medieval Spain.* The eventual result of such control, however, as in the Spanish instance, must be the complete collapse of competent government. There remains one final possibility, realised in Nazi Germany: the effective combination of hierarchies and cliques. This required an absolute boss over both, and the only logical candidate was a mass-murderer.

The tragedy of Germany had been prepared by a long series of unique stresses, dating back to the foundation of the First German Reich by Otto I in the tenth century A.D. This empire was born out of unstable conditions in the central strip of western Europe (from Italy to the Netherlands). As a political unit, it was a geographical impossibility, including both Germany and Italy, where there was already a nucleus of power in the papacy. By the end of the Middle Ages, the Empire had fallen to pieces. Italy fell under foreign domination for centuries. Germany, still more unfortunate, relapsed into chaos, and bore the main brunt of the seventeenth-century population crisis, as the chief victim of the ghastly Thirty Years War, which must have left its mark for generations. By the eighteenth century, Germany was divided between numerous (at one time 233) incompetent petty rulers, like the Duke of Pfalz-Zweibrücken (p. 235), and the state of Prussia, organised under an extremely rigid military hierarchy. It was this hierarchy, the German Army, which unified Germany in the nineteenth century, and fought and lost the First World War; by that time it was allied with another powerful hierarchical organisation, German Big Business. Because of her troubled history, industrialisation had come very late to Germany, and the rigid hierarchies in power resisted the drastic social changes it brought. Before any stability had been reached, Germany was struck by two terrible and very sudden economic crises, superimposed on a population problem already becoming serious for a European

* This development, and its consequences, are briefly described in Appendix Five, p. 295.

country with a 'colonial empire' which cost more than it paid and had absorbed only 5000 German immigrants by 1914.

The first crisis period began with the dislocation of economic life caused by the war itself, and continued with the catastrophic inflation. This disaster, which struck in 1922, was intensified by the senseless financial reparations demanded from Germany by the powers at Versailles (while the French people were distracted by the trial of Landru, p. 276). The war and the inflation suddenly ruined the large German class of small businessmen, traders and artisans. These people, who had particularly prized their economic independence, were suddenly deprived of their savings and means of livelihood. Meanwhile, in the complete collapse of economic life, the petty swindlers and spivs emerged into the open on all sides; they were the only people who understood the Black Markets and could fiddle their way through the disaster. It was this post-war period that saw the career of Haarmann, spiv turned mass-murderer (p. 277), the appearance of the Nazi Party, and the emergence of another petty swindler, Adolf Hitler. The first Nazi *putsch* and the trial of Haarmann coincided in the year 1924. They were the climaxes of several years of increasing public violence.

There followed a period of economic recovery, marked by a stay of execution for the democratic Weimar Republic and a temporary eclipse for Hitler and the Nazis. This period ended when Germany, already weakened by war and inflation, suffered the second frightful blow of the world depression, which produced a mass of new unemployed (over eight million by 1933) and a further crop of ruined small businessmen (ruined this time by deflation). It appears that by this time the formation of cliques or rat-gangs had gone a long way in the German lower middle classes, the chief sufferers from the war and the inflation. The earlier period of disaster had been a time not only of incredible public disorder, but also of phenomenally widespread pseudosexual activity, organised vice and perversion. In Hanover, the scene of Haarmann's murders, in 1918 there were 450,000 inhabitants; the police estimated that 40,000 of these were homosexuals, including 500 registered male prostitutes.

Everything indicated the appearance of rat-gang-like processes on an unprecedented scale.

The ruling hierarchies of the Army and Big Business, unable to control the situation, finally formed an alliance with the perverted cliques, of which the most active was the Nazi Party. When the coalition finally came to power, Germany was a strange mixture of traditional hierarchies with the clique system of the Nazis. The mass of the Party wanted a return to the system of medieval guilds, which had lasted longest in Germany: trade and manufacturing groups of small businessmen, rigidly restricted from competing with each other, fanatically devoted to absolute equality among members, ruthlessly monopolistic and exclusive towards everybody else. Big Business had enough influence in the coalition to prevent this. However, the Nazis organised the German population in a new and extraordinary way. The population was divided into ten somewhat overlapping categories: teachers, journalists, civil servants, young people, workers, women, students, university staff, farmers and entertainers. Within each category, everyone was supposed to join a mass organisation, which was completely controlled by a corresponding party clique, exclusively restricted to party members. This strange clique organisation operated side by side with the normal hierarchical chains of responsibility, with which it grossly interfered. Since the leading Nazis were, quite simply, criminals, the whole system was geared to the promotion of vice, crime and every kind of racket. The only organisations with a degree of independence were the Army and the biggest business corporations.

So strange an alliance could only work with one boss for both the cliques and the hierarchies. The boss who presented himself was Adolf Hitler. A swindler through and through, he may well have begun his career (to judge from his expenses and known income sources) by embezzling the Nazi Party funds, and before he was finished he had double-crossed all partners to the coalition, and made himself complete master of both systems. All Nazis who refused to accept the alliance were purged in 1934. But in 1938, by a neat coup, Hitler obtained the oath of allegiance of the Army generals. The German Army was so incredibly rigidly organised that it was, from then on, entirely at his disposal. He used it to carry out, on a scale available to no previous mass-murderer, his automatic and appalling fantasies. The Army's last realistic plan to dispose of the monster it had called up was frustrated when the British and French accepted the outrageous terms offered by Hitler at Munich.

The effective combination of hierarchy and clique made possible the most terrible outbreak of violence in history. As we saw in the Whipsnade Zoo, a hierarchy can have its outcasts (p. 104), treated without mercy as beings without rank. A clique, by definition, hates everyone outside. The Army may have had reservations about the Jews, but large sections of it were prepared to agree with the Nazis about the Slavs, and the German Army undoubtedly took part in the deliberate starving of millions of Russian prisoners of war. The society as a whole, however, gradually took on more and more of the rat-gang character, as the S.S. élite, in particular, were urged to get more and more babies promiscuously for an expanding Germany, ready to find its *Lebensraum* by exterminating other peoples. (A similar appeal for babies was made to the South African whites in 1965 by the Deputy Minister for Bantu Development.) The millions of murdered Jews and Slavs were to be replaced by an ever-growing German population. This at least is how it appeared to the German Nazi rank and file. They little knew that the swindler at the top was quite uninterested in Germans or Germany. 'I know perfectly well', he remarked to his intimates, 'that in the scientific sense there is no such thing as race.' And he went on to explain that he meant to destroy the whole concept of nationality. Potential breeding-stock was to be found in all nations (except perhaps Jews and Slavs), and he meant to breed a new ruling class of sadists, never mind where they came from, a kind of gang of super-rats.

Hitler himself conforms in every detail to the picture of the mass-murderer. A glance at his parents' photographs shows us the petty, pompous bureaucrat and his viciously resentful wife. The young Hitler's school career was a long record of failures;

he emerged, with no specialist skills, to join the ranks of the petty swindlers. He spent four years in the doss-houses of Vienna, learning to scrounge and fiddle, and no doubt experiencing much misery in the process. He then joined the Army, like most of his fellow mass-murderers. After the war, the unprecedented condition of Germany permitted him to extend his operations. He entered, swindled, took over the Nazi Party. He intrigued with the Bavarian separatists. He talked and talked, with his raucous voice and his execrable German. He made his unsuccessful first *putsch*. He spent (like most of the others) a few years in prison. After that he was in a position to intrigue with Big Businessmen and Army leaders, and later with the leaders of other nations. He swindled everybody, without exception. He stared madly in people's faces, a thing that confuses hierarchically-minded people, for it should indicate high status (p. 122). In time, so many people were taken in that they began to feel the man must have had some kind of political ability. Nobody likes to feel they have been taken in by a petty swindler. Even excellent modern historians of the period tend to concede Hitler some kind of political genius. Yet his proceedings were drearily automatic and repetitive, and he carried out faithfully the insane programme he had written up so badly and boringly in *Mein Kampf*.

It appears clever to tell endless lies and cheat everybody, but it is really a highly routine performance. The nature and course of Hitler's double-crosses was quite invariable. The Army and Big Business leaders were impressed by his capacity for endless loud talk; but this, too, was quite automatic. He was already doing it in his slum room in Vienna, shouting and waving his arms till the other occupants stopped him. He only needed something to start him off, then he would go on and on. At a party in 1923, his hostess made the mistake of mentioning the Jews. (Hitler had already made up his mind about the Jews; one of them had been kind to him in Vienna, so obviously the Jewish people were worthless as material for a ruling class of sadists.) Hitler 'began to speak', writes Konrad Heiden, who was there, 'and then he spoke without ceasing. After a while he

thrust back his chair and stood up, still speaking, or rather yell-
ing, in such a powerful penetrating voice as I have never heard
from anyone else. In the next room a child woke up and began
to cry.'

Hitler would talk rubbish about anything and everything,
but the only thing that personally interested him was cruelty.
He was personally responsible for the elaborate system whereby
men were manipulated into becoming torturers. He had films
made of executions and tortures, which he viewed repeatedly.
He had worthy companions, like Goering, the founder of the
Gestapo, but he also had the use of one or two intelligent dupes,
like the architect Albert Speer, who saved German industry
from complete collapse (under the pressure of crime and rackets)
in the middle of the war, and the Army experts who worked out
the new formula for mobile warfare, and (until Hitler double-
crossed him) the gifted financier Schacht. Without these men,
the Nazi State must have collapsed almost immediately.

The completely automatic nature of Hitler's proceedings became particularly clear when the outside world refused to accord
with his fantasies. After interviews with the only two men who
ever stood up to him (Franco and Molotov), he felt quite upset.
The invasion of Poland 'should' have proceeded exactly like
the invasion of Sudetenland and of the rest of Czechoslovakia.
Instead, the British sent an ultimatum. This was all wrong.
Faced with such a clash between fantasy and reality, he behaved in a way which made his insanity unmistakable. According to an eye-witness, he walked up and down saying to himself that Germany was irresistible. 'Suddenly he stopped in the
middle of the room and stood there staring. His voice was
blurred, and his behaviour that of a completely abnormal person. . . . "If there should be war, then I shall build U-boats,
build U-boats, U-boats, U-boats, U-boats".' Then he 'raised
his voice as though addressing a large audience, and shrieked:
"I shall build aeroplanes, build aeroplanes, aeroplanes, aeroplanes, and I shall annihilate my enemies"'. It is a simple
machine that has temporarily jammed. The Munich operation
must therefore have been just as automatic: it was through no

genius on Hitler's part that it came off. War with Britain was
simply not part of Hitler's plan, until the very last stages of
world conquest. He could therefore never fully realise that he
was at war with Britain. His conduct of this part of the war was
lukewarm and indecisive and full of obvious mistakes, designed
fitfully to punish the British for their obtuseness, rather than to
conquer them. British prisoners of war benefited from this misunderstanding: they were not, on the whole, starved to death.
To the end of the war, Hitler still expected an alliance with
Britain.

As events increasingly failed to coincide with his fantasies,
Hitler was forced to cut off more and more of his view of the
outside world. He refused to visit bombed cities — the British
should not be bombing them. After 1943, he scarcely left his
hide-outs. This cut-off on Hitler's part permitted Speer to dis-
obey the Führer's orders to reduce Germany to rubble. Before
he committed suicide in the Berlin bunker, Hitler sent the German people a last message. As the British historian Alan Bullock
has pointed out, it was entirely characteristic, 'containing at
least one striking lie'. The last words of the swindler, speaking
of 'unity with our soldiers unto death', were designed to make
the people believe he would die fighting at the head of his
troops.*

* The extraordinary process we have glanced at in this appendix,
the formation of cliques or rat-gangs under sudden stress, is obviously
worth much more study. It will be given more attention in a forthcoming book by Claire Russell, *Forbidden Fruit*.

Five/Leadership and Man

The criterion of violence-reduction (p. 79) is a simple and effective test for human, no less than monkey, leadership. Since discontent inevitably breeds either riots or precautionary government terrorism and/or mass redirection abroad, a community free from all these kinds of violence must be well satisfied under good economic and social leadership. On this criterion, good leadership on a small or medium scale is not rare in human societies, and examples of violence-reduction by leadership are common enough in everyday life. We watched a neat specimen in the autumn of 1965, from the interior of a coach in a coach station in Switzerland. A motorist had parked right across the nose of our coach, which was due to move out. The coach-driver, in the most tactless language he could use, asked the motorist to get out of the way. The motorist reacted to the words and the tone of voice, and refused to budge. In the ensuing argument, which was soon building up towards a punch-up, the problem of unsnarling the vehicles was lost from sight in mutual recriminations. At this point, a policeman sauntered up. He displayed the inimitable calm, effortless, relaxed posture of a monkey leader; if he had had a tail, it would have been high in the air (p. 73). He stood for a few seconds watching the scene with a placid smile, utterly devoid of impatience or threat. The motorist suddenly started up his car and drove off, the coach-driver subsided into muttering as he pulled out of the station, and the policeman strolled away. Many a London copper has produced similar effects, and, for that matter, many a man or woman with no uniform or official status at all. (On the other hand, many an official, backed by all the rigours of the law, and even by an army, has failed to do anything of the kind.) Nor is good leadership over a long period of time by any means rare in human communities and organisations. The effects of a change in leadership in a firm or institution are often rapid and striking: a bad new leader will create around him a widening circle of tension and redirection, a good one will produce co-operation and a common interest in the activities of the community.

On the very large scale, where one individual in high office can influence masses of people, the record of human leadership is less impressive. Of course the difficulty increases with the scale, despite the human advantages of intelligence, language and means of wide communication. But the selection and promotion of leaders in most periods and societies has shown little systematic regard for the criterion of violence-reduction, and sometimes a positively perverse disregard. Captain William Bligh, for instance, was the victim of the famous mutiny of the *Bounty* on the high seas, in 1789. This almost unique distinction did not prevent his appointment, in 1806, as Captain-General and Governor-in-Chief of New South Wales, where a penal settlement was gradually but successfully being transformed into a civilised community. Within less than two years, Bligh's outrageous aggressiveness had provoked the first mutiny in the history of the colony, and achieved (according to the Australian historian Manning Clark) 'the division of the upper ranks of society in Sydney and Parramatta into warring factions'.

This does not mean, of course, that human beings are sillier than monkeys. Those social arrangements which produce such admirable results in wild monkey bands are largely automatic, as will be clear from the description we have given (Chapter Two); under stress, they break down in the most disastrous way (Chapter Three). The selection of leaders, and the pressures upon them when in office, have been scarcely less automatic in human societies: that is why monkey politics look so familiar, and invite us to use words like 'establishment' in describing them. Ever since man began to raise crops and herds and to live in towns, human societies have been under almost continual stress, reaching great severity during the repeated periods of population crisis (Chapter Five). Hence even intelligent and potentially excellent leaders have only rarely been able to achieve large-scale reduction of violence, and all too often (especially in the crisis periods) high office or influence have been entrusted to more or less incompetent and aggressive candidates, as unsuited for leadership as the monkey Diablo (p. 106). Under severe enough stress, a society may even let a Hitler rise to the top (Appendix Four). On the overpopulated and declining Greek mainland in the fourth century B.C., when Isocrates was trying to develop criteria for intelligence, he was forced to admit that success in business or politics was no guarantee of ability. Writing in the ravaged American South in the early twentieth century A.D., James Branch Cabell observed, with pardonable exaggeration, that 'cleverness was, of course, the most admirable of all traits: but cleverness was not at the top of things, and never had been'.

Nevertheless, from time to time a balance of favourable local circumstances has enabled a good leader, firm, self-assured and unaggressive, not only to reach the highest office but also to obtain considerable freedom of action. By the use of human intelligence, such a leader can then produce remarkable results in the reduction of violence and stress. The outstanding examples (such as Cleisthenes of ancient Athens and Lorenzo dei Medici of late medieval Florence) naturally tend to come from non-crisis periods, when relief from population pressure permitted both their effective leadership and the brilliant renaissances which they did so much to promote. But perhaps the most interesting example, on the grand scale, is the reign of Elizabeth I of England. During this reign, the population crisis in Europe was already well under way (p. 182), yet conditions in England were still so finely balanced that this queen was able to delay the effects of the crisis there, and gain the respite for a great literary renaissance. Her period, indeed, has much in common with our own, and her work might suggest the great part which good leadership could play in the transitional time before us, while we are solving, once and for all, the central problem of population control (p. 252).

The reign of Elizabeth I was a time of great and rapid technical, social and geopolitical changes, and intense ideological conflict within and between nations. Elizabeth had to deal with the productive but tremendously dangerous upheaval that was finally turning England into an efficient modern nation, capable in due course of using her coal, iron and ships to become the first industrialised country in the world. While the queen could have done nothing without the support of her society, and could not always do all she would have liked (for politics is the art of the possible), she frequently acted against the advice of most or even all of her counsellors in the government and parliament, and always in the right direction, whether in the realms of economic or social leadership.

In Tudor England, the decline of the feudal nobles and the old Church institutions, the rise of the country gentry and the City merchants and financiers, and the breakdown of medieval farming systems, with consequent peasant unemployment, created a whole network of urgent problems, against the background of growing population crisis. The changes in human relationships, expressed in ideological terms, came to the boil in the English Reformation under Henry VIII. That king, brutal but realistic, managed the initial crisis by a series of oscillations in policy. By the end of his reign, a large body of public opinion was emerging, nationalist but conservative; it was to become the Protestant or Anglican Party. On either wing were Catholics favouring the old cosmopolitan order, and Puritans eager to push forward with ruthless haste the interests of the new gentry and their City allies. Under the boy-king Edward VI and his successor Mary I, the oscillations became more violent, and England experienced in turn the absolute rule of the Protestants, the Puritans, and the extreme Catholics. When Elizabeth succeeded her sister Mary, most people had had enough of extremes, and the majority of all classes were probably glad to support a moderate Protestant monarch. The Puritans had no choice but to support her, since the only other candidate for the throne (Mary, Queen of Scots) was a Catholic. The English Catholics were dividing (rather as they did in the Spanish Civil War in the twentieth century) into loyalists, prepared to support any legitimate English government, and extremists, prepared to aid any foreign invader who would forcibly reconvert England to the religion of Rome. England was somewhat in advance of Europe in making the usual transition, characteristic of population crises, from ideological to local allegiances (p. 203). The loyal Catholics supported Elizabeth on principle (one of them commanded the fleet that destroyed the Spanish Armada), and later with real enthusiasm, when they realised she was their only protector.

Despite this wide basis of support, Elizabeth had formidable difficulties. There was a strong prejudice against rule by a woman, hardly reduced by the disastrous reign of Mary I. The social upheaval was still pursuing its course, and party feeling became increasingly intense. Abroad, England had no reliable allies, and was just ending a particularly senseless war with France. Elizabeth was confronted by the most dangerous military power in Europe (Spain), ideologically Catholic and ruled by the Habsburg King Philip II. The personality of this king is well summed up in a secret despatch he wrote to his cruellest henchman, the Duke of Alva, about the strangling at Simancas in Spain of a Flemish ambassador, devoutly Catholic and personally loyal to Philip, who had ventured to present the objections of the Flemish nobles to the King's unconstitutional proceedings in the Spanish Netherlands. Philip had arranged this murder with such attention to detail that everyone in Spain believed the man to have died of a fever. He enclosed two letters, faked before the murder, for Alva to circulate in the Netherlands, as 'evidence' of the envoy's natural death. After describing the murder, Philip added that 'if the sentiments of the deceased nobleman had been at all in conformity with his external manifestations, according to the accounts received of his last moments, it was to be hoped that God would have mercy upon his soul'. The secretary who copied out the despatch thought fit to insert a suggestion that the murdered man had been encouraged in his last moments by the Devil. Philip struck out the insertion and scribbled in the margin that 'we should always express favourable judgements concerning the dead'. Philip was never in a position to write thus about the Queen of England; but it was certainly not for want of trying.

The fact that the Spanish people had to accept the proceedings of a ruler like Philip II provides a good example of the fate of a country under extreme stress. From being the most civilised country in Europe (in the thirteenth century), Spain had suffered a terrible decline. A corporation of Castilian sheep-rearers called the Mesta, exporting fine wool, had come to dominate the nation completely in the late fifteenth and early sixteenth centuries, using the Spanish Inquisition to secure its interests, which appeared to coincide with those of the centralising monarchy, eager to destroy local privileges. The Mesta shepherds and their flocks (3,453,168 sheep in 1526), moving over the whole country from summer to winter pastures, destroyed much of the forests of Spain, and rendered a great deal of land useless for cultivation. The country was vulnerable, because rainfall in most of Spain is nearly as irregular as it is in the dry belt (p. 10). At the same time, the Mesta monopoly ruined Spanish commerce and banking. By the reign of Philip II the Mesta was declining in influence, but it left Spain with a particularly disastrous population crisis and a ruined economic and political system. All that remained was an inflated army, which made Spain still dangerous to other nations until her bankruptcy became irretrievable in the next century. In these conditions, the Spanish people could do little to restrain an incompetent and aggressive ruler.

In England, where the damp climate threatened no irretrievable harm from large flocks, a flourishing wool export trade was an important source of national prosperity in the Tudor period. However, if Henry VIII had shown qualities of social leadership, his economic proceedings were anything but wise, and his successors were even more incompetent. When Elizabeth succeeded her half-sister Mary in 1558, she found the English finances in a desperate state. The price revolution of the sixteenth-century population crisis in Europe was well under way (p. 190). European monarchs tended to get their revenues as fixed sums of money, which bought them less and less as prices rose and the value of money fell. They found no solution for their problem except to mint debased coins (mixed with base metals) at times convenient for themselves; this only made matters worse. Previous rulers had repeatedly debased the English currency in this way. Two days after Mary's death, Elizabeth sent for the leading English financial expert, Sir Thomas Gresham; within three months she appointed a commission to solve the currency problem; within two years the problem was solved, by assigning a suitably low value to the debased silver coins, calling them in, and paying for them at the assigned value with coins of pure silver. Money totalling nearly £700,000 was exchanged in this way. Confidence in English currency was restored, and trade and industry were stimulated. Alone among European countries, England managed at least to slow down the rise in prices. By 1579, as a contemporary put it, 'the realm abounded in riches'. And, characteristically, Elizabeth herself made something like £45,000 on the deal, a windfall for her impoverished state treasury.

The currency reform may have been due to some adviser (probably Lord Paget), though Elizabeth was prompt in raising the problem and in applying the solution. But the maintenance of England's solvency from then on was almost entirely the queen's own work. She did it by heroic economy, often against the advice of all her ministers. Already, in 1560, at the age of twenty-seven, she would not accept the advice of her experienced chief minister, Cecil, to squander bribes on the nobles of Scotland; she rightly decided that they would not stay bought. Again and again, in the teeth of her advisers, she refused to embark on costly wars. After the defeat of the Spanish Armada, she demobilised with what everyone felt was indecent haste, to save wages. Yet on the rare occasions when she did use troops, she paid them more regularly than any other European government. In 1601, two years before her death, she spoke of her financial leadership. This summing-up may have surprised some of her subjects; but it was a fair statement. 'I never was any greedy, scraping grasper, nor a strait, fast-holding Prince, nor yet a waster.'

This herculean effort brought its reward in the stabilisation of the price of bread (pp. 26 ff.), and thus in the relief of the most serious stress in England making for violence. Meanwhile Elizabeth did everything in her power to control the ideological tensions. The Puritan party was small but tightly organised, and skilful in procedure inside and outside parliament; these Puritans invented most of the tactical techniques later used by Communist parties. Throughout the reign, they pressed relentlessly for persecution of Catholics as such, simply on ideological grounds. As the Catholic powers in Europe became steadily more menacing, this Puritan policy attracted increasing support from the Protestants, and Elizabeth was eventually quite alone, even in the government, in resisting it. Philip was sending assassin after assassin against her, and English extremist Catholics abroad were publishing propaganda in which she was described as 'an incestuous bastard', accused of 'unspeakable and incredible variety of lust', and labelled 'a common fable for this her turpitude'. Throughout all this Elizabeth firmly and alone retained a clear distinction between Catholic belief and political treason. In veto after veto and amendment after amendment to the endless bills sent up by the parliamentary Puritans, she fought a tireless rear-guard action against the witch-hunt. She took particular pleasure in the loyalty of the patriotic Catholics, particularly when she could show it off to Spaniards. When a subject approached her carriage, shouting 'Long Live the Queen!' in Latin, she turned to the Spanish ambassador and remarked: 'This good man is a clergyman of the old religion.' Her policy was admirably summed up by Francis Bacon: 'Her Majesty, not liking to make windows into men's hearts and secret thoughts, ... tempered her law so as it restraineth only manifest disobedience.' By the end of the reign, for all her efforts, English Catholics were having a rough time, but she had done everything to delay and moderate the persecution, and to establish principles of ideological freedom and compromise.

Firm but supple government at home was accompanied by firm but supple diplomacy abroad, which Elizabeth personally conducted or supervised, thanks to her gifts as a linguist. Despite his infinite duplicity, she ran rings round the slow-witted Philip and his plot-happy agents. Elizabeth played continually for time, and absolutely refused to engage in ideological crusades. Feria, the first Spanish ambassador of Elizabeth's reign, began by observing complacently, 'what can be expected from a country governed by a Queen, and she a young lass . . . without prudence?' He ended by complaining that England had 'fallen into the hands of a woman who is a daughter of the Devil'. Pope Sixtus V was a more magnanimous enemy than the Spaniards. 'She certainly is a great Queen', he enthused, 'Just look how well she governs! She is only a woman, only mistress of half an island, and yet she makes herself feared by Spain, by France, by the Empire, by all.' Elizabeth achieved this effect, between 1558 and 1587, at the cost of some four short military expeditions, as cheap in blood and money as she could make them. Indeed until 1587, when serious war with Spain could no longer be avoided, violence in the form of foreign war has rarely or never been on such a modest scale in the history of England.

As for violence at home, one simple measurement is supplied by the number of ideological and political executions. In the forty-five years of her reign (1558–1603) Elizabeth burned four heretics, all Anabaptists (regarded by all other sects as criminally insane, and massacred in droves by Protestant and Catholic rulers alike on the Continent). After the dangerous but brief rising of 1569 in the still half-civilised North of England, the queen hanged some 600 rebels. Apart from these, less than 300 Catholics died on the scaffold, often genuinely and always technically for political treason, never for their ideological beliefs. To see these figures in the perspective of their time, we have to add a few others from the same period, when Europe was in the grip of growing population crisis. Within three years (1555–8), Mary I had burned 300 heretics. In his six years as *gauleiter* of the Netherlands for Philip II (1567–73), the Duke of Alva *boasted* of having executed 18,600 people. Within a few hours, on 24 August 1572, on the orders of King Charles IX of

France, 2000 Calvinists were lynched by the Paris mob. It may fairly be said that, for that bloody century, the amount of violence in Elizabethan England was phenomenally small.

Towards the end of Elizabeth's reign, stresses began to build up which even she could not control. Disturbances on the Continent (where the market was) caused a slump in the English wool trade. The inevitable war with Spain, despite Elizabeth's persistent economy, gradually drained money away. Under the pressure of the rising population, the price revolution, though slowed in England, went inexorably on. Crown revenues dropped in value, and crown lands had to be mortgaged. The shrinking kitty at court was the object of bitter disputes between greedy courtiers out for what was left. Finally (p. 27), the European weather proved too much for the government, and violent crime and bread rioting resumed their old prominence. To the end, Elizabeth behaved as a great leader. In 1601 the incompetent and delinquent Earl of Essex raised an armed rebellion in London. Elizabeth (then sixty-seven years old) 'would have gone out in person to see what any rebel of them all durst do against her, had not her councillors with much ado stayed her'. She crushed the rising with a firmness that won the admiration of Henry IV of France ('She only is a king! She only knows how to rule!'), and then confined herself to six executions, pardoning all the other rebels: 'a thing the like was never read of in any chronicle'. But even she could not now halt the economic disaster, which produced increasing violence throughout the two succeeding reigns, to culminate in the English Civil War.

The reign of Elizabeth I thus shows that, in the long run, only the regulation of population by birth-control could permanently dispose of social stress and violence. Nevertheless, it also shows the remarkable ability of great leadership to tip the balance in a border-line situation where some freedom of action is left, and this may be of great importance in the present world crisis. It was Elizabeth's accomplishment to give England thirty of the least violent years in her history, and to obtain the respite that made possible the renaissance of the Elizabethan theatre.

The growing stresses of the population crisis, in the violent and squalid reign of James I, eventually proved too much for even the art of Shakespeare, who was forced to lay down his pen while still full of life and health. But, thanks to the Elizabethan respite, Shakespeare had already produced the great plays by which he is known, and the influence of his work on human relationships and emotional responses continues to this day. For in every respite from extremes of violence and stress, human civilisation has taken critical steps forward, and made gains which, in the long run, are permanent for mankind.

Notes

THE source or sources of each fact or group of facts are specified by the numbers in brackets, which refer to items in the Bibliography (pp. 313 ff.). The facts are grouped by pages on which they are mentioned.

Page

Page

310   Notes

Bibliography and Index of Sources by subject

THE numbers in italics at the end of each source entry refer to the page or pages of the text where the source has been used. Each source is briefly described unless it has a self-explanatory title, and the entries are arranged under various subject-headings. (Each source has been placed only under the most appropriate heading, even when it covers more than one subject.) It is hoped that this will make it possible to use the list as a general subject index.

Subject categories are as follows:

A *General*

B *Animal Societies*
   1) Insects
   2) Fishes and Birds
   3) Mammals other than Monkeys
   4) Monkeys

C *Human Prehistory and Tribal Societies*

D *History of Human Civilisations to Mid-Twentieth Century*
   1) World
   2) British Isles
   3) Continent of Europe
   4) Other Continents

E *Developments after 1950*
   1) Population
   2) Food Production
   3) Money
   4) Housing
   5) Health
   6) Education
   7) Labour
   8) Pseudosex and Drug Addiction
   9) Violent Crime and Murder
  10) Civil Violence and War

A *General*

1. ANDRZEJEWSKI, S. *Military Organization and Society*, London, Routledge & Kegan Paul, 1954. *109, 240.*

2. ANDRESKI, S. *Elements of Comparative Sociology*, London, Weidenfeld & Nicolson, 1964. *109, 172, 186.*

3. BOLITHO, W. *Murder for Profit* (Travellers' Library Edn), London, Cape, 1933. *274–7, 284.*

4. CARTHY, J. D., and EBLING, F. J. (ed.) *The Natural History of Aggression*, London and New York, Academic Press, 1964. *16, 33, 50, 81, 109–10, 146, 148, 262–3.*

5. KORTMULDER, K. 'On the Need to Popularize Basic Concepts' (Nature of Aggression), *Current Anthropology*, **7**, pp. 90–1, 1966. *16.*

6. LEYHAUSEN, P. 'The Sane Community — a Density Problem?', *Discovery*, **26**, 9, pp. 27–33, 1965. *55–7, 147, 150, 193, 218, 233.*

7. LEYHAUSEN, P. (interviewed by W. M. S. Russell) 'Of Cats and Men', *BBC Third Programme*, 15 and 24 Aug 1967. *55–7, 233.*

8. LORENZ, K. *On Aggression* (trans. M. Latzke), London, Methuen, 1966. *4, 124, 258–9.*

9. POWELL, H. A., RUSSELL, C., and RUSSELL, W. M. S. (Correspondence on Hunting and Aggression), *Listener*, **72**, pp. 845 and 887, 1964. *257–9.*

10. RUSSELL, C. *Forbidden Fruit* (Evolution of Human Behaviour), London, Macmillan, in press. *125, 134–9, 269–71, 281, 289.*

11. RUSSELL, C., and RUSSELL, W. M. S. *Human Behaviour: a New Approach*, London, Deutsch; Boston, Little, Brown, 1961. *123–5, 134–6, 274, 300.*

12. RUSSELL, C., and RUSSELL, W. M. S. 'Population and Behaviour in Animals and Man', *Mem. and Proc. lit. philosoph. Soc. Manchester*, **109**, 5, pp. 1–16, 1967. *166–8, 171, 177–8, 183, 218–20.*

13. RUSSELL, W. M. S. 'Art, Science and Man', *Listener*, **71**, pp. 43–5, 99–101, 113, 1964. *237.*

14. RUSSELL, W. M. S. 'Violence, Monkeys and Man', *Listener*, **72**, pp. 710–12, 753–5, 1964. *16–17, 48, 120.*

15. RUSSELL, W. M. S. 'Aggression: New Light from Animals', *New Society*, **7**, 176, pp. 12–14, 1966. *16–17.*

16. RUSSELL, W. M. S. 'Arms, Rules and Man', *BBC Third Programme*, 23 March 1966. *166–8, 171.*

17. STONIER, T. *Nuclear Disaster*, Harmondsworth, Penguin, 1964. *9, 12–13, 170, 266.*

18. STOTT, D. H. 'Cultural and Natural Checks on Population Growth', in *Culture and the Evolution of Man*, ed. M. F. Ashley Montagu, pp. 355–76; New York, Oxford University Press, 1962. *150, 157–8, 208.*

19. WRIGHT, Q. *A Study of War*, Chicago and London, University of Chicago Press (2nd edn), 1965. *7–9, 12, 28, 170.*

20. WYNNE-EDWARDS, V. C. *Animal Dispersion in relation to Social Behaviour*, Edinburgh and London, Oliver & Boyd, 1962. *4, 147, 153, 155–6, 159–60, 163.*

B *Animal Societies*

  1 Insects

21. HASKINS, C. P. *Of Societies and Men*, London, Allen & Unwin, 1952. *260–63.*

  2 Fishes and Birds

22. BASTOCK, M., MORRIS, D., and MOYNIHAN, M. 'Some Comments on Conflict and Thwarting in Animals', *Behaviour*, 6, pp. 66–84, 1953. *99, 123.*

23. HARRISON, C. J. O. 'Allopreening as Agonistic Behaviour', *Behaviour*, 24, pp. 161–209, 1965. *156.*

24. HEDIGER, H. *Studies of the Psychology and Behaviour of Animals in Zoos and Circuses*, London, Butterworth's Scientific Publications, 1955. *155, 231.*

25. IERSEL, J. J. A. VAN 'Some Aspects of Territorial Behaviour of the Male Three-Spined Stickleback', *Archives Néerlandaises de Zoologie*, 13, Supplement 1, pp. 383–400, 1958. *230–1.*

26. LORENZ, K. *King Solomon's Ring*, London, Methuen, 1952. *4, 124, 257.*

27. TINBERGEN, N. '"Derived" Activities; their Causation, Biological Significance, Origin and Emancipation during Evolution', *Quart. Rev. Biol.*, 27, pp. 1–32, 1952. *123–4.*

28. TINBERGEN, N. *Social Behaviour in Animals*, London, Methuen, 1953. *4, 123–4.*

  3 Mammals other than Monkeys

29. AUMANN, G. D., and EMLEN, J. T. 'Relation of Population Density to Sodium Availability and Sodium Selection in Microtine Rodents', *Nature*, 208, pp. 198–9, 1965. *158.*

30. BENIEST, E. 'Analyse du Comportement dit "Maternel" chez la Souris', *Mémoire pour Licence en Sciences Psychologiques*, *Université Libre de Bruxelles*, 1957. *268–9.*

31. CHANCE, M. R. A. 'The Role of Convulsions in Behaviour', *Behavioral Science*, 2, pp. 30–45, 1957. *137.*

32. CHANCE, M. R. A. 'An Interpretation of Some Agonistic Postures: the Role of "Cut-off" Acts and Postures', *Symposia of the Zoological Society of London*, 8, pp. 71–89, 1962. *121.*

33. CHANCE, M. R. A., and MACKINTOSH, J. H. 'The Effects of Caging', *Laboratory Animals Centre Collected Papers*, 11, pp. 59–64, 1962. *159.*

34. CHITTY, D. 'Tuberculosis and Wild Voles: with a Discussion of Other, Pathological Conditions among Certain Mammals and Birds', *Ecology*, 35, pp. 227–37, 1954. *158.*

35. CHRISTIAN, J. J. 'Physiological and Pathological Correlates of Population Density', *Proceedings of the Royal Society of Medicine*, 57, pp. 169–74, 1964. *157–8.*

36. CLARKE, J. R. 'The Effect of Fighting on the Adrenals, Thymus and Spleen of the Vole (*Microtus agrestis*)', *J. Endocrinology*, 9, pp. 114–26, 1953. *157–8.*

37. CLARKE, J. R. 'Influence of Numbers on Reproduction and Survival in Two Experimental Vole Populations', *Proceedings of the Royal Society B*, 144, pp. 68–85, 1955. *149–50.*

38. GODFREY, G., and CROWCROFT, P. *The Life of the Mole* (*Talpa europea* Linnaeus), London, Museum Press, 1960. *159.*

39. GRANT, E. C., and CHANCE, M. R. A. 'Rank Order in Caged Rats', *Animal Behaviour*, 6, pp. 183–94, 1958. *128.*

40. KABAT, C., COLLIAS, N. E., and GUETTINGER, R. C. 'Some Winter Habits of White-Tailed Deer and the Development of Census Methods in the Flag Yard of Northern Wisconsin', *Technical Wildlife Bulletin*, 7, Madison, Wisconsin Conservation Department, 1953. *147–8, 163.*

41. LEYHAUSEN, P. 'The Communal Organization of Solitary Mammals', *Symposia of the Zoological Society of London*, 14, pp. 249–63, 1965. *55–7, 147, 234.*

42. *New Scientist*, (Notes on need for variety in rats and canyon mice), *New Scientist*, 28, pp. 393–4, 1965. *237.*

43. STEINIGER, F. 'Beiträge zur Soziologie und sonstigen Biologie der Wanderratte', *Zeitschrift für Tierpsychologie*, 7, pp. 356–79, 1950. *278–81.*

4 Monkeys

44. ALTMANN, S. A. 'Field Observations on a Howling Monkey Society', *J. Mammalogy*, 40, pp. 317–30, 1959. *46.*

45. ALTMANN, S. A. 'The Social Play of Rhesus Monkeys', *American Zoologist*, 1, p. 27, 1961. *72–3.*

46. ALTMANN, S. A. 'Social Behaviour of Anthropoid Primates: Analysis of Recent Concepts', in *Roots of Behavior*, ed. E. L. Bliss, pp. 277–85, New York, Harper & Bros., 1962. *72–3.*

47. CARPENTER, C. R. *Naturalistic Behaviour of Non-Human Primates.* Pennsylvania State University Press, University Park, Pa, 1964. *43, 46, 48–9, 51, 59–60, 69, 78, 105–7, 157, 161–2.*

48. CHANCE, M. R. A. 'Social Structure of a Colony of *Macaca mulatta*', *British J. Animal Behaviour*, 4, pp. 1–13, 1956. *58, 73–4, 81–2, 84, 86, 90–1, 119, 122, 126, 128, 133.*

49. CHANCE, M. R. A. 'Social Behaviour and Primate Evolution', in *Culture and the Evolution of Man*, ed. M. F. Ashley Montagu, pp. 84–130, New York, Oxford University Press, 1962. *58, 73.*

50. CHANCE, M. R. A. *The Social Life of Rhesus Monkeys* (film). *58, 73, 90–1, 119, 126, 133.*

51. CHANCE, M. R. A. *The Dominant Set* (film). *58, 74, 90–1, 98.*

52. CHANCE, M. R. A., and MEAD, A. P. 'Social Behaviour and Primate Evolution', *Symposia of the Society for Experimental Biology*, 7, pp. 395–439, 1953. *58.*

53. CROOK, J. H. 'Gelada Baboon Herd Structure and Movement. A Comparative Report', *Symposia of the Zoological Society of London*, 18, pp. 237–58, 1966. *62–3.*

54. CROOK, J. H., and GARTLAN, J. S. 'Evolution of Primate Societies', *Nature*, 210, pp. 1200–3, 1966. *62–3.*

55. DEVORE, I. (ed.) *Primate Behaviour. Field Studies of Monkeys and Apes*, New York, Holt, Rinehart & Winston, 1965. *43–4, 46–7, 49–52, 59–60, 63, 69, 74, 77, 79, 84, 100, 128, 148, 161–2.*

56. HALL, K. R. L. 'Behaviour and Ecology of the Wild Patas Monkey, *Erythrocebus patas*, in Uganda', *J. Zoology*, 148, pp. 15–87, 1966. *50, 57, 77–8.*

57. HARLOW, H. F., and HARLOW, M. K. 'Social Deprivation in Monkeys', *Scientific American*, Nov 1962. *71–2, 269–71.*

58. HAYES, J. S., RUSSELL, W. M. S., HAYES, C., and KOHSEN, A. 'The Mechanism of an Instinctive Control System: a Hypothesis', *Behaviour*, 6, pp. 85–119, 1953. *125.*

59. IMANISHI, K., and ALTMANN, S. A. *Japanese Monkeys. A Collection of Translations*, Edmonton, Altmann, 1965. *45, 49, 59, 64–7, 77, 122.*

60. KUMMER, H. 'Soziales Verhalten einer Mantelpavian-Gruppe', *Beiheft zur Schweiserischen Zeitschrift für Psychologie und ihre Anwendungen*, 33, pp. 1–91, 1957. *74, 81–5, 99, 103, 119–20, 131–2.*

*

61. KUMMER, H. 'Two Variations in the Social Organization of Baboons (1), (in press). *50, 60–2, 72.*

62. KUMMER, H. *Social Organization of Hamadryas Baboons*, Basle, Karger, 1967. *48, 50, 57–9, 61–2, 67–8, 72, 76, 82, 84, 149.*

63. KUMMER, H. 'Tripartite Relations in Hamadryas Baboons', in *Social Communication Among Primates*, ed. S. A. Altmann, pp. 63–71; University of Chicago Press, 1967. *63, 131–2, 245–6.*

63A. KUMMER, H., and KURT, F. 'A Comparison of Social Behaviour in Captive and Wild Hamadryas Baboons', in *The Baboon in Medical Research* ed. H. Vagtborg, pp. 65–80; University of Texas Press, 1965. *48, 50, 82, 84, 131–2.*

64. KUMMER, H., and KURT, F. 'Social Units of a Free-Living Population of Hamadryas Baboons', *Folia primatologica*, 1, pp. 4–19, 1963. *48, 61–2.*

65. *Life International* 'The Social Ways of Monkeys', *Life International*, **38**, 9, pp. 38–53, 1965. *52.*

66. MASLOW, A. H., RAND, H., and NEWMAN, S. 'Some Parallels between Sexual and Dominance Behaviour of Infra-Human Primates and the Fantasies of Patients in Psychotherapy', *J. Nervous and Mental Disease*, **131**, pp. 202–12, 1960. *122, 125, 128–9, 137.*

67. MIZUHARA, H. 'Social Changes of Japanese Monkey Troops in Takasakiyama', *Primates*, **5**, pp. 27–52, 1964. *45, 59, 64–8, 75–7, 174–6.*

68. MORRIS, R., and MORRIS, D. *Men and Apes*, London, Hutchinson, 1966. *44–8, 51, 70, 124–5, 129, 148, 237.*

69. MOYNIHAN, M. 'Some Behaviour Patterns of Platyrrhine Monkeys. 1. The Night Monkey (*Aotes trivirgatus*)', *Smithsonian Miscellaneous Collections*, **146**, pp. 1–84, 1964. *50–1.*

70. REYNOLDS, V. 'The Social Life of a Colony of Rhesus Monkeys (*Macaca mulatta*)', Ph.D. Thesis, University of London, 1961. *81–94, 97–105, 119–22, 125–33, 272, 274.*

71. REYNOLDS, V. 'An Outline of the Behaviour and Social Organization of Forest-living Chimpanzees', *Folia primatologica*, **1**, pp. 95–102, 1963. *47, 69–70.*

72. REYNOLDS, V. 'Some Behavioural Comparisons between the Chimpanzee and the Mountain Gorilla in the Wild', *American Anthropologist*, **67**, pp. 691–706, 1965. *47, 69–70.*

73. REYNOLDS, V. *Budongo. A Forest and its Chimpanzees*, London, Methuen, 1965. *47, 69–70, 77.*

74. ROWELL, T. E. 'Forest living Baboons in Uganda', *Journal of Zoology*, **149**, pp. 344–64, 1966. *53.*

75. RUSSELL, C., and RUSSELL, W. M. S. 'Primate Behaviour and the Concept of Pseudosex', *Internat. Mental Health Research Newsletter*, 5, pp. 7–8, 1963. *123–5, 134–6*.

76. RUSSELL, W. M. S. 'The Animal Society. 2. Hierarchies', *Listener*, 77, pp. 487–8, 1967. *4, 73, 75, 174–6*.

77. SINGH, S. D. 'The Effects of Human Environment upon the Reactions to Novel Situations in the Rhesus', *Behaviour*, 26, pp. 243–50, 1965. *148*.

78. SOUTHWICK, C. H. (ed.) *Primate Social Behaviour* (Insight Book edn), Princeton, N.J., Van Nostrand, 1963. *43–6, 49–50, 52, 59–60, 63–6, 69, 71–2, 77–9, 157, 160–2, 269–71*.

79. SOUTHWICK, C. H. 'An Experimental Study of Intragroup Agonistic Behaviour in Rhesus Monkeys (*Macaca mulatta*)', *Behaviour*, 28, pp. 182–209, 1967. *146, 148*.

80. ZUCKERMAN, S. (Sir Solly) *The Social Life of Monkeys and Apes*, London, Kegan Paul, Trench, Trubner, 1932. *40–2, 83–5, 100, 125, 132*.

C *Human Prehistory and Tribal Societies*

81. ALEXANDER, T., and ANDERSON, R. 'Children in a Society under Stress', *Behavioral Science*, 2, pp. 46–55, 1957. *267*.

82. BBC 2 TELEVISION (Programme about the Hadja people), 7 Jan 1967. *258*.

83. FORD, C. S., and BEACH, F. A. *Patterns of Sexual Behaviour*, New York, Harper & Bros & Hoeber, 1951. *136*.

84. HAWKES, J. *Prehistory* (Vol. 1, Part 1 of UNESCO *History of Mankind*), London, Allen & Unwin, 1963. *18–19, 207–8*.

85. HIATT, L. 'Mung — a Theory of Dirt', *Balcony, The Sydney Review*, 3, pp. 15–21, 1965. *119*.

86. INTERNATIONAL UNION FOR THE CONSERVATION OF NATURE AND NATURAL RESOURCES *The Ecology of Man in the Tropical Environment*, Morges, Switzerland, IUCN, 1964. *59, 207–9, 258*.

87. LEY, W. *Dragons in Amber* (on Old Stone Age tools), London, Sidgwick & Jackson, 1951. *257*.

88. NAPIER, J. R. 'Profile of Early Man at Olduvai', *New Scientist*, 22, pp. 86–9, 1964. *258*.

89. RATTRAY, J. M., and BYRNE, F. O. 'Report to the Government of Uganda on a Reconnaissance Survey of the Karamoja District', *Report 1680 FAO/EPTA*, 1963. *214*.

90. RUSSELL, W. M. S. 'Farming the Forest', *Natural History* (Journal of the American Museum of Natural History), 77, 3, pp. 58–65, 76, 1968. *18–19, 208–9*.

D   *History of Human Civilisations to Mid-Twentieth Century*

1   World

91. CHILDE, V. G. *What Happened in History*, Harmondsworth, Penguin, 1942. *18–19, 173, 176, 207–8*.

92. CIPOLLA, C. *The Economic History of World Population*, Harmondsworth, Penguin, 1962. *38, 151, 171, 177–8, 182–3, 207, 216–18*.

93. FOOD AND AGRICULTURAL ORGANIZATION (UNITED NATIONS) *Fertilizers: an Annual Review of World Production, Consumption and Trade, 1963*, Rome, FAO, 1964. *9*.

94. GLASS, D. V., and EVERSLEY, D. E. C. (ed.) *Population in History*, London, Arnold, 1965. *152, 177–8, 182, 242*.

95. HARTMANN, F. H. *The Relations of Nations* (2nd edn), New York and London, Macmillan, 1962. *212*.

96. HUTTON, K. *Chemistry* (on synthetics), Harmondsworth, Penguin, 1963 (revised edn). *38*.

97. MUMFORD, L. *The City in History*, London, Secker & Warburg, 1961. *173, 184–5*.

98. ROSTOW, W. W. *The Stages of Economic Growth*, Cambridge University Press, 1960. *9*.

99. RUSSELL, W. M. S. *Man, Nature and History*, London, Aldus Books, 1967. *10–11, 18–19, 155, 171, 177–83, 196–7, 204, 207–15, 281, 295*.

2   British Isles

100. BARLOW, N. (ed.) *The Autobiography of Charles Darwin, 1809–1882*, London, Collins, 1958. *151*.

101. BEER, Sir Gavin DE (ed.). *Evolution by Natural Selection: Darwin and Wallace*, Cambridge University Press, 1958. *151*.

102. BLACK, L. (ed.). *The Love Letters of Henry the Eighth*, London, Blandford Press, 1933. *95–6*.

103. DE CHAMBRUN, C. Longworth, Countess, *Shakespeare: a Portrait Restored*, London, Hollis & Carter, 1957. *24–6, 298*.

104. CHUTE, M. *Ben Jonson of Westminster* (Four Square edn), London, New English Library, 1962. *24–6*.

105. COLE, G. D. H., and POSTGATE, R. *The Common People 1746–1946* (University Paperback edn), London, Methuen, 1961. *21, 113, 116*.

106. FORD, B. (ed.). *The Age of Shakespeare*, Harmondsworth, Penguin, 1955. *296, 298*.

107. GRAVES, R., and HODGE, A. *The Long Week-End* (Britain in the Nineteen-Twenties) (Four Square edn), London, Four Square Books, 1961. *113, 116*.

108. HALLIDAY, F. E. *The Life of Shakespeare*, Harmondsworth, Penguin, 1963. *24–6*.

109. HOSKINS, W. G. 'Harvest Fluctuations and English Economic History, 1480–1619', *Agricultural History Review*, **12**, pp. 28–46, 1964. *26–8*.

110. KENYON, J. P. *The Stuarts* (Fontana edn), London, Collins, 1966. *94*.

111. MacNALTY, Sir Arthur S. *Henry VIII: a Difficult Patient*, London, Christopher Johnson, 1952. *95–6*.

112. McCORMICK, D. *Pedlar of Death: the Life of Sir Basil Zaharoff*, London, Macdonald, 1965. *116*.

113. MAYS, J. B. *Crime and the Social Structure* (on rehousing observations), London, Faber & Faber, 1963. *224–5*.

114. MORRIS, C. *The Tudors*, London, Batsford, 1955. *27, 95–6, 273, 298*.

115. NEALE, J. E. *Queen Elizabeth*, London, Cape, 1934. *27–8, 296–9*.

116. NEALE, J. E. *Elizabeth I and her Parliaments, 1584–1601*, London, Cape, 1957. *296–9*.

117. NOTESTEIN, F. W. (ed.). *Three Essays on Population* (includes Malthus's last work), New York, New American Library, 1960. *152–3, 207, 251*.

118. OMAN, C. *Britain against Napoleon*, Readers' Union, London, Faber & Faber, 1943. *15*.

119. PEACOCK, A. J. *Bread or Blood* (East Anglian riots, 1816), London, Gollancz, 1965. *21–4, 109, 113*.

120. POLLARD, A. F. *Wolsey* (Fontana edn), London, Collins, 1965. *95–6, 116–18*.

121. READ, C. *Mr. Secretary Cecil and Queen Elizabeth* (Paperback edn), London, Cape, 1965. *296*.

122. SHAPIRO, H. L. *The Heritage of the 'Bounty'* (Anchor edn), Garden City, Doubleday, 1962. *22, 291*.

123. SMITH, R. 'Some Sociomedical Aspects of the Population Explosion' (on career of Malthus), *Proceedings of the Royal Society of Medicine*, **59**, pp. 1149–53, 1966. *151*.

124. SPENCER, H. *The Art and Life of William Shakespeare*, London, Bell, 1948. *24–6*.

125. TURNER, E. S. *Roads to Ruin. The Shocking History of Social Reform*, Harmondsworth, Penguin, 1966. *140*.

126. WOODHAM-SMITH, C. *The Great Hunger* (the Irish famine) (Four Square edn), London, New English Library, 1964. *223, 235, 268.*

127. WRIGLEY, E. A. 'Marriage and Fertility in a Pre-Industrial England', *BBC Third Programme,* 24 Jan. 1966. *243.*

3 Continent of Europe

128. BARNETT, B. 'Witchcraft, Psychopathology and Hallucinations', *British J. Psychiatry,* III, pp. 439–45, 1965. *199.*

129. BARRACLOUGH, G. *The Origins of Modern Germany,* Oxford, Blackwell, (2nd edn), 1947. *6, 113, 278, 283–4.*

130. BLOCH, M. *Feudal Society* (2 vols) (trans. L. A. Manyon) (Paperback edn), London, Routledge & Kegan Paul, 1965. *192, 200, 246–7, 273.*

131. BRUFORD, W. H. *Germany in the 18th Century: the Social Background of the Literary Revival* (Paperback edn), Cambridge University Press, 1965. *182, 235–6, 283–4.*

132. BULLOCK, A. *Hitler: a Study in Tyranny,* Harmondsworth, Penguin, 1962. *6, 8, 139, 278, 283–9.*

133. CARY, M. *A History of the Greek World, from 323 to 146 B.C.,* London, Methuen, 1932. *203.*

134. CARY, M. *A History of Rome down to the Reign of Constantine,* London, Macmillan, 1935. *66, 184, 192, 221–3.*

135. CLOUGH, A. H. (ed. and trans.). *Plutarch's Lives,* volume 2 (Everyman edn), London, Dent, 1910. *169.*

136. HEER, F. *The Mediaeval World. Europe 1100–1350* (trans. J. Sondheimer) (Mentor edn), New York, New American Library, 1963. *196–8, 203.*

137. HEMPHILL, R. E. 'Historical Witchcraft and Psychiatric Illness in Western Europe', *Proceedings of the Royal Society of Medicine,* 59, pp. 891–901, 1966. *199.*

138. HUGHES, P. *Witchcraft,* Harmondsworth, Penguin, 1965. *198–200.*

139. KESSEL, J. *The Magic Touch* (on Hitler and Himmler) (Pan edn), London, Pan Books, 1963. *288.*

140. KLEIN, J. *The Mesta: a Study in Spanish Economic History, 1273–1836,* Cambridge, Harvard University Press (Milford, London), 1920. *295.*

141. MOTLEY, J. L. *The Rise of the Dutch Republic* (3 vols) (World Classics edn), Oxford University Press, 1906. *294, 298–9.*

142. MUNDY, J. H., and RIESENBERG, P. *The Medieval Town* (Anvil edn), Princeton, N.J., Van Nostrand, 1958. *247.*

143. NOHL, J. *The Black Death* (Unwin edn), London, Allen & Unwin, 1961. *181, 197–8.*

144. OMAN, C. W. C. *The Art of War in the Middle Ages* (Great Seal edn), Ithaca, Cornell University Press, 1960. *203.*

145. ROSTOVTZEFF, M. *The Social and Economic History of the Roman Empire*, Oxford, Clarendon Press, 1926. *189, 192.*

146. SCHWEITZER, A. *Big Business in the Third Reich*, London, Eyre & Spottiswoode, 1964. *278, 283–5.*

147. SETH, R. *Petiot, Victim of Chance*, London, Hutchinson, 1963. *275–6.*

148. SHIRER, W. L. *The Rise and Fall of the Third Reich* (Pan edn), London, Pan Books, 1964. *6, 278, 283–4.*

149. SLICHER VAN BATH, B. H. *The Agrarian History of Western Europe, A.D. 500–1850*, London, Arnold, 1963. *26, 177–82, 189–94, 204, 210, 281.*

150. SPRAGUE DE CAMP, L. *The Bronze God of Rhodes* (Paperback edn), New York, Bantam Books, 1963. *190.*

151. THOMAS, W. L. (ed.). *Man's Role in Changing the Face of the Earth*, University of Chicago Press, 1956. *171, 173, 179–82, 204, 208–14.*

152. WHITE, L. *Medieval Technology and Social Change* (Paperback edn), Oxford University Press, 1964. *180.*

4   Other Continents

153. ANDRESKI, S. *Parasitism and Subversion: the Case of Latin America*, London, Weidenfeld & Nicolson, 1966. *109, 172.*

154. BUSCH, N. F. *Two Minutes to Noon* (the Tokyo earthquake) (Corgi edn), London, Transworld Publications, 1964. *266.*

155. CASH, W. J. *The Mind of the South* (Southern States, U.S.A.), New York, Knopf, 1941. *19–20, 107–9.*

156. CLARK, M. *A Short History of Australia* (Mentor edn), New York, New American Library, 1963. *291.*

157. FLEMING, P. *The Siege at Peking* (Boxer Rising) (Paperback edn), London, Arrow Books, 1962. *18.*

158. GALBRAITH, J. K. *The Great Crash* (Wall Street, 1929), Harmondsworth, Penguin, 1961. *87.*

159. GROUSSET, R. *The Rise and Splendour of the Chinese Empire*, Berkeley and Los Angeles, University of California Press, 1964. *7–8, 18, 213.*

160. HENRIQUES, F. *The Immoral Tradition. Prostitution and Society.* Vol. 2: *Europe and the New World* (Panther edn), London, Panther Books, 1966. *138, 140.*

161. JOESTEN, J. *Oswald — Assassin or Fall Guy?* (on Joseph McCarthy), London, Merlin Press, 1964. *195–6.*

162. KEFAUVER, E. *Crime in America* (the Senate Committee) (Four Square edn), London, Landsborough Publications, 1958. *200–1.*

163. KENNEDY, M. *A Short History of Japan* (Mentor edn), New York, New American Library, 1964. *111, 215–16.*

164. KRAMER, S. N. *History Begins at Sumer* (ancient Iraq) (2nd edn), London, Thames & Hudson, 1961. *29–30.*

165. LATTIMORE, O. *Inner Asian Frontiers of China*, Boston, Beacon Press, 1962. *209–15.*

166. NAROLL, R. S., and BERTALANFFY, L. VON. 'The Principle of Allometry in Biology and the Social Sciences' (on urbanisation in nineteenth-century U.S.A.), *General Systems*, 1, pp. 76–89, 1956. *183.*

167. NEEDHAM, J. *Science and Civilization in China*, vol. i, Cambridge University Press, 1954. *209–13.*

168. PAYNE, R. (ed.). *The White Pony* (anthology of Chinese poetry) (Mentor edn), New York, New American Library, 1960. *7.*

169. REIFENBERG, A. *The Struggle between the Desert and the Sown. Rise and Fall of Agriculture in the Levant*, Publication Department, Jerusalem, Jewish Agency, 1955. *10–11, 214–15.*

170. SANDARS, N. K. (ed.). *The Epic of Gilgamesh*, Harmondsworth, Penguin, 1960. *211.*

171. SINCLAIR, A. *Prohibition* (Four Square edn), London, New English Library, 1965. *144–5.*

172. WELLMAN, P. I. *Spawn of Evil* (violence in pioneer America) (Corgi edn), London, Transworld, 1966. *169.*

173. WHYTE, R. O. 'Report to the Government of Japan on Pasture and Fodder Development (8th and Final Report)' (on topography), *Report 1822 FAO/EPTA*, 1964. *45.*

174. WOOLLEY, Sir Leonard. *The Beginnings of Civilization* (Vol. 1, Part 2 of UNESCO *History of Mankind*), London, Allen & Unwin, 1963. *173, 176, 221.*

175. YANG, C. K. *Chinese Communist Society: the Family and the Village*, Cambridge, Mass., M.I.T. Press, 1965. *244–5, 248.*

E   *Developments after 1950*

1 Population

176. BERELSON, B., and FREEDMAN, R. 'A Study in Fertility Control' (in Formosa), *Scientific American*, **210**, 5, 1964. *249.*

Daily Mail, 1965. **177.** (S. Burch: birth control in U.S.A.), 15 Jun, p. 2; *251.* **178.** (J. Barton: birth control in India), 16 Jul, p. 2; *251.* **179.** (A. Macpherson: air traffic over Atlantic), 5 Oct, p. 13; *185.* **180.** (R. Smyth: birth control in France), 9 Nov, p. 2; *251.* **181.** (Couple who lost count of children), 30 Nov, p. 7; *165.* **182.** (P. Hawthorne: population policy in S. Africa), 1 Dec, p. 2; *286.* **183.** (Abandoned vehicles in Britain), 15 Dec, p. 9. *184.*

184. DRAPER, E. *Birth Control in the Modern World*, Harmondsworth, Penguin, 1965. *218, 243, 251.*

185. *Evening News*, 1965 (birth control in Australia), 6 Apr, p. 1. *251.*

Evening Standard, 1965. **186.** (M. F. King and R. Walling: traffic in London), 12 Jul, pp. 1, 15 and 28; *184.* 1966. **187.** (R. Wittman: the population explosion), 4 Apr, p. 11; *218.* **188.** (R. Wittman: the population explosion), 7 Apr, p. 10; *226, 241.* **189.** (C. Pickard: large families in Britain), 6 Jul, p. 11; *241.* **190.** (Birth control in France), 6 Sep, p. 16. *251.*

191. FREEDMAN, R. 'Norms for Family Size in Undeveloped Areas', *Proceedings of the Royal Society B*, **159**, pp. 220–40, 1963. *249, 251.*

192. GOODE, W. J. *World Revolution and Family Patterns*, Free Press of Glencoe; London, Collier–Macmillan, 1963. *249.*

193. HALL, P. (the population explosion), *Sunday Times Magazine*, pp. 18–20, 20 Mar 1966. *218, 226.*

194. McCANNEL, J. E. 'Expo's Agricultural Pavilion' (on world population), *Agricultural Institute Review* (Canada), **20**, pp. 30–1, 1965. *218.*

195. NEWMAN, P. *British Guiana*, London, Oxford University Press, 1964. *217.*

196. SAUZIER, A. G. 'Aspects of the Economic Structure and Development of Mauritius', *J. Royal Society for the Encouragement of Arts Manufactures and Commerce*, **113**, pp. 434–45, 1965. *217.*

197. SMEED, R. J., and HILLIER, J. A. 'Traffic Engineering Research — Some Recent Examples', *Transportation Engineering Conference Report*, pp. 60–70, 1965. *184.*

198. THOMPSON, W. S., and LEWIS, D. T. *Population Problems* (5th edn), New York, McGraw–Hill, 1965. *151–3, 183–4, 216, 250–1.*

199. *Times*, 1966 (President of British Association on British population policy), 1 Sep, p. 9. *241.*

2 Food Production

> *Daily Mail* 1965. **200.** (P. Whaley: encroachment on farmland
> in Britain), 4 Feb, p. 6; *220.* **201.** (Three Mountain Shrine
> ritual, Japan) 4 Jun, p. 7; *212.* **202.** (Drought and famine,
> 1965–6), 10 Jun, p. 2; *219, 225.*
>
> *Evening Standard,* 1966. **203.** (Famine in India), 5 May, p. 1;
> *219.* **204.** (P. Marshall: factory farms), 1 Dec, p. 16; *220.*
> 1967. **205.** (C. Pickard: malnutrition in Britain), 12 Jan,
> p. 5; *220.*

206. FOOD AND AGRICULTURAL ORGANIZATION (UNITED NATIONS)
Production Yearbook 1963, Rome, FAO, 1964. *218–19.*

207. FOOD AND AGRICULTURAL ORGANIZATION (UNITED NATIONS).
Production Yearbook 1964, Rome, FAO, 1965. *218–19.*

208. FOOD AND AGRICULTURAL ORGANIZATION (UNITED NATIONS).
The State of Food and Agriculture 1965, Rome, FAO, 1965.
218–19.

209. FOOD AND AGRICULTURAL ORGANIZATION (UNITED NATIONS).
The State of Food and Agriculture 1966, Rome, FAO, 1966.
217–19.

210. SEGAL, R. *The Crisis of India,* Harmondsworth, Penguin, 1965.
14, 38, 186, 218, 246.

3 Money

211. ABEL-SMITH, B., and TOWNSEND, P. *The Poor and the Poorest,*
London, Bell & Sons, 1965. *37, 164.*

212. COLE, D., and UTTING, J. *The Economic Circumstances of Old
People,* Welwyn, Codicote Press, 1962. *36, 250.*

> *Daily Mail* 1964. **213.** (V. Mulchrone: poverty among old
> people, Britain), 4 Dec, p. 10; *36.* 1965. **214.** (B. Kidel:
> Great Society programme, U.S.A.), 8 Apr, p. 2; *115.* **215.**
> (A. Cook: inflation in Vietnam), 9 Jun, p. 2; *138.* **216.**
> (Cost of living in Britain), 25 Jun, p. 11; *191.* **217.** (W. For-
> rest: cost of Egyptian intervention in Yemen), 25 Aug, p. 2;
> *13.* 1966. **218.** (B. Kidel: war and welfare expenditure,
> U.S.A.), 25 Jan, p. 2; *13–14.* **219.** (Prices, U.S.A.), 28 Jan,
> p. 2; *14.*
>
> *Evening Standard.* 1966. **220.** (Sir Robert Thompson: cost of
> Vietnam war), 19 Apr, p. 7; *13.* **221.** (R. Purdue: currency
> circulation in different countries), 12 Jul, p. 3; *33, 38.* **222.**
> (J. Prosser: government bonds in different countries),
> 6 Sep, p. 3; *191.*

223. FLETCHER, R. *£60 a Second on Defence,* London, MacGibbon &
Kee, 1963. *12–14.*

224. GANS, B. 'Experiences in a Coloured Children's Welfare Clinic', *Proceedings of the Royal Society of Medicine*, 57, pp. 327–8, 1964. *36.*

225. GIBSON, T. *Breaking in the Future* (on British housing prices), London, Zenith Books, 1965. *191, 218.*

226. KEFAUVER, E. *In a Few Hands* (Senate Committee on monopolies), Harmondsworth, Penguin, 1966. *35.*

227. KOLKO, G. *Wealth and Power in America*, London, Thames & Hudson, 1962. *29, 33–5, 37, 141, 193, 229–30.*

228. MILLER, M. *Rise of the Russian Consumer*, London, Institute of Economic Affairs, 1965. *32, 34.*

229. SOULE, G. *Men, Wages and Employment* (Mentor edn), New York, New American Library, 1954. *38.*

230. *Sun* 1966 (food prices in Britain), 13 Oct. *219.*

231. TITMUSS, R. M. *Income Distribution and Social Change*, London, Allen & Unwin, 1962. *34.*

232. TOWNSEND, P. (poverty in Britain), *Poverty*, 1, pp. 5–9, 1966. *37, 164, 220.*

4 Housing

233. BBC 1 TELEVISION. 'Who are the Vandals?' (London housing developments), 2 Feb 1967. *194–5, 227–8, 233.*

234. BEATTY, R. T. *Hearing in Man and Animals* (on noise), London, Bell & Sons, 1932. *227.*

235. BEST, R. H. 'Against High Density', *New Society*, 8, pp. 787–9, 1966. *226, 232–3, 236.*

236. *Daily Express*, 1966 (noise in London), 18 Feb, p. 4. *227.*

237. *Daily Herald*, 1964 (M. Jones: effects of high-rise housing), 6 Aug, p. 4. *228, 236.*

Daily Mail, 1965. **238.** (P. Whaley: housing in London), 12 Mar, pp. 6–7; *229–30.* **239.** (B. Kidel: water shortage in U.S.A.), 11 Oct, p. 2; *225.* **240.** (S. Burch: housing in New York), 5 Nov, p. 10; *230.* 1966. **241.** (B. Kidel: slump in house-building, U.S.A.), 31 Aug, p. 2; *14, 115, 190–1.* **242.** (House-building decline predicted in Britain), 12 Nov, p. 7; *226.* **243.** (Decline in quality of British housing), 24 Nov, p. 9; *226.*

Evening Standard, 1966. **244.** (Refrigerators in Britain), 2 Feb, p. 3; *229.* 1967. **245.** (C. Lyte: personal territory in open prisons), 20 Feb, p. 7; *231–2.*

246. GRANT, E. C. 'An Ethological Description of some Schizophrenic Patterns of Behaviour', *Proceedings of Leeds Symposium on Behavioural Disorders, 25–27 March 1965*, chap. 12. *232.*

247. Low, I. 'Cities Fit for People', *New Scientist*, **30**, pp. 35–6, 1966. *221, 224.*

248. Moore, R. S. 'The Profits from Misery', *New Society*, **5**, pp. 18–20, 1965. *222.*

249. Schorr, A. L. *Slums and Social Insecurity*, London, Nelson, 1964. *37, 226–30.*

5 Health

250. Collins, P. 'Urbanization and Filariasis', *Span*, **8**, pp. 169–71, 1965. *183.*

Daily Mail, 1965. **251.** (Search for nurses in Malta), 5 May, p. 14; *187.* **252.** (K. McDowall: Indian and Pakistani doctors indispensable in Britain), 8 Sep, p. 6; *188.* **253.** (Staff shortage in British mental hospitals), 10 Sep, p. 11; *187.* **254.** (J. Starr: staff shortage in German health and education services), 8 Oct, p. 2; *188–9, 238.* **255.** (I. Campbell: mistakes in British hospitals), 8 Oct, p. 10; *187.*

256. *Evening News*, 1966 (S. French: doctor shortage in France), 8 Jul, p. 4; *188.*

Evening Standard, 1966. **257.** (H. Jillings: a doctor's day), 23 Aug, p. 7; *187.* 1967. **258.** (P. Fairley: mistakes in British hospitals), 25 May, p. 32; *187.*

259. Illingworth, R. S. 'The Changing Pattern of Paediatrics in a Children's Hospital 1876–1961', *Proceedings of the Royal Society of Medicine*, **54**, pp. 1011–13, 1961. *187.*

260. Taylor, J. 'Modern Life and Salmonellosis', *Proceedings of the Royal Society of Medicine*, **58**, pp. 167–70, 1965. *220.*

6 Education

261. Albrow, M. C. 'The Influence of Accommodation upon 64 Reading University Students — an *ex post facto* Experimental Study', *British J. Sociology*, **17**, pp. 403–18, 1966. *238–9.*

Daily Mail, 1964. **262.** (P. Keiran: nursery schools in Britain), 16 Dec, p. 8; *237.* 1965. **263.** (R. Nash: large classes in British schools), 28 Apr, p. 10; *188–9, 238.*

Evening Standard, 1965. **264.** (Encroachment on playing-fields), 8 Jul, p. 5; *238.* 1966. **265.** (School demands in Surrey), 17 Aug, p. 12; *188.* 1967. **266.** (V. Lederer: crowding in British schools), 12 Jan, p. 7; *238.*

267. Frieslich, V. 'The Extent to which the Use of Language Inhibits Violence in Situations of Aggression among Five-Year-Old Children' (unpublished thesis). *238.*

268. HIGBEE, E. *The Squeeze: Cities without Space*, London, Cassell, 1961. *238.*

7 Labour

269. MAY, E. *The Wasted Americans* (Signet edn), New York, New American Library, 1965. *35, 186, 230, 251.*

270. *New Scientist* (correspondence on shortage of skilled labour in British industry), **419**, pp. 594–5, 1964. *188.*

271. SHANKS, M. 'The Stagnant Society' (extract) (shortage of skilled labour in British industry), *Time and Tide*, **42**, pp. 1390–1, 1961. *188.*

8 Pseudosex and Drug Addiction

272. CLARK, J. A. 'Opiate Addiction', *Proceedings of the Royal Society of Medicine*, **58**, pp. 412–14, 1965. *202.*

273. CONNELL, P. H. 'Adolescent Drug Taking', *Proceedings of the Royal Society of Medicine*, **58**, pp. 409–12, 1965. *202.*

Daily Mail, 1965. **274.** (H. McLeave: drug addiction in Britain), 28 Apr, p. 8; *202.* **275.** (I. Smith: drug addiction and crime in New York), 8 Jul, p. 2; *200.* **276.** (H. McLeave: drug addiction in Britain), 25 Nov, p. 10; *202.*

Evening Standard, 1966. **277.** (Prostitution in Vietnam), 26 May, p. 18; *138.* **278.** (Social status raised in divorce case), 15 Jul, p. 5; *142–3.*

279. KINSEY, A. C., POMEROY, W. B., MARTIN, C. E., and GEBHARD, P. H. *Sexual Behaviour in the Human Female* (Giant Cardinal edn), New York, Pocket Books, 1965. *136–7.*

280. *Observer*, 1966. (Drug addiction in British schools), 17 Jul, p. 10. *202.*

281. O'CALLAGHAN, S. *The Slave Trade* (Consul edn), London, World Distributors, 1965. *138.*

282. RUSSELL, C., and RUSSELL, W. M. S. 'The Natural History of Censorship', in '*To Deprave and Corrupt*', ed. J. Chandos, pp. 153–74; London, Souvenir Press, 1962. *139–41, 300.*

9 Violent Crime and Murder

283. *Daily Express*, 1966. (P. Hoskins: British police, technical improvements), 18 Feb, p. 9; *31.*

Daily Mail, 1965. **284.** (H. McLeave: battered children in Britain), 22 Apr, p. 10; *166, 168.* **285.** (I. Smith: crime in New York), 23 Apr, p. 2; *31.* **286.** (Unsuspected murders in Britain), 7 Jul; *31.* **287.** (S. Burch: crime in U.S.A., 1964), 27 Jul, p. 2; *7, 31–2, 143–4, 168, 224.* **288.** (A. Tietjen:

British police, technical improvements), 27 Aug, p. 1; *31*. 1966. **289.** (Murder in England and Wales), 7 Jan, p. 1; *31*. **290.** (K. Morfett: crime in Moscow), 27 Jan, p. 2; *32*.

291. *Evening News*, 1966. (D. Wainwright: guns in London crime), 13 Aug, p. 4; *145*.

Evening Standard, 1964. **292.** (J. Campbell: crime in New York), 23 Sep, p. 15; *32*. 1966. **293.** (R. Carvel: attitude of girl prisoners in Britain), 31 Aug, p. 32; *272*.

Guardian, 1965. **294.** (High-rise housing and crime), 4 Sep, p. 8; *228*. 1967. **295.** (Newcastle housing study), 6 Sep, p. 4; *224*.

296. HENRY, A. F., and SHORT, J. F. *Suicide and Homicide* (Paperback edn), Free Press of Glencoe; London, Collier–Macmillan, 1964. *19–20, 223, 227*.

297. JONES, H. *Crime in a Changing Society*, Harmondsworth, Penguin, 1965. *31–2, 109*.

298. KEMPE, C. H., SILVERMAN, F. N., STEELE, B. F., DROEGEMULLER, W., and SILVER, H. K. 'The Battered Child Syndrome', *J. American Medical Association*, **181**, pp. 17–24, 1962. *165–6, 268*.

299. McCLINTOCK, F. H. *Crimes of Violence*, London, Macmillan, 1963. *30–32, 144, 168, 223–4, 227*.

300. MORRIS, J. N. 'Capacity and Incapacity for Work: Some Recent History' (on timing of crime explosion), *Proceedings of the Royal Society of Medicine*, **58**, pp. 821–5, 1965. *225*.

301. MORRIS, T., and BLOM-COOPER, L. *A Calendar of Murder. Criminal Homicide in England since 1957*, London, Michael Joseph, 1964. *31, 143–4, 166–8*.

302. POWER, M. J. 'An Attempt to Identify at First Appearance before the Courts those at risk of becoming Persistent Juvenile Offenders', *Proceedings of the Royal Society of Medicine*, **58**, pp. 704–5, 1965. *238*.

303. REPORTS ON CRIMINAL STATISTICS FOR ENGLAND AND WALES, 1964, London, HMSO, 1965. *7, 31*.

304. SONDERN, F. *The Mafia* (Panther edn), London, Panther Books, 1961. *145, 200–1, 282*.

305. *Sunday Mirror*, 1966. (R. Champion: Chicago mass-murder of 1966), 17 Jul, p. 3; *276*.

306. WIGHTON, C. *Dope International* (Four Square edn), London, New English Library, 1964. *145, 201*.

307. WILKINS, L. T. *Delinquent Generations*, London, HMSO, 1960. *268*.

10 Civil Violence and War

BBC 1 TELEVISION **308**. (Panorama: on recruits and casualties in Vietnam), 31 Oct, 1966. *114*. **309**. (Revolt in the Cities: John Conyers on Detroit and Newark riots), 26 Jul 1967; *109, 115*.

Daily Mail, 1965. **310**. (G. Vine: displaced persons in Europe), 28 Jan, p. 8; *10*. **311**. (Water and conflict in Near East), 30 Mar, p. 2; *211*. **312**. (J. Starr: water and conflict in Near East), 12 Apr, p. 2; *211*. **313**. (Water and conflict in Near East), 13 Apr, p. 1; *211*. **314**. (R. Churchill: Soka-gakkai), 4 Jun, p. 2; *249*. **315**. (A. Macpherson: nuclear weapons), 19 Nov; *9*. 1966. **316**. (A. Cook: children in Vietnam), 20 Jan, p. 2; *170*. **317**. (A. Cook: compilation on medical statistics in Vietnam), 26 Jan, p. 2; *114*. **318**. (A. Carthew: revolt in S. Sudan), 31 Jan, pp. 1 and 9; 2 Feb, p. 6; *8*. **319**. (J. Blyth: recruits in Vietnam), 2 Feb, p. 2; *114*. **320**. (Revolt in S. Sudan), 3 Feb, p. 1; *8*. **321**. (B. Kidel: Vietnam war), 8 Feb, p. 2; *8*. **322**. (Indonesian Civil War), 14 Feb, p. 2; *8*.

Evening Standard, 1966. **323**. (Kurdish revolt), 26 May, p. 6; *7*. **324**. (J. Campbell: Chicago riots of 1966), 15 Jul, p. 1; *115, 276*. **325**. (New York riots of 1966), 22 Jul, p. 15; *115*.

326. GETTLEMAN, M. E. *Vietnam. History, Documents and Opinions on a Major World Crisis*, Harmondsworth, Penguin, 1966. *114*.

327. RUMMEL, R. J. 'Dimensions of Conflict Behaviour Within and Between Nations', *General Systems*, **8**, pp. 1–50, 1963. *110–11*.

Index of Proper Names

Names of *individual* animals (monkeys unless otherwise indicated) are included in this index, marked with asterisks for easier recognition. Animal types are entered in the final index on p. 340. For purposes of order, all names are treated as single words (e.g. New Haven, Newmarket, New South Wales).

Index of Proper Names

Index of Animal Types

The 'types' in this index vary from species to much larger groupings. Only common names are used. Those interested in pursuing the technical classification of monkeys will find a wealth of information in *A Handbook of Living Primates*, by J. R. Napier and P. H. Napier (London, Academic Press, 1967). Names of *individual* animals are included in the previous index, on pp. 333–9.